THE FROG POND

JOYCE MacIVER

• • • • • • •

THE
FROG
POND

• • • • • • •

GEORGE BRAZILLER

NEW YORK

1961

TO BILL,

best frog in pond.

This book is a fragment of an autobiography, or a piece (a seven-year piece) of my life. The events insofar as they concern the narrator are true. But while truth is stranger than fiction it sometimes requires the needle of fiction to pull it together for a book. That is where the other people come in. These characters are composite pictures made from the elemental parts of many real people. No one character was or is an actual living person and any resemblance to any person living or dead is not intended.

J.M.

"Once there was a little man—and he led a little life—and one day he began to pack a little bag. And They said, 'Where are you off to? Where are you going?' And he said, 'I'm packing my bag and I'm going to Connemara.' And They said, 'You mean, you're going to Connemara, God Willing.' And he said, 'I mean I'm going to Connemara.' So God changed him into a frog and put him in a frog pond and kept him there for seven years. And then God changed him back again—and what did the little man do? He began at once to pack his little bag. And They said, 'Where are you off to? Where are you going?' And he said, 'I'm going to Connemara.' And They said, 'You mean, you're going to Connemara, God Willing.' And he said, 'I mean I'm going to Connemara, or back to the frog pond.'"

F. CABELLERO'S OLD SPANISH FAIRY TALES
(As adapted by Phillip Barry in *Here Come The Clowns*.)

THE FROG POND

CHAPTER ONE

· · · · · ·

WHAT IS IT?

I asked myself that question many a time those days, during the summer of 1942, when I foolishly supposed the problem might be solved by thinking. What is this *Thing* that has me in its iron grip, forcing me to go its way—not only against my own desire at the moment of the crisis, but against all that I hold dear or even pleasant in this life? What is it? Where does it come from? I would ask of myself or of the silence in the room. And at other times, in a more pointed, desperate mood, *Who are you?*

Questions, framed of words, usually lead to more words, but not these questions. They led nowhere and to nothing. There was always just the question, and then the sense of a deepening, widening silence. Sometimes I felt *It* knew I was trying to discover its identity, and then the silence became threatening. The thing to do then was to move quickly: go take a shower, go buy a dress, or call up a friend and have a drink.

One fine day *It* will be gone, I thought. The *Thing* will leave me as quietly and mysteriously as it arrived. Then the skies will be blue again, I'll be happy, at peace, and alive, too, as I felt somehow I was born to be.

This was not an unreasonable idea, for there were days when *It* wasn't in evidence and then I was joyous. Then everything I saw or touched or sensed had a special radiance. Maybe it has gone and will never come back, I would tell myself, and enjoy the luxury of imagining living without it. I didn't quite believe this, but it was fun to think about it and live normally, move freely and see clearly the smiling face of life. The earth felt good then, it was fun to be alive, and everything seemed just about right.

11

I never knew when *It* would strike or what it would do with me. Sometimes, after *It* had swept in and out, leaving me down at the very bottom of the barrel, I would even pray, although I had no faith and was slightly frightened of the idea of God. "Dear God," my prayer went something like this, as if I were writing a letter, "You whom I do not know and in whom I do not believe, You whose Being is wrapped in such devilish, unnecessary mystery, have mercy enough to let me out of this—not because of what I have done and will do again, *but because I am compelled against my will to do it.* Hear me, You out there, You Endless Shadow in that endless space. And if you are not that Great Shadow, if you are instead some dim, lost part of me where there is still the power to see and to control this *Thing,* then wake up and let me awaken, and show me the way to be as I was intended to be."

But the prayer came afterwards, never before *It* struck or while it was striking. While the *Thing* was striking I was a hypnotized subject just like the man in Dr. Caligari's cabinet, obeying his master's will, and prayer for the master's vanquishment was certainly not one of the master's commands. So perhaps that was in itself part of the trouble: that I always prayed too late.

It seems almost funny now, looking back over the hill to that summer, but I vaguely imagined or assumed that I alone was *Its* slave— that I, of all the millions in the world, was the only one who was marked in just this way with the *Thing's* ugly burning brand. I knew, of course, that there were others known to have committed great evil, sometimes against themselves and sometimes against their brothers, and often against their will: murderers, dope addicts, or alcoholics, people whose bad acts had brought them public notoriety and punishment. They were mostly people whose acquaintance I had made through the pages of books and newspapers. I read of them with deep, absorbing interest, especially when they said "something got hold" of them, or they "didn't know" what they were doing, and other things of that kind, but I didn't connect them with myself. And, as for the rest, the whole world seemed to be populated by people who evidently were not dominated, controlled, driven by what dominated, controlled, and drove me.

I certainly had no idea then that everything that lives is blessed *and* cursed with *It*, starting with the lowliest insects and ending in a blaze of glory in man. I had no idea that those who are blessed and feel its powerful benevolence are fortunate indeed, and those who are cursed and feel its malevolence are always asking the same damned question as I, What is *It*? Some of them make jokes, tell funny stories, pretending *It* does not exist. Others run away in the hope of escaping—in the hope that *It* may not be in Arabia or in Paris, the Foreign Legion, or a new love affair, and sometimes their very running satisfies it for a while.

I ran, too, but whenever *It* was ready *It* stopped me. *It* had the drop on me and I had to turn and face it, which is like being murdered slowly while you know you must continue to live. Young, alive, and full of longings, I was impaled on its shaft.

There was a good spell that summer when *It* was not in evidence. I remember especially the marvelous weather, the long, soft, golden days when, busy and contented, I began to feel certain the *Thing* had gone forever.

I had come to New York from Hollywood and, having been away for three years and wanting to get my bearings, I had taken a job writing for a news service. I had been fortunate in finding an enchanting place to live, a completely furnished duplex with fireplaces and a garden, which a friend was just vacating to go overseas. I had no financial problem, I had saved much of my Hollywood money, I had a good many friends back East, and with the men being gobbled up by the army, jobs for women were opening everywhere. Besides, there was a special feeling of excitement in the air, a sense of haste and urgency, with the unexpected happening every day, that pushed up the pace of living.

There was one beautiful summer day when I awakened early, bathed and dressed carefully—I was looking forward to a lunch date with Liza, my closest friend—and thought to myself, Everything is clear now. Whatever the trouble was, it has gone at last. I remember putting on a remarkable two-piece ensemble of dark blue wool and light blue silk, purchased just before the war, and delighting in the combination of innocence and sophistication. In fact, glancing in the long mirror, I saw myself clearly that day, as, most of the time, I could not. I saw a fair-haired girl with bright, clear skin, with a certain tentative, friendly look in her sleepy blue eyes, with good legs and a good figure. Why, I wondered, why was I so embarrassed when people commented on my looks—but even as I wondered I knew the answer. "It is because of the *Thing*," I thought. "I'm afraid they will see it on me, and then—*will they run away?*"

But I was smiling. It was gone, wasn't it? And now I could think of things like that as of other unpleasant or frightening events in the past.

I had an appointment to meet Liza for the weekly luncheon of the European Club. Liza, a tall, stately, titian-haired girl, with perfect, iridescent white skin, green eyes, and a remarkable speaking voice, after some success on the stage and in radio, had just found a sponsor and was launching her own radio show. She had telephoned me to say, "I'll save a seat beside me at Table 7, Joyce. Wait till you see the job I've fixed up for you." There was something about a "really big deal" with some Washington big shot whose name I "must have seen in the paper last week" and who was doing some "fine heroic job" or other to help speed up the war production. He wanted a publicity assistant, and Liza had recommended me.

Some hours later, walking up Park Avenue in the sunny afternoon to keep my appointment, a feeling of kinship with all other living beings flowed through me like a stream of fresh, warm blood. I was looking forward to meeting Liza and thinking fondly of her. Liza was a good friend, and a person with extraordinary powers to make things happen. When I saw it was quarter to two, I realized I was late and promptly signaled a taxi.

In the crowded hotel ballrooom, some three hundred people were sitting around tables, their faces raised above half-empty coffee cups and soiled ice cream plates toward a man standing on a dais at the center of the speaker's table, talking into a microphone. I spied Liza and settled quietly into the one empty chair beside her.

All that I saw was vague those days, seen "through a glass darkly," and most of what I heard seemed to come from a distance, the sounds becoming distorted as they rumbled on to me over the dark hills of fear. What I saw now in the semi-darkened room was a short,

1 4

intense man peering through bifocal glasses, his mouth opening and closing, and what I heard were some sounds like these:

Ack ack ack . . . bang bang bang . . . boom boom boom . . . dead dead dead. Then other sounds. *Hate hate hate . . . wait wait wait . . . hope hope hope dead dead dead.* Superman . . . Blitzkreig . . . Luftwaffe . . . Mot Pulk. Beachheads . . . redheads . . . no heads . . . bang. Hate hate hate . . . work work work . . . ack ack ack . . . dead dead dead. Occupied Europe . . . end of blitz. People lie dying . . . broken in bits. French, Poles, Russians . . . and Norwegians and Dutch. Belgians and Yugoslavs . . . die in the Putsch. Goering and Hitler . . . Goebbels and Krupp. Ack ack ack . . . bang bang bang . . . swastika up. Where will it end, boys . . . will history repeat. Death walks the ocean . . . Death stalks the wheat. The Don and the Caucasus . . . Rostov, the Ukraine. The Caspian, the Volga. That man's here again. Freedom, Democracy . . . Safety ahead . . . Ack ack ack . . . boom boom boom . . . bang bang bang . . . Dead.

That was a very informative speech, Mr. Bifocal, and I'm sure we're all . . .

The party was over now, the crowd breaking up. I found myself being whisked into a taxi with Liza, cool and lovely as always, in spite of the heat, and two men, Mr. Eckhart and Mr. Whyner, who seemed to be partners. The place was bursting with VIP's, and these two were right up front. They worked together like a knife and fork; Mr. Eckhart speared the meat and Mr. Whyner ate it up. Mr. Eckhart had barely said, "Let's get a taxi," before Mr. Whyner had found one and placed us all in it.

My first impression of Mr. Eckhart, who was obviously the dollar-a-year man Liza had mentioned on the phone and obviously the boss, was not pleasant any more than it was easy to forget. He was a tall, heavy-set man in a dark blue suit, with small, heavily lashed dark blue eyes to match bushy brows that were in odd contrast to the rosy cheeks in his large, smooth face, and his small, tight little mouth that would have looked nice on a girl. The entire hulk was topped by a big head covered with thick black, crew-cut hair. The other man, Mr. Whyner, was much slimmer, lighter, and almost nebulous by comparison.

"Better hurry," Eckhart announced, as soon as we were settled in the taxi. "I've got a five o'clock appointment."

1 5

Whyner instantly leaned forward and told the driver, "Hurry, will you, buddy?" and the driver ignored the remark. I was sitting in the middle, with Mr. Eckhart on one side and Liza on the other, and Whyner trying to accustom himself to the pull-down seat. I noticed that Mr. Eckhart was looking out the window, exactly as if he were driving alone.

"You're coming back to the hotel with us, aren't you, Liza?" Whyner asked.

Liza said, "I'd better not, Bill. My car is double-parked on Central Park South."

"We're in the business of fixing summonses, huh, Hank," Bill Whyner pleaded. But Liza, who always knew the right word, ended the matter. "Now that you three know each other, you don't need me."

"Tell the driver Central Park South," Mr. Eckhart told his stooge, and Whyner again instantly obeyed.

"I hope *you're* not in a hurry," Mr. Eckhart said. I knew he was addressing me, but he was still looking out the window.

"Oh no, she's going to stick around a long time, huh, Joyce, baby?" Whyner asked and answered for me. "Matter of fact, she's free until tomorrow morning—if that's all right with you, Hank."

This was supposed to be a joke, everybody laughed at the same time. I said, "Not quite." Hank Eckhart, still looking out the window, said, "That's great." Now Liza and Hank were talking seriously, something about her coming down to Washington next week and calling him at ten o'clock. Then Liza left to get into her car. I heard her saying good-by, and asking me to call her later, and then I was sitting between these two strange people, wishing to God I were somewhere else.

Next thing I knew I was sitting in a big expensive-looking hotel suite, with a planted terrace just off the long living room, with waiters wheeling in tables of food and bottles of wine in iced buckets. As Whyner, whom Hank Eckhart called Junior, received the food, signed the checks and answered the telephone, Eckhart told me about himself. Short compact statements hit my ears. "Never eat the food at public affairs," he informed, still looking in the opposite direction. "Stomach won't take it." Disturbed by the tension, I conversed in platitudes such as, "You're so wise," and, "What did the cannibals serve today?" And examining the far side of the room, he replied, "Don't know. Drank mine," which he seemed to find amusing.

Listening, I had an unpleasant sense of having entered the wrong place by mistake, and this impression became more acute as Mr. Eckhart went on in a depressing monotone, telling me all about his personal habits.

"Boys downstairs all know when I'm here. They see me coming in and going out—so they keep the food ready for when I come back. Of course, I have my own liquor—keep it right here in the apartment. I take this place by the year—signed a five-year lease. Nice little place, too—don't you think? You can sun yourself on the terrace whenever you want."

I said, "Thanks," wondering vaguely if the main reason I disliked him so was the offensive mannerism he had of not looking at the person to whom he was speaking, or if it was more the absolute dullness of his conversation about himself, combined with the assumption that it was completely fascinating?

"Well, here we are. . . ." Junior was back, the waiter was serving the champagne. "You like Veuve-Cliquot, don't you, baby? You'd better. We drink it around here like water, huh, Hank?"

Hank didn't bother to answer. He was too busy breaking his not-looking rule and had turned his face in my direction as he lifted his glass and said, "Happy landing." I was now getting desperate to bring the situation around to its original purpose. "We'd better start talking about your project," I said. "I can't stay here long—" Plates appeared, filled with turkey, roast beef and salads, and the two men fell to on the food as if they hadn't eaten for days. The waiter kept refilling the glasses with the wine, which both men instantly seized and drank off. Then there was fruit compote and coffee and then—suddenly and miraculously—I saw the food was being wheeled out, Junior was disappearing, and Hank was moving near me—then standing near me—a mustache of milk around his unpleasant little mouth. He was looking straight at me and saying, to my absolute amazement, "Well, here I am."

I remember saying, "I can see you just the same over there," and hearing him burst out laughing, a loud, raucous laugh that stopped suddenly.

"You mean you don't want to kiss me?"

I was floundering now, hypnotized into inaction by the sudden move, my voice was gone, my hands were cold, my body was stiff with apprehension. It was his sudden, "What's the matter—you're not a child," that roused me, and after that I could hear and see with more awareness of what was happening.

"Here I am!" Milkmouth was hollering out loud. "I said don't you want to kiss me?"

I must have found my voice, too. I heard myself saying, "Not now, please—I've got to go—" And him hollering, "Go where? You don't have to go anywhere. What's the matter—don't you like me?" And me trying to say something, not making it, working hard to—and then suddenly hearing a single small, soft word come out. "No."

Mr. Eckhart started to smile. He turned around, looked at me with great interest—and when he finally spoke he lowered his voice as he asked, "What don't you like about me? There must be something?"

I had started to walk toward the door, the voice following me. "Wait a minute. Not so fast. You've got a deal here, girl. Liza said—" Just then he moved in front of me quickly and half-smothered me with a frantic, wet, nasty kiss. When he let go, I fell back against the chair. I was in a panic now. Things were becoming very vague, with only his figure enlarged bigger than life in the smoky twilight that had suddenly swept into the room before my eyes. I heard myself whispering foolishly, "Not now," something like that, and then my voice went, and I was like a doll, like a rag doll with all the life gone.

What was the matter with me? I wondered vaguely, as I watched myself in horrible fascination, complying *against my will,* in one last panic-ridden flash of insight. I didn't have to do what I was about to do. Milkmouth was right. I was not a child. I could at any minute have changed the situation. Other women did it every day—perhaps every hour—often converting the wolf into the lover or at least the friend. They did it with a word or with a glance, and after that the situation was changed.

Try! The word was there in the smoky light. Try again, and maybe somehow, just this once, you'll win! Do something, say something, make some move to stop him.

I did try . . . and found I couldn't move or speak. The I who could have done all this so easily, the I who was wise, alert and fearless, was not there any more. Rough, unpleasant hands seized me, then they were leading me, and then pushing me down, down, down. And I obeyed, silent and powerless, feeling nothing but the vague sense of an unwanted animal lashing against me, telling myself, "You won't smother, you won't die, it won't take long . . . ."

I was alone now. Junior must have come back. I could hear the two men talking in the next room.

"Now she hates me, boy!" Eckhart sounded joyous. "I'm not kidding with this one. I tell you, Junior, it's just what the doctor ordered. She hates my goddamned guts."

It sounded like Junior was congratulating him. I heard him say, "You couldn't have planned anything like that—huh, Hank?" But I wasn't thinking about them any more. What had happened between Hank and me had at least created a temporary kind of safety, and now I could think, though what I thought about was certainly not pleasant.

I must get out of here, I thought, *and quickly!* Then, *Oh God, I've done it again—as I have so many times before. The same damned helplessness, the same terrifying coma, the same pattern. Why? why, oh, why? . . . And with this horrible man. . . .*

And now, afterwards, it would be the same, too. The same sense of humiliation, the same shame, the same God-awful inconvenience and futility, for what could be worse than this—the giving of your own self, the most personal part of it, against your will to the very people you wanted least?

I was looking for the bathroom when I heard Hank close behind me, talking in a tense whisper.

". . . be busy for a while now, honey. Junior'll tell you all about the deal. Crazy about you, understand? We'll get up a letter . . . tell Junior anything you want. . . ."

Then I was in another room, a camera out of focus picking up a blurred picture. Everything looked overwhelmingly big and strange. I saw studio couches covered with Chinese red, bookcases filled with those phony cardboard covers, sets of Tennyson and Sir Walter

Scott. I heard words and phrases, names of munitions makers I recognized from the newspapers, as Hank's voice floated in now and then from the next room. Commissions, percentages, sums of money: ten thousand, five thousand, fifty thousand.

There was Junior walking up and down, yakking away at me.

"You've just walked into the sweetest little setup you ever saw. You won't even see the boss—except for week ends. Now listen, I'll give you all the info, see? Hank wants the whole business to be patriotic as hell. Over-all picture of the emergency. Telling civilians and manufacturers how to operate! First title we thought of was *YOUR COUNTRY NEEDS IT NOW*, but maybe you can think of something more spectacular—like for instance *SALVAGE*."

Words. *Scrap iron, Steel* and *Allied Metals, Rubber*. And talk. And more talk. "Angle is—well, it goes something like this, see? In a democratic nation why, every man and woman is a volunteer— not like with the Axis where you get forced into action. Great, huh? I was always fast with ideas. Every executive—every superintendent —every foreman in every plant—it's for them! And it's for every worker—every automobile mechanic—and for garage owners and junk dealers—and every goddamned housewife and husband—and their kids—it's for every boy and girl."

The man who was "head of the biggest sales engineering firm in the country" and had "handled more Navy contracts in the past six months than any other six firms" apparently wanted a public relations job to create an aura of patriotism around his name, and a helpmate in his deals—sex, female—who would set up parties to entertain Army and Navy brass, newspaper people, models, actresses and anybody else who happened to be floating around. And, *him*.

At one point in the proceedings Junior opened a closet full of women's clothes, taking time out from the information to touch them lovingly—especially the fur coats, the boxes of nylon stockings and the bottles of expensive perfume. "He got them for Melba—that was his last girl—but it's all yours now. He told me to tell you, you can take them home! Now I ask you, is he a regular guy?"

Junior was busily typing a letter when I discovered and opened a new door, and started out.

"Wait a minute!" He could hardly get his breath. "You're not leaving! Say, I thought you were putting on an act. Jesus, maybe you mean it. Well, I'm a sonofabitch. You don't seem to get it, baby—you've hit the jackpot!"

I said No, I didn't get it, the champagne had gone to my head, I wasn't feeling well and wanted to go. Words ran out of Junior faster and faster . . . so fast in fact they had a queer compelling fascination that kept me there, listening.

"Look, he loves it when they hate him. I tell you, you two are made for each other—why, you go together like ham and eggs. Melba was putting it on—*but you mean it.* He told me, he said you're the real thing, but I didn't buy it."

"Buy what?" I managed to ask.

"Look, like I'm trying to tell you. See, he likes it when they're revolted by him. That gives him the thrill, see—the thing he needs, get it? I tell you, you've hit the jackpot, baby. Now do you get it?"

I said, "No—not quite."

"He's a sadist, you dope. He likes to hear their bones breaking!"

A woman at the desk in the corridor stared at me curiously as she asked what room I wanted. I told her I was looking for the elevator.

"It's right in front of you."

It was too, but in my anxiety to get out I hadn't seen it. *Again,* that was all I could think of. *I had done it again.*

Always, after one of these experiences, I would have to force myself into going on. Take hold of myself with my mind and talk, talk fast. This was no exception. In fact, coming as it did literally out of the blue, on the heels of a spell of freedom and hope, I knew the aftermath would be bad.

Walking out in the hot street, I talked to myself, trying to still the clamor of the heavy, mortified creature inside me, something like a mother trying to soothe a child. *You're in the street now and nothing more can happen. Your name is Joyce MacIver. Just keep on walking and soon we'll be home.*

But the street is filled with strangers, it would whisper back. There is no love in the street. The street is filling up with big cold

2 1

people, men and women with cold eyes like fish. It is dangerous walking in the street.

Not now, the enemy is gone. You got away, he didn't kill you. Hold up your head, and walk on. Some day things will be better. Hold on to me, and maybe one day somehow we'll find our way together.

Some day. That was what I promised my child self. But when would some day be? Tom-toms were beating behind the buildings. The sun stared down with its red-hot, blinding eye. The air was hot, hotter than before. The child I dragged along with me whimpered harder. If you loved me, you would know I am burning alive down here—and you would let me out.

But I was a stern mother. *I can't let you out,* I went on. *I must go along with you into the fire. I don't know where the exit is. Come on,* I commanded, *I'll take you home—home where the nice quiet furniture is. Here, I'll even take you home in a taxi. I'll show you the pretty tree in the back yard.*

And so somehow I was home again. Taking a shower, letting the water pour over me. The water, dashing against my skin, washed white flesh into pink and warm flesh into cool, but it stopped short of washing away the black memory that would be staring me in the face now for days. It was not so much the actual recalling of what had transpired, or the re-enactment of the crime—I could brush that away somehow, push it down into the limbo of other memories. It was the quiet, deep-seated, terrible knowledge that I had capitulated against my will. I had collaborated in my own undoing.

And worse: it was not only to Hank Eckhart, it was to anyone who attacked, who demanded something of me, for that was the signal for the trance. Hence, in a sense, I capitulated to the entire adult world.

22

CHAPTER TWO

. . . .

THE TELEPHONE WAS RINGING. IT MIGHT BE HE, I THOUGHT INSTANTLY.
It probably is he. Oh, if only the maid were there. Trafinia, the
West Indian woman who came down from Harlem to clean the
place, she would tell him I had gone out, gone away. But she wasn't
there.

Now the new trouble was beginning, or a new phase of the old
trouble. I had to get out of it, as quickly, politely, evasively as possible—preferably without a trace. I had thought often of discon-
necting the phone, but I knew I didn't dare—the apprehension
would be worse without a telephone. Besides, I needed the telephone,
not only socially but in connection with my work. I didn't dare
leave it unanswered.

I lifted it up gingerly, tried disguising my voice. Hello. . . . Ah,
it wasn't he, or any of the others. It was Red, old friend, Red the
safe, the man who was not a threat.

"Hello, Joyce. You haven't forgotten—we're due at the Sarensens
at seven-thirty."

Ah, the Sarensens: more safety, a lovely spell of no-attack in
which to recover. "No, I haven't forgotten. I'm dressing now," I
told him quickly, gratefully.

"What are you wearing—what color, I mean?"

I pleaded, "Don't bring me any flowers—please, Red. After all,
there's a war on."

"Oh, that, sure. Only I'm going away soon, you know. Mightn't
get another chance to hang some flowers on something sweet. . . ."

I dived away from the emotion there at the other end of the
wire as I told him, "The black dress," and something sharp, like

a knife, leapt and twisted inside near my heart, and the blood of guilt was dripping somewhere, and I could hear it as I dressed.

That summer. Whenever I spoke of it later, I called it "the first time the floor caved in" or "my first try," or sometimes, writing in a diary for relief, "my first inquiry." But to myself in secret I called it "my first round with *Devman*," for that was the name I called *It. Devman,* the curse, or the Thing.

Devman was no stranger to me. I had met him as a young child. Aunt Rose, the wonderful, warm Negro woman who came to our house from time to time, introduced us all to Devman. Whenever we were bad, quarreling and fighting among ourselves, it was simply because Devman, the Devilman, had come in. I can still see Rose's thick pink lips muttering, "Looka that! Devilman come and got my babies." If the situation grew worse, as it often did, and Rose was forced to use pressure to keep us from hurting one another, she would talk more sternly to it. "Get out of here, Devilman. Clear out, and doan come back." Never once did Rose admit that we had misbehaved and needed stern treatment. It was always Devilman who deserved the punishment, and her admonitions to him often had an instantaneous effect, for we quickly picked up her thought and felt innocent of all wrongdoing.

I can remember her holding me screaming on her lap and saying, "Wait a minute now, honey—I got t'make sure he's gone." She would wait, her eyes half-closed, and speak only after the clamor had died down. "There now. He's cleared out."

When Rose herself was angry, cursing her stove, her cake batter or her pots and pans, it was always Devilman. "Turns up in this kitchen like an ole penny." It was never Rose herself. Rose talked to other unseen "people" too, went straight into the face of those mysterious parts of herself and called them by name, but Devilman, or *Devman* as we called him, somehow seemed the more personal and powerful to us as he had mysterious ways of entering us, and that was in itself a fascinating matter to contemplate. I thought of him as a great black shadow in which something was hiding, a bad thing, and it came and went as it pleased.

Throughout my life I had often thought of *Devman*. I knew him as a man of many faces, capable of extraordinary doings. He it was who struck suddenly, making me into his creature. One day, powerful and wily, he forced me to do things I did not want to do, and another day, he had me cringing with terror. Now I was being pushed into the arms of people I didn't even like, and now I was being turned in disgust from the gentle, loving ones I needed so badly.

It is all *Devman,* I thought, picking up the one sound note in the crazy symphony of childhood, handed down to me by an African Negro with the desperate abiding wisdom afloat in the old slave ships: "It isn't *me* and, therefore, someday he will go."

And it was this conviction, given to me so early in the battle, a great gift, too, and a gift of love, that stayed my spirit in the critical times ahead and somehow carried me through.

I always felt better when I was dressed. Safer, that is—*alerted.* Someone was going to get me sometime, it was a question of time and . . . well, somehow it seemed wiser to be fully clothed and ready . . . if one is ever ready to be murdered . . . But now, to-night, there would be a reprieve, a few hours of safety. Red was coming, a pleasant evening stretched ahead, and Red would protect me from all harm. He wouldn't if he really knew, of course. He was doing it because he loved me—but that was in itself a problem and an accusation, one more thing I didn't want and couldn't face, one more demand. . . .

We were going that night to a party for Russian War Relief and, having decided to pass up the long dinner, speeches and entertain-ment and arrive in time for the dancing, we'd planned to enjoy a leisurely dinner together before meeting the Sarensens and the rest of the crowd. It should have been a pleasant evening, in spite of the holocaust of the afternoon—that had been before and would be again—but as soon as we arrived at the restaurant, things began to happen. . . . I had gone up the stairs to claim a scarf I'd checked on arrival, and as I came on back down the steps, I noticed Red had moved to a table in the bar. There he was, having a drink and watching me, all the way down the steps. He stood up and smiled as I came toward the table. For some reason I disliked him when he stared at me as he did then. His eyes seemed suddenly to grow bigger and soft, very soft—why, they actually seemed out of place in a tall man with a strong jaw and bright red hair. There was something wrong, or something that rubbed me the wrong way. The crispness seemed to have left him, and he looked limp and kind of broken, as he said, "Joyce, will you do me a favor?"

"What?" I asked, but I was irritated; whatever it was I knew I wouldn't want to do it. His voice had changed, too, I thought. Wasn't masculine, the way it had been when he arrived. Sounded low and—pleading.

"Go up the stairs again and come walking down—just like you did just now."

"Oh, come on, Red—*why?*"

"Because I want to see you come down again."

Resentfully I flounced back up the steps. He is queer, I thought. Sentimental. A real man wouldn't ask anybody to do such a foolish thing. I hated him for it—much more than the occasion warranted—that I knew. Besides, he was going away soon, and perhaps he was a normal human being capable of storing up happy memories, but I hated him just the same. The headwaiter looked bewildered when he saw me coming down the steps again. I felt uncomfortable, but Red was pleased.

"You don't know what that meant to me," he said, still with that soft, mushy look on his face. We had a whole drink together at the table in the bar, without his saying another word or taking his eyes from my face. The place buzzed with chatter, made a safe little island in which I could float for a while.

"The resemblance is remarkable." Red was still looking at me, but talking half to himself. "It's not an actual resemblance, I guess. It's the feeling of the resemblance. It's the—the sense you give me. It quickens me. Everything lights up and starts moving."

"What's the matter with you tonight?" I knew he wanted me to ask who he thought I resembled, but the whole thing annoyed me and made me feel spiteful. "Making people put on a show in public—seeing resemblances—talking to yourself." But he actually seemed not to hear me. He went on staring at me, with that strange wide-eyed look on his face, until I became so annoyed I began to eye the mound of cold salmon in the dining room and to dream of escaping into food.

"Don't be angry, Joyce. It's a teacher I used to know—when I was a young boy, he was a young man. A teacher and a poet. There's something about your face—and about you, altogether—that brings him back to me very keenly."

"What was he like?"

"Like you—around the face. He—he leaned on me pretty hard later on."

"I'll watch out for that."

"You needn't. What he wanted from me was nothing to what he gave me. He was a cripple, Kenny was. He had a clubfoot, and so he could never get the things he wanted—girls, jobs, anything. He took what was left and as a result he was full of hate."

"Well, thanks—"

So he had seen. Maybe he knew, I thought, as he went on, drinking more and more, talking on deeper levels than he meant . . . "Why can't you swim out of this muddy water, Joyce? It's blue and clear somewhere. Other people reach it, and maybe you can, too. I'll help you—and maybe we can make it together."

I sighed and drank more. Why couldn't I like Red, I wondered, as I felt myself moving away from him, running. A good thing showed up, and I stood still in my tracks, or moved away in the opposite direction. "What do you say, Joyce? Tell me. I'm no oil painting. Just a businessman who hates business. I'm likely to make a brilliant flop of everything—but then maybe not, maybe not. You have something I need. . . ."

I arrived at the big sprawling party for Russian War Relief in a new mood, with a certain keen sense of anticipation I often had upon entering a new place. Red had left me to go and check his hat. As I walked up to the bar, stopping to talk to friends, it hit me so hard I must have been stunned for a few seconds. I remember staring absentmindedly at the Sarensens' nice long pleasant faces as they chattered away, without actually seeing them. Then, as other friends came by, I must have looked distractedly at their familiar faces. Somebody said, "Where are you?" and I came back, realizing I had let greetings go unanswered—as I searched with frenzied excitement among the faces in the crowd.

I was looking for someone—someone I must have lost somewhere long ago. It was almost not a person, in the sense that all these other persons were. Something bigger and greater and somehow different.

Thinking: maybe he's here tonight, in this very place. Maybe he's here, looking for me.

There was more to it than this. The one I was looking for was not any specific person I had ever known or could remember. It was more like—the rest of myself. The other half with which, or with whom, once I came together I would be complete. The one who had the key to my being, and who would instantly unlock the closed door and let me in. The one who had that which I needed to live, and without which I was doomed.

Late that night, after the drinking and the dancing, when the party was tapering off, it hit me. He is not here. All the guests have come—a thousand faces, moving around, and I have seen them all, now I know. He has not arrived.

The scene changed. The faces dulled. I didn't care now. I remembered Red saying, at one point near the end of the evening, "What happened to you all of a sudden?" and my answering, "Nothing—why?" and his saying, "Don't kid me. You had a date with somebody —and he stood you up," and my denying it, and his final flare of temper. Then, "Come on. You're a dead duck on the dance floor. You might as well get loaded."

CHAPTER THREE

· · · · · · · · ·

IT HAPPENED A FEW MONTHS LATER ON ONE OF THE WORST OF THOSE
August days when the heat comes at you early in the morning like
some nagging old harridan, and wakes you by breathing her fetid
breath in your face. I remember practically the minute it happened,
the way you remember the minute you began falling in love or having
a heart attack. Shortly before noon, about a quarter to twelve. It
came to me like a message: *You are in danger. The bluff won't work
any more, you can't stay where you are if you want to go on living.*

They had caught up with me at last. I had hidden out from them
for a long time. Eaten, slept, loved and worked, in hiding. All the
time, of course, they had been tailing me, but I had kept on the jump,
year in, year out, sacrificing anything to keep from being caught. Now
they had hit town and spotted the house. Now, *this minute,* they were
watching, waiting, biding their time. The jig was up.

I was sitting at my desk in the upstairs living room of the duplex
apartment on East Thirty-seventh Street. I remembered the sentence I
had just finished typing—about Japanese pilots dressing in black silk
robes, a pre-suicidal funeral before taking off in planes to bomb the
Allies.

I looked at the furniture in the living room—the sofa by the fireplace covered with chintz, the two big chairs facing it, my desk with
the green lamp; but they seemed to draw away, silent, staring. I
walked to the window in the bedroom, looked down at the back yard
with its one plump little tree like a plateful of green salad surrounded
by the long, grim buildings, and vaguely sought some strength, some
hint of a plan.

I lit a cigarette, and sat still, thinking. Something terrible is going to happen to me, *soon.* I walked across the living room and looked out the front windows. Three soldiers were passing on the other side of the street, walking in the hot sun. Probably on their way to one of the endless rows of bars on Third Avenue. I remember what they were singing—*April in Paris.*

I followed them with my eyes, listening, clinging, but they turned at the corner and were gone, taking their melody with them.

Who would help me? I thought of Red. He was at camp now at Fort Benning, Georgia, eating bad food, cursing the training, and writing frantic letters trying to get switched into some safer spot, any little cubicle in the protective breast of the Pentagon. No, I couldn't ask Red. He was looking for help himself. I thought of writing him a letter. *Dearest Red: Don't be depressed when you find I am no longer here.* I knew I never would. I'd write him the same kind of letters I'd been writing. *Everything here is fine, honey. I am expecting good news for you by the minute and then you'll be back home. It can't be long. . . .*

It wasn't any good standing near the window, looking into a hot street spotted with strangers. I walked back into the room, and as I did I saw somebody coming toward me through the long mirror in the next room. That's me, I thought. That girl with the light hair, a shiny sunburned face and big, scared eyes. I looked and looked, as I often did. I wasn't admiring myself, I was looking to see if it was showing yet. But it wasn't showing, it never had been, and when I was completely certain that it wasn't I felt slightly better.

The bell rang. I was always afraid when the doorbell rang. A wave of terror, and in it was a thin thread of hope. It might just possibly be the one who was coming to save me . . . the remarkable strong person I was always looking for, who knew my side of the story.

It was hot in the downstairs part of the duplex.

"Who's there?"

"Hello, Joyce. It's Mat. Open up."

Relieved, I opened the door and a tall soft man in a seersucker suit walked in. His round red face with the sharp gray eyes looked fresh as an open melon. "I tried to call you but your line was busy so I thought I'd drop over." He was in the room now. "Say, what's the matter? Have you got a hangover?"

"No, I'm fine. Glad to see you. Come on upstairs."

Matthew Davis was an ambitious lawyer who had migrated from Brooklyn to Park Avenue. Now there was another live human being in the place, and with this temporary protection I started feeling better.

"What would you like, Mat—coffee or a drink?"

"Liquor. A nice cold drink'd be great. It's ninety outside, going up to ninety-four the paper says."

As I sat drinking with Matthew, the terror moved a few steps away. Matthew had wide cold gray eyes, completely indifferent until livened by just two expressions that seemed to say, I think I'm going to get sex, or I think I'm going to get money. When he was in a relaxed state, in the company of friends, his conversation went easily into a series of personal resentments beat out of his mouth like news off a ticker tape.

"Saw Colonel Richards last week," he was saying. "Had to go into the Pentagon anyway so I thought I'd try and get Red straightened out. The sonofabitch gave me the prettiest brush-off you ever saw. So scared of being shipped out himself he wouldn't do a damned thing." He waited. "Don't look so worried. I heard something about the Colonel. Seems Dickie boy accepted a bribe for helping a certain German dentist on the Coast. If it's true, it's just enough to have his ass kicked out of the army."

The terror had moved up. Anything I saw or heard that brought home the evil in the world could bring it up front, and now I wasn't seeing too clearly. I remember seeing Matthew as a blob of sunburn above a seersucker suit. I looked again and he was like some strange fish swimming toward me through water. He was talking, too. "I'm going now," he said. I remember thinking, he's going . . . even the sunburned fish is turning away from me. I'll be alone, caught down here in the dark cold waters, unable to move or cry out.

I stood still, feeling the wild flood tide come rushing in, tearing at the roots of everything I knew. I could still see the blob of seersucker suit, the face with teeth and a pair of eyes, but now the parts of a man were running into each other like a water color left out in the rain. And it was speaking.

"Hey, what's the matter? You want me to fix you a drink?"

I nodded. I was coming back now. Slowly. The room and its furnishings began to seem smaller and further away, shrunken down to some crazy scale as a city street appears after the spaces in the country. I could feel myself again, the old familiar fears. Matthew

3 1

was putting ice into a glass, I could hear the cubes tinkling, and I knew I was in danger.

I had to detain him at all costs. I thought desperately of hiring him to stay with me. I might offer him a hundred dollars a day—he would never be able to turn that down. That great solid rock of a Matthew, that man of gold and steel. I could hear him talking again.

"Well, here you are. You've got enough Scotch to float a ship. Where'd you get it, you hoarder?" Then, "You're not pregnant, are you? Sally gets like that when she's pregnant."

"Could be." I knew I wasn't, but pregnancy was at least mentionable, whereas what I had was better left unnamed.

My eyes stayed riveted to his face as I swallowed the whiskey. These few minutes we were sharing together in time were crucial now. Come to think of it, he was the only strong person I knew. I could win or lose, depending upon how I handled the next few minutes.

I heard him say, "Well, I'll be going." There they were again, the fatal words. I heard myself say, "Not now. Don't go. I'm scared."

He gave me a sharp look. "What are you scared of?" he asked. And I said, "I'll try to tell you."

I wouldn't tell him the truth, of course, but maybe I'd think of something clean and respectable, I thought, as I heard him say, "I'll have to get that Lincoln character on the phone, he's meeting me for lunch."

Those footsteps again, such a nice crunchy sound. And his voice, reassuring.

"Women. Tell you, guy's gotta have second sight to figure out what goes on."

Then Matthew was on the telephone, and his words were a lifeline in the void. The minute he stopped speaking I felt the terror rising and stirring toward me. The red flag was up, and murder was in the air. And then he was back and talking calmly to me.

"So you're scared, huh? Well you're not the only one, I know all about it. Comes on you out of nowhere, is that right?" I nodded. "Sure, I know. I had it crossing the San Francisco bridge. Got it so bad I felt like jumping. Couldn't keep my hands on the wheel. Sally had to hold me and take over the car."

"What did you do about it?"

"Soon as I got back to town I went to a psychiatrist and got cured. I've never had it since."

"Cured! How long did it take?"

"Three months."

"You mean in three months this doctor cured you of a thing like that?"

He nodded. "Now listen, Joyce, you're in a panic. You need help. I think my doctor would see you. Ramsey's his name. Here, take this pen and write it down. Doctor Ramsey. Circle five seven five nine eight. I'll call him first."

I wrote down the name and telephone number and Matthew went off to telephone the doctor. There was a possibility of my going overseas—in fact, I was to hear about the job that afternoon. It was in London, and what with London being bombed those nights, I'd stand as good a chance as anybody else of being killed, and then I wouldn't need this Dr. Ramsey. I went to get fresh drinks and when I returned with the glasses Matthew was waiting.

"Well, I fixed it." I felt hope, long choked, rising like a bird in my breast, winging its way up. "He can see you. You call him as soon as I go."

"I'll never forget what you've done for me," I whispered as I followed him to the door, so flushed with hope and bursting with gratitude I hardly heard his parting words.

"Never mind that stuff. You hang on to that bank account. I've got the Indian sign on you. I like sad women—especially when they're young and rich."

The minute the door closed on Matthew, I hurried upstairs and dialed the number. I had by then conceived a vague but thrilling image of this Dr. Ramsey who had saved Matthew from the demons of the San Francisco Bridge and who was waiting at that moment a few buildings away to do the same for me. I pictured him as being extremely tall, about eight feet. I couldn't quite make out his features at that point, but I knew he was handsome without being showy, a cross between Cary Grant and Jesus Christ, with the beard removed and with an enormous extra scuttle of masculinity thrown in. Say as if the Rock of Gibraltar should become a man, that would be about it.

The telephone rang three times. Then a soft voice, located way down at the bottom of the line, said Hello.

I said, "Hello. Is Dr. Ramsey there?"

"This is Dr. Ramsey."

I told him my name. "I seem to be having some trouble," I blurted out, and giggled, finding it suddenly funny.

"Ye-es?" The voice cooed like a bird. "Can you be here at two o'clock?"

I said, "Yes," and he went on cooing, "All right, then I'll see you at two o'clock."

CHAPTER FOUR

. . . . . .

IT WAS TWELVE THIRTY-FIVE. ONE HOUR AND TWENTY-FIVE MINUTES to wait before I could see Dr. Ramsey.

What would I tell this doctor? Matthew had only one symptom, or so he said—fear of crossing a bridge—whereas I, I had as many as I could count on my two hands.

I too was afraid of heights. The minute an airplane took off from the ground, my insides shrank in terror. I was afraid to be alone, but I was often terribly disturbed in the presence of large groups of people. I was afraid to go to sleep, afraid of lying awake, and afraid of people walking behind me on the street. I was afraid of any threat of attack, a voice raised in anger, just or unjust, afraid of any demands made upon me, forced to comply at once, afraid of success and afraid of failure.

Not afraid of love, oh no, I loved everybody, taking people at face value and being constantly surprised and delighted by their interest in me, doing anything they asked as long as it was for them and not for myself. I could still work and hold down a job, as long as it wasn't anything I really wanted. I could deliver as long as someone else got the credit. I already showed signs of becoming a confirmed ghost writer, while my house was filled with my own half-finished books, the half-alive people screaming in the steel drawers of the filing cabinet, two with contracts stuck like pacifiers in their open mouths. These books had all begun in a great blaze of energy, but just as they were getting near the finish, I would be stopped, just as surely as if a hand had reached out and turned off the current, and from then on, the stuff would turn into dust. Strange dust, too. Sometimes, picking it up, I could barely recognize it.

About sex now, I loved the stuff, I'd tell him that fast, but the thrilling peak of human closeness, the Great Ride Over the Mountain where you were supposed to go off into star-studded space, with the female pearls inside bursting and flowing into the lava of life, that experience so ineptly and functionally labeled *having an orgasm,* had I ever had that? I didn't think so.

At two o'clock I entered a building on West Fifty-third Street, found the office and went into the waiting room. I noticed the faded chintz covers on the sofa and chairs, the small glass ashtrays, the old copies of the *New Yorker* mailed originally to J. R. Burroughs in Spuyton-Duyvil.

Behind a closed door, I heard voices growing suddenly louder. The door opened, and a woman came out, followed by a tall, thin man who glanced at me, closed the outside door softly on the woman and said, "Won't you come in?"

The inner office was heavy with smoke. Through the fog I saw a man with a long, soft, yellow face, and pale eyes and light straw-colored hair. There was weakness and pain in the face, but the deciding characteristic was pain. I noticed his tobacco-stained fingers, and his thin wiry neck. He looked something like a chicken, I thought. A depressed chicken.

"Do you feel like talking?"

"Yes. There's only one trouble. I don't know where to begin."

He glanced at me and smiled, and I smiled back. I had heard about patients falling in love with these mental-help boys, and quickly decided I could have no such feeling toward Ramsey. Nobody with a face as soft and yellow as that, or with hair that long, could attract me. Didn't he ever see a barber? He had as much sex appeal as a milkshake, I thought, and might therefore be as soothing. I felt safe.

"It hit me this morning," I said.

"What hit you this morning?"

"This *thing.*"

"Ye-es? What is this *thing* like?"

Should I tell him, or would he decide immediately that I was crazy and draw away in disdain? Oh well, I thought, if what I have is going to cause my being snatched and confined to the booby hatch, perhaps after arrest by the police, better to have the first accusation made by somebody like this. With his long nasty face and stained fingers, he wouldn't stand up very well in court, or, better still, he might even die before he got there.

"I'm afraid."

"What are you afraid of? Do you know?"

"Yes. I know."

"What is it? Could you tell me about it?"

"Of being killed."

There! I had gone and blurted it out. He looked up with interest. You look scared yourself, I thought.

"Is anybody after you?"

"No one that I know of."

"Have you ever done anything—that would make anyone want to kill you?"

I thought carefully before I answered "No," and he seemed to relax, at least he lit another cigarette.

"Anything more?"

"That's enough, isn't it?"

"I imagine there's more—much more. How long have you had this feeling?"

"A long time, I think. It comes and goes. Only this morning it got so bad—something seemed to *crack*."

"Did anything happen to bring this on?"

"Nothing I can think of. Matthew came by—but I had it before he got there. Then, when he said he was going to go, I was afraid to be left alone."

"Then Matthew had nothing to do with bringing it on?"

"Oh, no. In fact, he helped greatly. He told me he'd felt like that— or something like that. And he came to you—and you cured him in three months. That was the best news I had ever heard. I'd never thought anything like this could be cured."

"But you found out from Matthew it could be cured—so you took the step, is that it?"

Dr. Ramsey was beaming now, and I was rattling on.

"In three months. It sounded quite wonderful, so I called you immediately. Do you think mine can be cleaned up in three months— like Matthew's?"

"I don't know yet. We'll have to find out more about it first. What did you do this morning?"

3 7

What did I do this morning? Why, this morning I woke up and—there it was. A hot summer's day with the sunshine pouring into the room, it was there looking at me. The quiet furniture, the emptiness, the sounds from far away, all were charged with apprehension. I got up, had my shower, drank coffee, went to my typewriter, did my work. It was all so easy to describe. I was writing about the Jap pilots chained to the controls—about their having a pre-suicidal funeral—when the message came. The sense of immediate danger. *The past has caught up with you. They know where you are. They're closing in.*

"You were writing about death," he said. "The pilots chained to the controls. Do you think that had anything to do with your panic?"

"No. I've had it before when I was writing about Christmas."

"But you were alone. Are you afraid of being alone?"

"Yes, often. But I'm often afraid in groups."

Uncomfortable, lonely in a group of gay people, looking for someone who isn't there. Who. . . ? I don't know, but I will know him when I see him, and he will know me. Someone deep and sweet and familiar as the water in a long-forgotten well. If he had come, I wouldn't be here.

It was quarter to three now, and I had told him almost nothing.

"Do you know what it is I have? I mean—can you tell from my description?" I asked hastily.

"Yes, I believe so."

"Is there anything different—anything special about my case—I mean, something that might set it apart from the others you've cured?"

"Every case is different, just as every person is different. But there's nothing incurable in your case—if that's what you mean. Nothing that I can see as yet."

He went with me to the door, muttered a nice soft muddy "Good-by," and there I was again, walking through the lobby and out into the hot street. I was bursting with the joy of my new hope. Imagine being cured! Imagine going to sleep at night and waking up in the morning without that damned thing lying in wait! Listen to me, I was already calling it *that* damned thing instead of *this* damned thing, as if it had miraculously become a thing of the past.

Monday, promptly at two o'clock, I was back at Dr. Ramsey's. Again on Wednesday at the same time, and again on Friday. The waiting room began to seem less ominous than it had at first, the sessions like an hour of reprieve, a suspension of the execution.

"Why?" The birdman cooed this question into the cigarette smoke. "Why were you so frightened of Mr. Eckhart?"

How could I describe the burning memory of that big evil blue man who stood over me, complete with custom-made suit and milk mustache, warming up to the demolition of a new flame? Just a man, another man, so many pounds of protein. It all reminded me of someone—or something. . . . I couldn't remember. I kept going back.

"Stay with the present," the doctor said, but there was no clue in the present. Against instructions I began turning the key, and glanced quickly into the chamber of horrors I kept inside me, going from one dusty face to the other. My mother, a sad pretty face. My father, a pair of big red eyes. My uncles, warm shadows and cold shadows. My aunts, oh yes, my aunts, the big breasts and the gentle hands. My grandpa and my grandma, two silver angels. And Aunt Rose, a hot brown angel. The silky touchable people and the people who were dry and gone. There they all were, standing in my head. And the sounds. My mother's piano playing, my father, he liked to crack his knuckles. . . .

"That stooge Whyner said Hank Eckhart liked to hear bones cracking." I was talking fast. "But it wasn't his own bones. It was women's bones. He liked to hear their bones cracking when he made love to them—or murdered them. . . ."

"Why do you always come back to murder?"

I thought, Why? and stared into a great black silence—in which, after a time, I could barely discern a threatening swallowing movement—was it inside me or out there in the room?

Certain facts I knew as only a child knows in the deep clear wisdom of the new cells. The first wisdom. *I don't belong Here. This is The Wrong Place.* Something went wrong somewhere and I got shoved in Here by mistake. I wish, oh how I wish I could go where I belong, and where they will know me. But I don't even know who *they* are, much less where the place is or how to get There.

Wrong Place was interesting, there was no doubt about that, but never was it interesting to me in the same way as to those to whom it was home and who were supposed to be Here. Wrong Place was alive with fascinating new sights and sounds, ever new objects to smell and taste and feel. In Wrong Place you could look up and see an immense blue bowl far above your head, or you could smell the flowers, feel the sun warming your skin and listen to the friendly drone of insects. You could walk in bare feet on the grass, feel the cool damp earth or the warm delicious sand, smell hot bread baking in an oven, bite into a freshly baked pie, or jump into the big wide-open laps and hug and kiss or go to sleep.

There was a great deal of trouble Here, I could see that all right. Largely because the people Here didn't seem to know where they were and kept up a constant useless communication with some Other Place where there were supposed to be other more important people whom they called at various times—God, Jesus, The Lord, Our Father, or that scary name, The Holy Ghost. And these were all people about whom they seemed to know almost nothing.

It was dangerous Here, and anything could happen, for some kind of battle was raging all the time. There was murder in the air. Once, when I was very little, between two and three, I heard them talking about it in the dining room: my Aunt Penny (for Penrose), my mother, and my Aunt Margie, while I was playing in the kitchen. *He* had done something *terrible* to *her,* but she was *little* and didn't *know* or couldn't *understand.*

I was instantly alert in every fiber of my being. A *man* had attacked a *baby.* I saw a big naked ugly hairy man coming up against a little frightened baby. The baby was a girl baby, oh I knew that all right. I could see her clearly too, no matter how hard they tried to keep their voices down, I knew: this was a male and female situation. *It* was *terrible* what this big crazy ugly hairy man had done. *It* might have *broken her bones. It* might have *smothered her. It* might have *killed her. He didn't realize,* they said. *He didn't know what he was doing,* and that made it somehow better. *He was in one of his spells,* and of course the baby *didn't understand* what had happened . . . but I knew different. The big ugly crazy man knew perfectly well what he was doing, and so did the baby know.

There was more. Someone had come in right in the midst of the terrible thing the man was doing to the baby. He had quickly recovered his senses, hidden the weapon, and pretended that nothing unusual was happening. It would never happen again, of course. Lightning never strikes twice in the same place.

I didn't believe a word of this last part of what they were saying because their words didn't fit with the pictures that came through to me. If the crazy man didn't know what he was doing, why did he stop suddenly when he was caught red-handed? The shadowy outlines of the big hairy crazy man with the wild eyes was with me there in the kitchen, and so was the little girl baby. And I was with them, too.

Next I heard my name being called, "Joyce, are you asleep?" and then Aunt Penny came in, carrying the big tray with the coffee cups. "Little pitchers have big ears," she announced, as she discovered me standing near the doorway.

This was not the first time I had heard these stories of violence being discussed by adults. I had heard tales of terrible fights and stabbings in the alleys, kidnapings and even murder, and these were all exciting, even though terrifying. The names of the killers, whenever they cropped up, were more scary even than the name of the Holy Ghost, that Great Big Cold Shadow with a Man hiding in it.

It was already fascinating to be scared, and no wonder either, for that was one thing the inmates Here knew all about. They were all afraid, and they knew how to pass it on.

At some point during those weeks I began to think Dr. Ramsey did not resemble a chicken at all. I did not fully understand his method. He believed in having his patients "utilize" their drives, he said. I should seek out stronger and healthier people, he suggested, and see how I felt in their company. I had thought of sharing my apartment, but in discussing this with him, the combination of Florence Nightingale and Abraham Lincoln he suggested seemed impossible to find among my current group.

My job kept me busy all day and sometimes in the evening, rounding up war news and interviewing people. I found my problems did not interfere with my doing the work, and because I was out of the office most of the time, I was able to keep the three weekly appointments with Dr. Ramsey. The hours flew by, the weeks turned into months, but the panic kept on. I was afraid alone, and afraid in company. I was even afraid of the doctor, fearful of displeasing him and thereby losing whatever help I was receiving.

I kept wanting to talk about murder, as this was uppermost in my mind. No matter how much I tried to focus on my current life it seemed to me that it was somehow irrelevant because, by ways and means I couldn't understand, the past was still going on. I kept going back to my early life, especially to my father, who was cruel, moody, capable of violent tempers, and whom I considered to be mysteriously responsible for most of my difficulties. Dr. Ramsey did not agree with me, and kept bringing me back to the present. He was, of course, right, I assumed, and I must be wrong.

"Your father was a rider, wasn't he?" Dr. Ramsey asked. "Why don't you ride horseback?"

"Is that a suggestion—I mean, something I should do—that might be curative?"

"Yes, it is. I think it will make quite a difference."

I walked out into the beautiful autumn afternoon thinking: So now I'm to imitate my father. He was just about the last person in the entire world I would want to imitate in anything, I would just as soon have identified with Hitler, but Dr. Ramsey's suggestions were sacred to me so I knew I would do whatever he said would help. I got out my jodhpurs and went horseback riding in Central Park every morning when the weather permitted.

CHAPTER FIVE

. . . . . .

ONE AFTERNOON AS I WALKED HOME, STOPPING HERE AND THERE on Third Avenue to do my marketing, I thought of the evening stretching ahead. I had a date to interview a man from inside Germany who knew Hitler and was busily advising the military about the German plan. I was just thinking this would be interesting when the child inside whined: "Just another evening, another step down the wrong street." I drew away from the voice in fear, trying to lose myself in the strange sweet excitement of the city.

A sliver of a moon floated in the soft blue sky overhead like a smile. The street was alive with servicemen wandering in and out of bars, older, wearier people coming out of pawnshops, standing in doorways or shuffling heavily along, murmuring and complaining, and other men and women hurrying by with those nice brown bags filled with groceries. I had learned certain things I could do to ease my apprehension. Sometimes working, sometimes a few drinks, sometimes going out of my way to help other people worse off than I.

This particular afternoon I arrived home, mixed myself a drink and had just settled down to work when the telephone rang and Fate herself, the dilatory old hag, offered me a brilliant opportunity for trying out the last of these stunts.

"Hello."

I recognized instantly the childish but very deliberate, thoughtful voice of Toni Gower, an appealing, intelligent young actress, and was delighted at the interruption.

"Hello, Toni."

"Oh, Joyce, I'm so glad I got you. I've been calling you all day."

"Well, you got me. Here I am. Lucky you."

She giggled a full minute before going back into her remarkable dialect that sounded like nothing so much as a pixie from Brooklyn.

"Listen, honey, I've got to see you. As soon as possible, I mean. How is your time fixed?"

"I guess it's fixed for tonight. What's the matter?"

"Oh, God, honey, don't ask. Everything is terrible. Cal is being shipped out—he's taking the train tonight."

"What time?"

"I don't know. Maybe like midnight—or like early in the morning. Look, I'm up at CBS and somebody wants this phone. I can't talk long. When can we see you?"

"Would you like to come by tonight?"

"Sure. What time?"

"I'll be back by eleven, or shortly after."

"That's okay. Look, Joyce, can I stay with you tonight? You see, I had to give up the apartment, you remember—I told you about that —and I haven't got anywhere to stay."

"Certainly. I'd love to have you. How's Cal feeling?"

"Like death in a bucket. He thinks somebody at the draft board double-crossed him. They were out to get him, he thinks. Look, somebody's knocking on the door of this booth. But listen, when I come tonight, can I bring some of my things?"

"Bring everything you've got and stay as long as you want."

"Joy-y-y-y-ce, you don't me-e-e-e-e-an it, do you? Because if you do, that's just what I was going to ask you about tonight. My doctor is threatening to raise the price of my hour and if he does I'll have to get another radio job quick—so if I could just stay with you for a while, why that would be spec-tac-u-lar."

"All right, girl, your dream has been answered."

"Oh, Joyce, I'll never forget it—not even when I get on Broadway again—if ever. You're the first person I've spoken to about shacking up that wasn't a sonofabitch. They're after this phone like mad. Listen, honey, before I scram, don't say anything to Cal about me going to an analyst, you hear?"

"I won't—but why?"

"Well, he'd think I was quitting him—if he thought I was seeing a doctor—and that would make him extra insecure. I've been going for two years now—but I've never told him. You won't forget now, will you?"

I said I wouldn't, and she screamed the rest. "I've got to go now. Some eavesdropping bastards are listening to every word I say."

I left an envelope for Toni, with the key to the apartment, protruding from the mailbox and when I returned home I found Toni and Cal comfortably ensconced in the upstairs living room, bidding each other a gloomy but discursive farewell. Cal, a tall, good-looking man, a radio director, who usually spoke in a kind of satirical jargon, had recovered from his army blues enough to enjoy a last fling at civilian life.

"It's certainly nice to see you living in Buckingham Palace—with us other poor rats trying to find a damp cellar somewhere," he commented.

"This place is spectacular, Joyce," Toni chimed in. "Four fireplaces—and a back yard."

"Garden is the word," Cal corrected, as he turned to me. "Look, Queenie, we're kind of depressed, see? Uncle Sam sent me greetings, as you no doubt heard—just as I was about to corner a G a week in Hollywood. I'll be in my zootsuit tomorrow, so this is the end of me."

"You'd like a drink?"

"Well, girl, you're telepathic. It all comes with the place no doubt."

Toni stopped being sad long enough to giggle, a high hysterical laugh she had that usually stopped other people, as they watched her with interest. I waited politely, but noticing Cal motioning to me to get the drinks, I turned to go downstairs, whereupon Toni stopped giggling suddenly and came running down the steps after me.

"Jeepers, Joyce, you've got a dining room, too—with a fireplace— and get a load of those dishes. Brother, this is dreamy. If I lived here I'd marry Rockefeller—or Einstein."

"A sublet," I informed her. "Man's gone overseas. Nothing is mine."

"But it's sensational, honey. It must cost a fortune."

Out in the kitchen, she lowered her voice.

"Listen, honey, don't forget what I told you on the phone. I mean about not mentioning my analysis upstairs. Cal's off his rocker anyway about going into the army and losing that Hollywood money— it's only five hundred, not a G like he said, but I guess it looks like a G to him. I'm all he's got to hang on to, and if he thought I was in analysis, he'd go real nuts."

I looked at her with interest. Toni was a little girl, with an exquisitely perfect face, and with her miniature body, hands and feet, the head of reddish curls, she looked like a doll—with the wrong kind of eyes, I mean, not doll's eyes at all. The minute she spoke, it was almost impossible not to give her your undivided attention, the combination of her childish drawl and the stark seriousness of what she was saying created an outlandish effect that hit you like dynamite. You could almost see the crude but searching mind turning over behind the baby-doll face.

"Why?" I asked. "Why are you so afraid of Cal's finding out?" You're doing something to help yourself, aren't you? What's so awful about that?"

"Yes, I am doing something to help myself—but maybe it's something that's not going to help him."

"Oh." I thought of the similarity of my own situation; I hadn't wanted to tell Red I was going to a psychiatrist. "Can you give me more on that?"

"Well, listen, honey—you see he wouldn't like the idea of any changes in me. How does a baby feel when it sees its mother getting ready to go away?"

I thought that over, delighted with her wisdom. No wonder, two years in psychoanalysis! Here was a girl who knew the answers. She wasn't lost, like me.

"Come on, you two!" Cal was calling from upstairs. "Cut out the girl talk. You've got plenty of time for that—and I'm a doomed man."

"I'll tell you later about these baby men, honey. Tonight, maybe. After he's gone. It's a long story—a very long story."

"I can see that," I said, feeling very cheerful just the same as I picked up the drinks. "Well, it's going to be a long winter."

At three o'clock that morning, sitting opposite Toni before the fire, and listening to her with rapt attention, I began to get an eerie feeling that I was being catapulted into a new place. I was certainly entering a new era, I knew that, but now I thought perhaps it was even a whole new world.

Out beyond the high shadowy rooms, the black night stared in at us through the wide French windows. Listening, I thought, here I am in the Alley of Change, of Nightmare and Metamorphosis, leading into that blazing street called Reality. That's the place I've never even seen, whereas Toni, this fighting, searching New Woman, has walked this street for two whole years, and now here she is describing the sights for me, the dumb but eager tourist.

"What I'm getting, Joyce, is the real thing. Freudian psychoanalysis. It takes two or three years, sometimes longer. You go back to your childhood—to your infancy in fact—and relive the whole thing and then you relate it to the present. And after that you are reborn."

"Reborn?"

"That's right. Reborn. Just as if you were born into the world all over again—under different circumstances, of course. A second chance."

"When does this happen?"

"Somewhere during the treatment it begins to happen; when you're finished, it has completely happened. You become completely new. It's the only way for people like me because I have very serious problems."

She, too. But respectable problems, most likely. Regular problems. Nothing like mine.

"Like what?" I ventured.

"Well, I'm very insecure. And I have to operate in a very insecure group who suffer from every anxiety known to man. So I have to be doubly secure—just in order to survive. You see, take like the men you meet in the theater. Well, the men I meet I know are all looking for their mothers so they can just lie down and rest up. If a person tried to lean on one of them you'd be surprised how quick you'd both fall over. That's one of the reasons why so many American women are sexually frigid."

I pricked up my ears. "Say that again, please. Slowly. Why are so many American women sexually frigid?"

"Because they are confronted with baby men who don't like any women except their mothers. All other women are whores. They don't really like sex."

"Who don't—the men or the women?"

"I was talking about the men and how they are babies—instead of lovers or husbands. They were made like that originally by their mothers because their mothers didn't like sex or men or people. It's an endless chain. And they are kept like that because of the pressures put on them by our economic system which is set up against life and against love—just like our parents were."

4 7

Hmmm. I'd never thought of that angle. "But if it's the setup or the environment that's at fault, how can psychoanalysis help that?"

"It can't. But we, people like you and me, we have to be extra strong to survive in this kind of ruthless society, Joyce. And after the war, it's going to be worse. We have to become so strong we can live in any system. We have to, in effect, make our own system."

"How can we do that?"

"Well, take like me. I have to grow up and become a real woman—and then maybe I won't attract any more of these baby men. That's why I don't want Cal to find out I'm being reborn—because he's one of the very kind of men I don't want to attract any more of—when I am finally reborn, now do you see? And when I am one of these real females, why, then I'll attract a real man. If any."

I was hearing these words for the first time, and they fascinated me, coming as they did from a fellow-sufferer—at least she seemed to be a fellow-sufferer—who had gone further along the way and found out a few of the answers. So it wasn't just three months as Matthew had said. It was more like three years to reach the Promised Land. The antennae of my hopes, now electrically charged, stretched forward responsively as I recognized the names of many of Toni's pains. Anxiety. Insecurity. Frigidity. Nameless terrors, too. She nodded, acknowledging acquaintanceship with mine. I even told her of my fear of being murdered.

"I have an anxiety something like yours, Joyce. I'm crazy to get married but I can't let a man stay overnight in my apartment. I guess I could have a husband—if there was any way of hanging him outside the window overnight."

"Is it any better now?" I asked eagerly.

"Oh yes, it's much better. I've thought a lot about it and in fact I'm getting ready to try it again. Having a man stay overnight, I mean. My doctor and I are working on it very hard. We're bearing down. He feels part of it is because I am still childish—I'm not a real woman—and I've been unable in the theater to find anything like a normal man. Only babies, other babies. And mean. And competitive. And being a baby myself I'm not strong enough psychically to carry other children but I've had to do it just the same. And I hate their guts."

I was amazed and delighted by Toni's articulateness and, listening, drinking in the new words, I couldn't help thinking: Here is a human being who is not hiding out from the enemy, here is a female who is not a craven coward like you. It seemed to me she had investigated the areas of distress inside and out, examining and naming everything she saw. Her safari was already halfway through the psychic jungle, the number of wild beasts she had slain was mounting by the day and, what was more, she was not secretive and aloof about the difficulties of the journey but ready to share her conquests with a tenderfoot like me. I thanked my lucky stars that the fates had thrown her my way at the most opportune moment, as my mind stared up at her words like those people in Times Square watching the neon-lighted news.

"It's because of our backgrounds that we are sick, Joyce," she was saying. "My background is from hunger."

"Mine's from Dixie."

We thought the application of these show-business phrases to Our Trouble was very funny and went off into peals of laughter—actually more of a hysterical reaction, a simultaneous outburst of joy and re-lief at finding company in our misery. She described some of the hor-rors of the Brooklyn pattern of her past and, listening, I found the people far more normal than the unpredictable Southerners from whom I had sprung. "By and large, Toni, I mean in general, the Jewish people seem to have much more of a *family* feeling than gentiles."

"Not by me they don't. Not when you got poverty and kids and—brother, are they puritanical! My mother still thinks anybody who has sex without marriage is a prostitute. My father didn't want to let my sister into the house because he said a divorced woman didn't belong in a decent home."

"That's pretty unfriendly—but it's more of a normal neurotic pat-tern. I'm afraid my father wasn't all there—"

"What did he do—talk to himself, for instance?" I nodded, and she continued, "Same here. By the hour."

"And my mother—the poor woman had her troubles—but what a martyr—a real early Christian martyr."

"Wait a minute. You mean she was always crying—going on about what a hard time she was having—how everybody was doing her in?"

"That's it. She used to say, 'You'll never miss the water till the well runs dry.' Referring to when she'd die and leave us. Scared us half to death."

"Jesus, Joyce. You're not *kidding?*"

"No, of course not. Why?"

"Well, honey, the gentiles ain't got no copyright on that martyr stuff. My mother still says, 'My children are killing me.' If I have a fellow, I'm killing her, if I don't have a fellow, I'm killing her."

"But at least you've got her. She didn't prove her point by dying."

"I got her—yeah, and that's one of my troubles. I can't come home and stay there. She just doesn't want me around. She thinks I put a curse on the place—now do you begin to get the idea?"

The thought that Toni, this solid, courageous and beautiful girl, was not wanted by her mother went straight to my heart and I felt better, a lot better somehow. When, later, she indicated she would like to hang up her clothes, I showed her the three bedrooms in the apartment, determined to let her have her pick, even to give over my own room if she wanted it. She chose the one downstairs because it had its own bath, and I went on upstairs, the general idea being that we had better turn in.

I was just putting on my robe when I heard her calling from downstairs.

"Are you sleepy, Joyce?"

I leaned over the banister and hollered eagerly, "No, Why? Want to talk some more?"

"Yeah. I'll be right up. Shall I bring the Scotch?"

"Sure, we'll kill the bottle."

"You *goys* kill bottles, that's what my mom says, but not us Jews, nosirree. Whiskey is strictly for colds in the head and after an operation. If she thought I was down here killing a bottle she'd blow her top."

"In that case, we've got to kill the bottle. It's practically dead, anyway."

I poured us each a double slug on ice and threw another log on the fire; it had grown very cold in the early morning hours.

"Joyce," Toni was suddenly serious, "have you discussed sex with this psychiatrist you're going to?"

"Yes, as much as I know about it. Why?"

"Because sex is very important for your psychic health—good sex is, I mean—sex on a mature emotional level."

"What's that anyway, Toni? Please tell me—how is it supposed to be?"

"You mean you don't even *know?*"

"I don't think so. Does that indicate I've got something terrible?"

"I don't know what you've got. But, listen, Joyce—are you frigid?"

"I don't know. What does it mean?"

"Are you cold?"

"No," I answered with relief, "I'm not cold, I'm hot. I like sex a lot. Frigid women are the ones who don't like it—isn't that right?"

"No, not necessarily. You can be hot and frigid. Well, what I mean is, frigidity means much more than just people who don't like sex, it may apply to people who like it a whole lot. Frigidity has a very definite sci-en-tif-ic meaning."

"Well for God's sake, what is it?"

"You mean you don't know what frigidity is?"

"No. I've heard so much talk about it, and read so many conflicting opinions, how can anybody know? I looked it up in the dictionary, and I remember what it said."

"What?"

"Something like this: cold in feeling or manner—I think—haughty or forbidding and lifeless. I know the word. Comes from the Latin *frigeo,* to be cold, and *rigeo* means numb."

"That is *not* what it means at all. Why didn't you look it up in a medical dictionary?"

"I did. It isn't in the medical dictionary."

"Did you look up *orgasm?*"

"Yes, that's in it. Here, wait a minute. I'll read it to you." I found the medical dictionary, opened to the page and read the definition of *orgasm.* " 'The crisis or climax occurring in sexual intercourse, ending in the male with ejaculation of semen.' "

"And what about the female?" screamed Toni.

"It doesn't mention her."

"Well, I'll be goddamned."

"Yeah. Me, too."

"Well, honey, frigidity means when a woman can't have a climax or an orgasm. You can be hot as a pistol and sexy and glamorous as anything, most frigid women are, but if you don't have an orgasm, you're frigid."

"Gee whizz!"

"Now, do you have orgasms?"

"I don't know whether I do or not."

"You don't know? You mean you don't even know what it's like?"

"No. But I'm sure as hell waiting to find out."

"Oh, you poor kid. You've never had an orgasm."

"I guess not."

"And did you tell that to your psychiatrist?"

"No, not yet. He didn't ask me."

"Well, you'd better tell him, Joyce, right away. Oh, that's ter-r-ible."

"I'll tell him. But look, Toni, it's frigidity I've got, not leprosy. Don't keep looking at me as if you could catch it."

"Oh, but I can't help it, I'm so sorry for you. With all your sex appeal and your personality and everything, you still can't have an orgasm. Oh my God!"

"Yeah." I was beginning to feel depressed myself. "Well, maybe I will sometime. Anyway, let's not cry in our beer. At least I want to hear about it—from somebody like you, somebody who's been there. The stuff you read in books is so confusing. Please just go ahead and tell me about it."

"Sure I will, Joyce. Well, you see, there are two kinds of orgasms women have. First there's the clitoral orgasm. You know what your clitoris is, don't you?"

"I think so. It's up front."

"That's right. The clitoris is like a small penis. A very small penis. Now in certain neurotic women, a great many, I guess, all they can ever have is an orgasm of the clitoris. The doctors say a great many women don't even have that. But as for the real big deal, the complete vaginal orgasm, you can't have that until you're completely well."

"What's that like?"

"Oh, that's something spec-tac-ul-ar. That's practically like going over the moon, I guess. My doctor says it's no good for me even to think about that kind of thing yet. He says I can't expect anything like that for a long time."

"Like how long?"

"Oh, maybe like years—or maybe like never. He's of the opinion a great many women just never have that kind of sexual fulfillment because the con-di-tions have to be so good. They have to be completely *well* and feel completely *safe*. And who goes to heaven?"

"I'd like to make it. But now tell me this, Doctor Gower. I guess it's pretty important to get to this over-the-moon complete type sex, wouldn't you say? What I mean is, if you can't make it, it means in a sense you just haven't gotten out of the hospital—or out of the cradle —isn't that about it?"

"Oh, it means even more than that, honey. Why, if we could ever get to have a real bona fide, honest-to-God vaginal orgasm, why that's like getting your Ph.D."

"I see. And this clitoral orgasm, when you get to that—why it's more like being in grammar school maybe, huh?"

Toni nodded, giving the question her sage assent. I was thinking, if what she said was true, and I had no reason to doubt her, then sex, in its most personal aspect, was even more important than it was rated in human society, for besides being the great magnetic force that drew people of opposite sexes together, thereby shepherding peoples of the world into couples and family groups, it was also the one sure measuring rod for the mysterious workings of the inner man—and woman. I began to feel pretty gloomy as, using this newly discovered ruler to measure my own state of psychic health, I found I was not even in kindergarten, whereas Toni, with all her problems, had gravitated way up to grammar school. Things were certainly not looking up, but I had at least learned a great deal more than I had known before and, since understanding was the only way out, I was grateful for the large chunk Toni had thrown my way.

It was nearly four o'clock, the conversation had ended at last, I was in bed again and just about to turn out the light, when I heard her calling me again as she mounted the stairs.

"You're not asleep, are you, Joyce?"

"No," I hollered back. "Us hunks of ice don't get to sleep so easy. Why? Is there anything you want?"

She opened the door and came in.

"I just wanted to tell you something."

I saw she was deadly serious, her forehead pressed into a deep frown, her small face so twisted and contorted from the pressure she was exerting that lines showed under her night cream.

"It's about this clitoral orgasm I was telling you about. You see, they're hard to have, too."

"My God, not that."

"Yeah, very hard. You see, that has to be done with hand manipulation, and usually everybody gets pretty exhausted before it comes off. So you see, if you decide sometime to try it, why don't be discouraged at first. But the point is, I didn't want to give you the impression that I have them all the time."

"You mean you don't . . .?"

"I did have one during the summer—that was around July, I think—yes, I remember, we went away for a week end in July. Well, that was one. And then before that, I had one in December— I think it was December, yes I'm sure it was, because it was around Christmas, maybe it was Christmas Eve. Oh, but that was last year, wasn't it?"

"You mean that's all you had—one a year?"

"Yeah—but that's not such a bad average. This is only October. I've got nearly three more months to bring up my average. Rome wasn't built in a day. I'm going down to see Cal at camp next month. And after it's two, why then it's three, and after that, who knows? I tell you, Joyce, it's a question of time for all of us, so don't you be depressed. Well, good night, honey. Next year in Jerusalem."

CHAPTER SIX

· · · · · ·

BY NOW DR. RAMSEY HAD BECOME THE CENTER OF THE UNIVERSE inside my head.

On one side he was the essence of maturity, benevolence and wisdom, on the other mysterious, frightening and unpredictable. Altogether a man possessed of infinite powers. Sometimes, remembering my first impression—he had looked so sallow I'd wondered if he mightn't have tuberculosis and had felt some of the physical revulsion of the healthy toward the sick—I wondered how I could ever have felt so cold-blooded. Now, seeing the long yellow face, I was conscious of wellsprings of compassion, tenderness and fear for his future. How was it possible that this same face, which had so recently resembled a cigarette left out in the rain for a month, now appeared beautiful? And outside in the daily routine of living I found myself turning from the healthy, sunburned males in favor of sickly, yellow people, convinced that all men who weren't yellow just hadn't mellowed.

On one occasion, I'd arrived early to keep an appointment; while waiting and thinking idly of nothing very important, a poem began forming in my mind. It came so quickly, like a bolt out of the blue, I reached for my pen and wrote it down. It was a love poem, and in it I called my lover Death.

"What makes you think the poem is about me?" Dr. Ramsey asked.

"I know it's about you. I'm calling you Death. Love and death are the same things to me—unconsciously. Love very likely means murder."

I went on as if he weren't there. "I'm calling you my Knight, my lonely Knight. My father was lonely. He used to wander off by himself at night, the family never knew where he went. I tell you to stop wandering and come home to me. Come home, Death. I'll let you kill me. I'll return your kiss. Did I think my father was a murderer too? This is scary—but I begin to feel where it goes. What do you think?"

"I don't approve of this probing." I had made him angry. My insides contracted in panic at the thought of losing him. Coward that I was, I spent the rest of the session agreeing with him and trying to get back into his good graces.

"Now we know your father liked to hunt. Have you ever tried hunting?"

"No, never."

"I want you to go hunting as soon as possible," he went on. "Did you ever shoot a rifle?"

I said I hadn't, but could learn. The entire idea of shooting animals is utterly repulsive to me, I hold most hunters in contempt, and was about to explain, but it was quarter to three. The buzzer announcing the next patient had already sounded.

With Toni sharing the apartment and often answering the phone for me, especially when Trafinia wasn't there, I felt better. And with the apartment shortage becoming more acute by the day, we were both well satisfied with the arrangement.

"You don't know how lucky we are," Toni commented. "An actor on the show told me he spent last week sleeping in Saks Fifth Avenue."

One day another actress named Daphne Johnstone called to tell us her two weeks were up in the hotel where she was staying. "They've moved me out of my room—lock, stock and barrel—and animals. I've got no place to go." Somewhere in her desperate telephoning around she had heard of a big duplex with only two people living in it, and if she could possibly share it, just for a while, of course, until she could wangle herself a place. . . .

Toni had appeared on a couple of radio shows with her and found her quite interesting.

"I can't imagine her needing a place to live. She's always going out with senators or cattle barons—people like that."

"What else does she do?"

"Oh, she's been a model and she's been in a couple of movies—nothing big. She was in a play last year. Now she's around radio row like me. Maybe you've seen her on magazines—I guess she uses the modeling to fill in. She's terrific-looking. She told me she's posed as a bride so much she's got a phobia she'll never be one."

An hour later the statuesque brunette arrived, loaded down with suitcases, fur coats, packages of books about how to be happy or how to be thin and a beautiful red-and-white cat named Cheetah. Daphne hung up her many coats in the upstairs bedroom and brought us both up to date on her life situation. She had been lured away from her many-splendored aristocratic life in the state of Alabama by the Technicolored wink of Hollywood, on which city she frowned impatiently. As I helped her put away her things, I learned she was now busy frowning impatiently on the theater, the model business, radio and the coming new terror of television, those vulgar stop-offs a girl had to endure on her way to Dream Town where fame, position and security awaited her arrival.

"Vulgar!" She kept repeating the word, shaking her pretty black, thick hair and frowning. "It's all so vulgar—and cheap. The people are so cheap, don't you think so, Toni?"

"Well, yes—but sometimes I think maybe it's good they are," Toni consoled. "I feel kind of uncomfortable with very high-class people. I'm not so high-class myself."

"She's not kidding," Daphne whispered to me, and laughed out loud.

People had "no education" she said, and "no manners." Why, if some of her British friends could have heard what that hotel manager said to her they'd have him put in jail. She was widely acquainted with British royalty, and was ready to share her acquaintanceship, especially with me, at the drop of a duplex. She knew Sir Harry Morsby.

"You know who he is, of course. Here on a mission—it's very hush-hush. As Sir Henry says, after the war there'll be nothing left. Everything is getting hard, dear. I want you to meet Sir Harry. You'll like him, and he'll like you."

Sir Harry had "education," which apparently Daphne admired above all other things, and which I suspected she was fresh out of, even though her perfect white teeth flashed in and out as she mentioned the universities she'd attended; there were so many it began to sound as if she'd sprung full-grown from the dean's foot. The day after Daphne's arrival, and from then on, the telephone rang oftener than ever as Daphne's admirers called to check on their dates with the dark-haired beauty or the boxes of flowers, gifts, or happiness-and-philosophy books they kept sending her.

Within a week Daphne had fitted into the place as if she had been living there forever. Her personality kept me constantly guessing. She could change from amiable to forbidding and back again in a matter of seconds; somehow each mood was as unreal as the next, but it was all spoken in a carefully modulated voice and with excellent diction, and the total effect was pleasurable. To my surprise, she did indeed know all the important people she had claimed to know, they did show up at the apartment, and she did share them generously with Toni and me.

After a time the relationships among the three of us acquired a pattern.

"That one is real loony," Toni commented of Daphne. "I guess she has to be, her goals are so impossible." And I would say, "She is realizing some of them. She wants to know nobility—and she does." And Toni, "Royalty? These people she sees don't really know her and she doesn't really know them. It has to be like that because she's one of those wax women. If she ever got wise to herself, she'd go to pieces—but she can't because she's wax." And I would say, "Maybe it's good to be wax. If you're absolutely certain these people don't feel anything, and never can, then maybe they're to be envied." And Toni, "You can never get like that, honey, so don't try. There's no way of ever knowing what they're really like inside—but they're bastards, I can tell you that much. They can be meaner than all hell. And smug. These goddamned waxies, they just assume that's all there is to life. And the minute you show them anything that's un-wax, they'll claw you to death." And I, "Men seem to like it, though. They like Daphne plenty." And Toni, "But of course, honey. It makes it so easy for them. They take her out to be seen with her. She's a typical magazine cover girl. It makes them look masculine—and successful. Every time they appear somewhere in public with her, they're saying, 'Look how good I am, look what I've got with me.' But a real man wouldn't be caught dead with her."

"Why not?" I asked. Toni was always talking about "a real man."

I wasn't quite sure what she meant, but she didn't want to talk any more about it. All she would say was, "Don't ever strike a match near her face."

And of Toni, Daphne confided, "That Toni Gower, she'll never succeed in the theater—not with that voice." And I would say, "But she's trying to succeed first in living. She's trying to find peace." And Daphne would scoff, "Peace! She'll never find it that way. If she had any sense she'd take the money she's paying that psychoanalyst and give it to a voice teacher." And I, "When she feels more secure, maybe her voice will change." And Daphne, "How can she ever feel secure the way she's going? She makes no effort to change herself. And Broadway producers don't like girls from Brooklyn. They're from Brooklyn themselves."

I, being the in-between character—*and* a writer, of all things— was regarded by them both with alternate respect and pity. Respect, because they wondered how anybody could ever have the something-or-other to sit down all alone and string words together, and pity because who in hell would want to? As for me, I liked them both, Toni of course more than Daphne, she having entered somewhat the same purgatory I had entered, but unlike me, I thought, she was well on her way to leaving it and entering heaven. I was pleased that they accepted me so wholeheartedly and felt inferior to both of them. To Toni for her earthy fighting spirit, because she had fought her way up. To Daphne for the mystery surrounding her, the secret something from which she drew faith and sustenance, that made her, by comparison to me, seem cool and swift as someone flying by on skis.

I was just beginning to discover and to think about something I had known deep down for a long, long time. Everybody in the whole world, even the lowliest of God's creatures, had something I didn't have, and Toni and Daphne, being people, had it too. Just me, I didn't have it. Just me, alone of all the world.

The place on Thirty-seventh Street met all our needs. During the cold weather, we kept logs burning in the fireplaces. At night, with the street and garden showing through the parted draperies at either end of the long, high-ceilinged rooms, it took on a special enchantment resembling a theater setting of a past era. We often speculated about the people who had lived in this house years ago. I believed the men and women who had walked these rooms were more graceful and less desperate than we, but Toni thought not. "Eh, they were full of *souras,* too," she commented, "only they were so dumb they probably thought it was indigestion."

Daphne had her own odd and very personal ideas about all people's troubles, and the ghosts of a past America that haunted our apartment were no exception. "Their troubles came because of the awful amount of clothes they wore—those awful corsets and petticoats. And the way they filled their stomachs!" Daphne was of the opinion that going naked or "letting the body breathe" and eating uncooked vegetables could cure anything from a mild depression to leprosy. She also believed the apartment was haunted and that it "picked up bad vibrations" which were the exclusive cause of our problems, but the vibrations were much worse on the ground floor. We thought the vibrations she mentioned were caused by the characteristic darkness that hung over the first floor because it was slightly below street level and with the low ceilings and heavily carpeted floors it was bound on dark days to feel musty. Toni, who slept in the lower bedroom off the garden, liked the lower floor because it was quiet, especially in the back, but Daphne still insisted it was "bad—very bad."

There was little social planning in our lives yet often at night, after a day of what seemed like incessant movement, we would find the rooms had filled with people and the movement of the day was going on into the evening. I found myself listening to all kinds of information about the war from people on their way to or just returned from Washington. The people who knew President Roosevelt tried to top the people who knew Ben Cohen, only to be contradicted by the people who knew the Litvinoffs. We heard horror stories from Frankfurt and Okinawa, told casually by people from Emporia, Kansas. Servicemen Toni and Daphne had met at the Stage Door Canteen talked wisely or bitterly or not at all.

No party was ever complete without the "other talk" that was becoming current, about "the emotional plague." As its victims arrived, in groups or singly, and wherever you moved, the air burned with the human illustrations of the success or failure of Good Relationships, Growth-making Relationships, Good Working Conditions, Security and Insecurity, and Sexual Fulfillment. People were no longer happy or unhappy, lucky or unlucky, now they were Sick or Well. No single phase of current existence was as it was pictured to be. The women suffered psychically because they wanted to be men. This disease, now diagnosed as Penis Envy—a phrase that flew about the room like a batch of wild butterflies—occasioned, according to Toni and her cohorts, "a very definite disturbance of the sexual functioning."

It was all new to me and fascinating at first. Besides, I felt some deep identification with most of these people, especially with Toni. It seemed as if we had all felt the stirring of some sixth sense, perhaps even resembling the instinct birds and animals feel when they hurry along in groups on their way to some warm place before the snow falls. *That's it,* I thought, *before the snow falls. Before the blizzard, in which all life and movement may be blocked off and lost forever.*

Now about this business of being Reborn, this arrival at Fulfillment Island, Toni was of course much nearer to it than I was, everybody was nearer to it than I—but she, too, I began to suspect, hadn't arrived. This made me like her more than ever. Daphne ignored the entire matter, maybe she was made of wax as Toni said, but Toni and I, we were more human, worse luck.

"It's this place," said Daphne. "It has a bad influence. We had the same trouble in our house down home. Why that old house had vibrations from the people who'd lived there before. Of course you people don't believe in anything like ghosts—or picking up other people's thoughts—but I can *feel* things."

These remarks always sparked Toni's lecturing wire. "What you feel is not a real ghost. It's the ghost of the dying economic system. The ghost of American money. The bad vibrations come from the era we live in. Women in Russia don't feel insecure, because there the state stands solidly behind them. They have their emotional security in the only real parents there are for anybody."

Daphne would stand very straight, smiling that dental smile, looking down at Toni and me, as if from some unseen tower. "It's too bad you and your friends from the Jefferson School can't get over there and get adopted by these nice parents in Russia. That's an idea now, Toni. Why don't you take the money you're paying that doctor and go back where you came from?"

Toni would reply, "I don't know where I came from. That's what I'm paying him to find out."

Daphne would cross to the window, and stare down at the street.

The block on Thirty-seventh Street went downhill at a sharp angle into the black arms of Third Avenue. Third Avenue was dark those nights because of the blackout, with only the neon lights showing cold and lurid from the bars, with now and then a beam of yellow flashing out as a door opened, falling briefly upon the searching faces of the servicemen who seemed to be forever walking from bar to bar. I nicknamed Third Avenue *Sinister Street,* so whenever we were rushing out to shop for groceries we'd say we were going "down to Sinister Street," but it remained for Daphne to interpret its power.

Returning from the window, she'd stand straight and still beside the fireplace, speaking in a measured, elegant manner, soft gusts of words delivered so precisely it sounded sometimes as if another person were speaking through her.

"It's that street. It gets the vibrations from all those soldiers and sailors and marines. That's why we're confused. We're picking up all their thoughts. They don't know where they're going or why—and neither do we. And that's our trouble."

CHAPTER SEVEN

· · · · · · ·

ONE NIGHT I AWAKENED FROM A NIGHTMARE IN WHICH I WAS BEING smothered by someone, or some thing, covered with hair. Opening my eyes in the dawn-lit room, I noticed to my horror the outlines of the figure were there in the room before my eyes. As I stared, it faded quickly into the familiar lines of the bed, desk, fireplace and window of my bedroom, leaving me sitting up in bed shuddering with terror but reaching frantically for the disappearing thread of the dream. Wasn't there something familiar about the creature with the furry skin—and, yes, there was some familiar odor . . .

As luck would have it, Dr. Ramsey had been ill and unable to see patients for two weeks, so I was forced to wait to analyze my nightmare. His telephone service finally called to say he was well again and set my first appointment for five o'clock on Friday the thirteenth, a day that was to be memorable for me. By then I was desperate to be back unraveling the mystery of my distress, to discuss where I thought he'd gone off in my case, and above all to dig into the volcano that had erupted in the nightmare.

It seemed as if five o'clock would never arrive, but it did, and there I was in Dr. Ramsey's waiting room, ready to spring. The room looked dusty and neglected, with only one light turned on. A dark day, too. At five past five I started feeling impatient. The gray stones and empty trees in the courtyard outside looked ugly in the murky day. At five ten I was just beginning to wonder if something had happened when I heard the old familiar chair scraping inside. A minute or so later the door opened.

In the first glance I caught, Dr. Ramsey looked still quite ill, but once inside, sitting in my old place beside his desk again, talking away, I quickly forgot the first impression. He was looking down at the open folder on his desk—my case, I thought eagerly, as I wondered how he was able to read in the dim light—and I talked on, describing the nightmare.

He listened, his head bent over the folder, a puzzled expression on his face, from time to time nodding his head. Once, when he glanced up, his eyes were so heavy-laden he looked half asleep. Poor man, I thought, he ought to be home in bed, but this is no time for me to sympathize with him.

"Dr. Ramsey, wake up now, please," I said. "I know we're on to something. The thing that was smothering me was big—a big creature —covered with fur—or hair. And there was something familiar about it—an odor . . ."

"What kind of an odor?"

"I'm not sure, but I'd know if I smelled it again. I thought it was maybe a cat—not a real cat—but something or some*one* that looked or felt like a cat—"

Something was happening. A corner was breaking off the glacier and as it crashed through my head it left fragments. I raced on now, frantic to recover and examine these fragments. It was not like a dream, it was more like an experience being relived on another plane, complete with feel and smell. I could feel myself sliding around the arc of time, entering my grandmother's house where the big mystery figures were walking about, when I heard his voice saying, "Take it easy now. Talk about the present."

I felt angry at the interruption. "Damn the present. You're always after the present. Don't you understand—it's more vague to me than this past—where the thing happened that keeps me in chains?"

What was my present life anyway but the other end of a rope I wanted to burn? The present; I hated the words, seeing miles of twilight and one inch of sun.

"I mean the real present. What did you do yesterday? How is your job?"

"Oh, that present." The frothy egg-white that disappears when you beat it up. Why can't this man understand, I have no real present because I am not in control of myself? I, some semi-human thing whose vital life juices are being extracted, an automaton obeying commands coming from far off, from the killer in the nightmare. The present is nothing but an illusion, a reflection of the past. But the past is real. The past has fingers to choke you to death.

What was he saying? "You don't want to become—a victim looking for a murderer. It is very disturbing to you—this dredging back into the past. Come on back now."

"But why?"

"Well, for one thing, I promised your mother, and I don't like to go back on my promises. I know you discuss everything with your mother—"

I felt a shock go through me. My mother! My mother was dead! Long dead! My MOTHER! He said it twice, too. "I promised your mother . . . you discuss everything with your mother." He had known my mother was dead, we had discussed her death. I knew instantly he had either completely forgotten my case, or else was confusing me with some other patient. And on this particular day.

I tried to say something—what's the matter with you, Doctor?— but my lips wouldn't move.

"Oh, I'm not criticizing," he went on. "Most of my women patients tell their mothers everything. But she has repeated the things you've said and I've said, and I promised her we'd keep away from those things in your childhood that you think happened."

Now I was beginning to feel really queer. Dr. Ramsey didn't know who he was talking to, that was obvious. As for me, I felt as if I were sitting in the air. There was nothing solid under me anywhere, in the chair, in the floor, in the world. That man sitting there, that doctor who had become the central figure of the universe inside my head, he didn't know who I was! In the silence I heard a thin voice. "Dr. Ramsey, my mother is dead."

I saw his face change color, a dark red shadow settling over his cheeks like an old bloodstain. He pulled the cord on the lamp, lighting another bulb, and looked quickly down at the folder, then up at me, just as the buzzer sounded outside. He must have seen something disturbing in the folder, the way he was coughing and lighting cigarettes, he lit one and then another before smoking the first.

"Oh. . . . Well, we changed your hour. I'm sorry, I must have forgotten—I thought you were another patient—"

It was nearly six, the minutes were ticking away, but he went on.

6 5

"Funny thing is, you look so much like her—I'm awfully sorry. I won't charge you for this treatment. You just forget this session—and let's see—I'll call you in the morning—and we'll set up another appointment for tomorrow—"

The street outside was dark, and I felt queer and alone. I had lost him, him whom I needed most in all the world. I must have lost him long before this, I thought. Today he didn't even know me.

I tried to reason with myself: he's just a doctor, after all, and there are others. It wouldn't work. He was everything to me: this was what they call a "transference." This man was mother, father, doctor, lover, all in my mind, of course, but that was where everything was with me just then, and he had the key.

It had started raining. I kept on walking, with this funny feeling that there was no solidity anywhere, that I was walking in the air. . . . Sitting there staring right in my face, he didn't know who I was. I had nothing now, no one in the world. There was left only this vast loss everywhere.

I tried to think logically. Not only was I losing him, but maybe he was losing something, too. His mind. It was possible . . .

Where would I go now, and what would I do, I wondered, knowing I hadn't the power to go far. I couldn't go back to the office— I felt altogether too queer. Any place to sit down and get through the next half hour where I could be alone and unwatched in my shame. A nice, dark bar would do, somewhere to sink into deep anonymity. There was one nearby, big and loud and dark, as I remembered, and that was where I headed in the rain.

It got better after the second drink, and I leaned back against the velvet upholstery, watching a group of servicemen and girls singing. I found the raucous medley soothing. I still felt queer, uncertain of everything, as if all of life had suddenly been swept away from me— swept way up there on the ceiling with the small lights and frescoes of cherubs, far over my head.

A new idea hit me. Suppose Dr. Ramsey's mind was all right, but he had just forgotten me. There now. Just me. Could remember everybody else, of course, just not you-know-who. Why, it would make a lyric. "Forgettable You." Maybe it was only a question of time before nobody would remember me. This might be just the beginning, with Dr. Ramsey the forerunner of the new era. People would look at me blankly, then back away, embarrassed. And if enough people did this, they would be right and I would be wrong. My case might even start a new department in the *Reader's Digest*. The Most Forgettable Character.

I thought of accosting Ramsey in his office and taking a poke at him, but the idea began to seem ridiculous. Then I thought, It's I, there's something I haven't got, there's something about me that's just so awful it caused him to black out. Then, As for you, Ramsey, cold or no cold, I hope you break your nasty little neck!

I don't remember much about the next few days. Dr. Ramsey had dealt me some kind of a mortal blow. I didn't understand it at all.

I noticed I had started forgetting important appointments, sometimes even neglecting to write them down. Then one day I forgot to keep an appointment with a famous man who promptly called the office and reported the incident, whereupon the editor just as promptly called me into his office and asked me for an explanation. Actually I had none, I didn't know why I was forgetting things lately, but the incident brought me up short. I rushed to the telephone and caught the important gentleman barely in time to get to his place and get the story, but this activity wasn't enough to erase the downward trend that was becoming obvious to everyone, including myself.

I couldn't remain in this state. I knew that much, walking around in the empty apartment over one of the longest week ends I had ever known. Everything in the place looked old and worn, going to pieces. How had I ever found it beautiful, I wondered; and then I remembered, that was when I had hope. Now I had left only these rubber hours in which I was operating mechanically, going to my job, buying food and cooking meals occasionally, in a dull, lifeless daze. Then came Sunday, and Sunday afternoon, and suddenly the hours felt too heavy to walk in. I felt abandoned, like an animal watching the family move away and leave it behind in the empty house.

I needed help. I couldn't stay in this state. I had to talk to someone. Toni was up at a hall on Second Avenue, rehearsing for the opening of a new radio show. Daphne was away for the week end. I found myself half wishing she were home, I'd even welcome hearing about "vibrations."

Desolately rereading my messages, I saw one I hadn't noticed. "Call

Red. Important." I must have been blind indeed to have missed that message. Red was back, staying at a hotel right around the corner. I called him immediately and heard the good news. "Look, I'm okay, see. Transfer came through at the last minute. Don't worry about me any more, baby. I'm safe in the arms of the Pentagon."

An hour later, having ferreted out of me the reason for my blues, Red walked up and down the room, using his highball glass as a pointer for his comments.

"Forgot your case, hah? Now suppose a surgeon got his patients mixed up. Instead of removing a cancer from *A,* he thinks it's *B* and removes a lung. Now *A* wakes up from the anesthetic. *A* still has the cancer but now he has lost his lung."

"So . . .?"

"So that could be you. At least he forgot before the operation went any deeper. Don't you get the point? You ought to find out about this Ramsey. Who the hell is he anyway? Look, I've got an idea. I know a dame in Washington Square knows every head-shrinker in the business. I'll bet a quarter Irene Wardman knows him."

"But what good would that do—at this point?"

"From the looks of your face, practically anything would do some good. Besides, if this character forgets people's faces—your face in particular—think what he's likely to do to the lesser schmos he's treating. Where's your social indignation? Where's your curiosity? Where's your guts?"

I started to explain. "Maybe there aren't any lesser schmos. Confidentially, I'm a worm."

He wasn't listening. He was dialing some number on the telephone, and then talking.

"Irene? . . . Hello, sweetie . . . how the hell are you anyway? . . . Are you? . . . Great! . . . Irene, do you by any chance know a psychiatrist named Ramsey? . . . You do? . . . I thought you would . . . You don't say! . . . Well, I'm here with a friend of mine . . . Joyce . . . Yes, the same one. She's been going to this man. She's in quite a state . . . It seems he thought she was somebody else . . . They were discussing something and he said they'd better not because he had promised her mother . . . Her mother's only been dead for about twenty years . . . Isn't that a dilly? . . . Oh, thanks, Irene . . . Wait a minute—I'll ask her . . ." Red turned to me. "Irene says would you like to come down there for supper? . . . She's having some people in. She'll tell you all about Ramsey."

I soon found myself in a beautiful apartment in an old brownstone where some twenty-odd people were scattered in groups, holding well-stacked plates and talking excitedly. The place, furnished in antiques set on lush carpets, looked more like a stage setting than a home, and the people showing off against the dramatic backdrop fitted in perfectly. Irene Wardman turned out to be a tall, handsome brunette whom I liked on sight. I admired her green satin coat dress, her merry gray eyes with the long black lashes, her thick black curly hair, her laughing mouth with the orange lipstick, from which a low, purring voice came as a surprise, emanating as it did from the big bright package of her face. From time to time she would float out of a group of guests and talk to me.

"So you're going to Henry Ramsey . . . My, my," she purred, then burst into a soft guffaw. "Do you know, you're the first person I ever knew who *went* to him?"

It seemed ages before she finally beckoned me into the kitchen. At last relaxed that her party was now going on its own momentum, she poured us each a cup of strong coffee, stretched her big head forward and began to purr more seriously.

"How on earth did you ever find Henry?"

I told her, and she nodded.

"So he forgot your case?" She burst out laughing. "It's funny, but of course it wasn't funny for you. I'm surprised at Henry, too. He should like you. His wife is something of your type."

"I didn't know he was married."

"Maybe he isn't any more. I don't think they're exactly living together these days. Haven't heard from her in a while and . . . maybe they're even divorced by now." I listened, fascinated as a woman listening to the private hidden life of her lover—or worse, as a wife hearing she is "married" to and in love with a bigamist, learns about the other woman.

"I've never known the doctor side of Henry. He may be all right, for all I know. The strangest people make excellent psychiatrists."

I saw her watching me now, a shrewd look on her big handsome face. Meantime, Red had wandered in and was listening at the kitchen door.

"Why don't you tell her the truth about the guy?" he demanded. "Tell her what you told me over the phone."

"Stop it now, Red!" She was suddenly serious. "His private life has nothing to do with it—and I won't say one word about it."

"Why the hell not?"

She crossed the room and spoke to Red. "Can't you see how disturbed she is? Can't you see she has a transference to Henry a mile high?"

"No! Has she? Have you, Joyce?" I stared back at him foolishly. "Well, don't worry, baby. You'll get over it. If Irene won't give, I'll get the facts for you—and then the transference will be out the window."

"You'll get the facts for her? How—I'd like to know?" Irene was indignant now. "You can't find out anything more about Henry Ramsey than you know right now. He's a bona fide M.D. He went to a good medical school, I forget which. He's been practicing for about ten years. That's all anybody can find out. The rest isn't known."

"But you know it. Why don't you tell her? You got us down here under false pretenses. I think a whole lot less of you, I can tell you that much."

"I don't care what you think. All I know is, she's still going to Henry Ramsey. She hasn't officially broken with him."

It had been a sleeveless errand. I was still up in the air, but I kept on working, coming home, going out again. Sometimes, in the midst of a busy hour, pictures would float up, complete with color and sound. Dr. Ramsey would appear saying, "I knew you'd tell your mother . . ." "You needn't pay for this session . . ." "I'm so sorry—"

And the days stretched into weeks.

CHAPTER EIGHT

· · · · · · ·

AT ELEVEN O'CLOCK ONE NIGHT THE TELEPHONE RANG.

"Hello. Irene here. Are you all right?"

"Fine. How are you?"

"Well, I'm relieved. And in that case, I'll go about my business."

Just as she spoke, a window appeared, a small square in the stretched rubber hours, and something seemed to prod me like a voice. "She knows something. Find out what it is."

"Are you still going to Ramsey?"

"No."

"I have an errand I must do. It's important. I'm coming uptown in a taxi and if you'll be waiting outside your door, I'll take you with me. We can talk later."

"Where are we going?" I asked her, as we rode together in the taxi.

"Someone's in trouble. You'll see."

"Worse than mine?"

"Yes," she purred, then laughed that low guffaw. "Much worse than yours."

We smoked silently. So someone was worse off than I. Good. So I let her alone.

Now we were going up the steps of an old brownstone. Irene rang the superintendent's bell, and after a wait the basement door opened.

"What do you want?" a woman's voice asked.

"Oh, Mrs. O'Connor, it's me again, Mrs. Wardman. I've been trying to get you on the phone. Give me the key to 4A, please."

"What's the matter up there?"

"I'm not sure. Give me the key—"

Mrs. O'Connor disappeared, muttering, then returned and handed over the key, still muttering.

"Haven't seen her all day. She had a package come . . . I've got it here if she wants it. Looks like a dress. I can bring it up."

"Never mind now. I'll see you later."

The door opening into 4A revealed nothing but darkness. Irene closed it quickly, whispering: "Shh, you be quiet now. Just wait here."

She turned back, opened the door long enough for us to see our way about, and switched on the light.

"There's a chair. Just sit down and wait."

I saw I was standing in a dusty foyer.

"Chloe!" Irene called into the dark apartment. "Are you all right?"

A woman's voice, dulled with pain or fatigue, called back:

"Hello, Irene."

"Are you all right?" Irene repeated.

"Yes, I guess I'm all right, I'm still here. I couldn't have dialed you if I wasn't . . . *but hurry.*"

Irene had left me now. I could hear her speaking in the other room.

"My God, have you been in the dark all this time? Where's the light switch?"

"Over by the sideboard—on the right."

I waited in the foyer. There was a dusty table with a small chair beside it. On the floor a hooked rug had been pushed against the door, as if someone had fallen over it in leaving hastily. I sat down and listened to the voices inside.

"You poor girl—sitting here in the dark." Then, "My God, Chloe, your hands—I can't get this damned thing untied! How long have you been here?"

"Since this morning," the dull voice answered. "Took me till four o'clock to get the chair over to the telephone—so I could dial you. I'm so hungry—I'm starving."

"And look at your feet. You've cut them badly—"

"Had to—to get to the phone—"

Now I knew someone had tied the woman up. Irene wanted me for a witness, no doubt. We'd call the police. I thought it should

7 2

be done immediately and was just about to call to Irene when I heard her calling me, "Joyce, come quick," and I hurried in.

In the bedroom a girl, or was it a woman, I couldn't tell, was sitting on a stiff high-backed chair, her feet and legs tied with ropes to the legs of the chair, her hands tied behind her. Her feet were bare, badly swollen and bruised, they looked like an ugly mass of purple, red and blue, showing the marks of the rope. She had long ash-colored hair, I couldn't tell if it was blond or gray, but her face, bare of make-up, looked young.

In the quick glance I caught I saw she was suffering from some kind of acne, two spots were inflamed, with points standing out on her pale cheeks. The faded blue robe she was wearing had come open in front, revealing a long, shapely, pink-and-white body, in odd contrast to the unhealthy color of her face, from which big blue-black eyes with deep circles beneath stared inquisitively at me as Irene talked rapidly, and worked frantically with the ropes.

"You don't mind—I brought a friend—we'll undo you together —she'll help me, then you can eat. Where are the scissors?"

"In the sideboard—no, somewhere in the kitchen—hanging on the closet door, I think."

I looked frantically for the scissors in a very disordered kitchen. Not finding them in the place Chloe had mentioned, I moved stained cutlery in drawers, and was just opening the closet beneath the sink when Irene appeared.

"There they are—over the stove—looking you right in the face!"

"Who on earth did this to the poor thing?"

"Shh now, I told you to keep quiet. Get the scissors."

"But I think you should call the police—before doing *anything*. I can get the precinct on the phone right now."

"No. It's the delicatessen you can call right now. She's hungry."

"All right, but this fiend should be arrested."

"First her hunger has to be arrested. Then her masochism—the way she puts up with it. Then maybe later—maybe never—*his sadism*—"

It was hard work cutting through the heavily knotted clothesline with the rusty scissors, with Chloe groaning and perspiring freely, no doubt from weakness.

"We could burn through the rope quicker than trying to cut with these things," I suggested.

"Oh no, the last time I tried that, I burned her. You go call Irving's Delicatessen, I'll keep on with this. Hurry now. Ask for two turkey sandwiches. White or dark meat, Chloe? I've forgotten—"

"White's all right. Cole slaw, and black coffee. No cream or sugar. You have to tell them or they'll make it sweet and I'd be sick."

I was just leaving the room when Chloe began pleading.

"You better call, Irene. He knows you so he'll send it quick."

"All right. Here, Joyce. You keep cutting—it's beginning to break here."

Irene was about to dial the number on the telephone in the bedroom when Chloe almost jumped out of the chair in alarm.

"Not on that phone, for heaven's sake, Irene. Keep that phone free. Use the house phone."

"But why—?"

"He might call any minute now."

I went on where Irene had left off, determinedly cutting through the rope. I felt a slight revulsion toward the girl in the chair—or was it the odor in the room, a musty smell of an unventilated room in which medical ointment and perspiration were extraordinarily strong?

I noticed her looking at the ceiling, and, glancing up, I saw to my amazement that the entire ceiling was mirrored. I remember meeting her glance in the mirror overhead, and feeling embarrassed.

"Do you know the person who did this?" I asked quickly, to cover up.

She laughed, a quick chuckle, then turned her eyes back to the ceiling, without answering. It was not until her hands were completely untied at last and she was examining the ugly cuts in her wrists that she started to talk.

"I don't know why he does it," she said. "Nothing to eat all day, and this pain, this awful pain. Why must he punish me so— why?"

I went on cutting—I was at the feet now. I knew somehow she didn't want an answer. She was not even looking in my direction, her attention was focused entirely on the ceiling mirror where she got a full view of herself.

Shortly afterward, with Chloe sitting in the living room, ravenously devouring the turkey sandwiches, I noticed her glancing up again, and discovered the living room also had a mirrored ceiling.

Irene was in the bedroom, answering the phone.

"Yes, she's all right, I told you. Yes, she has something to eat, she's eating fine. I'll call you later."

During the conversation Chloe stopped eating and listened to Irene. A wild look came into her eyes. Her mouth came open, showing her tongue and teeth, and she breathed heavily.

"When is he coming?" she asked, as soon as Irene had hung up.

"He says in about half an hour."

The food finished, Chloe walked around in the living room—smoking, talking, and looking into first one mirror, then another.

"Look at my hands—the bruises. Will that be enough for him, Irene? Or must there be more—more—more?"

"I don't know." Irene's cool purr sounded mighty sane and pleasant. "There'd better not be any more tonight. If there is, it's on you, girl. I'm going home—"

But Chloe clung to us at the door, and now genuine fear seemed to be operating in her.

"Be careful what you tell him, Irene. I didn't say a word, remember. I only called you because I was getting faint from hunger. Nothing else."

"You didn't say a word. Now stop looking in the mirror!"

"I will, oh I will. I didn't know I was doing it any more. Don't tell him about that. You'd better go now, quick—he might be coming."

"Who is she?" I asked the minute we got outside and started down the stairs.

"Chloe. A woman. Masochist Number 2762."

"But the man—the fiend who tied her up—is he her lover?"

"Yes, in a manner of speaking. He's also her husband."

"But who is he?" We were at the door now, but Irene wasn't answering. "What kind of man? What does he do?"'

I noticed Irene looking at the names on the buzzers. I heard her say, "There." My eyes followed where her finger was pointing. I looked but I couldn't believe my eyes, there must be some mistake. I looked away and then back at the name, and as I read it again

my feet seemed to move further away from me, then my body felt
queer as if it were being drawn apart like an accordion. What I
read was just a name.

HENRY RAMSEY, M.D.

I was still feeling the shock as we settled at a table in a favorite
restaurant of Irene's on Sixth Avenue. She was talking away. "Henry's
a bad boy and . . . Well, now you know about the private life of your
Doctor Ramsey."

But this wasn't the Dr. Ramsey I knew. There was one Dr.
Ramsey, the psychiatrist who forgot my case—but this other Henry
Ramsey, M.D., the invisible hand-tier, that must be someone else.
But it wasn't. It wasn't. *They were both the same man.* These two
separate human entities were suddenly joined together on a piece
of cardboard containing a printed name, Henry Ramsey, M.D. But
they didn't fit—or did they?

"Now then, let's celebrate. After all, I've done it. I'll have a
drink first—then the pea soup and the roast beef."

"Done what?"

"Cut the umbilical cord—or haven't I?"

"Oh yes, that—I see what you mean. I—I guess some day I'll
be glad you brought me along. If you'd told me about this I wouldn't
have believed a word of it."

"Let's start with a double Scotch on the rocks, and then, maybe
another."

Irene's big, handsome face became startlingly alive in the blue
restaurant lights, the purr rose and fell contentedly over the horrors
she was mentioning, as casually as if she were reading off items on
the menu.

"A narcissist—that's what Henry is. . . . You mean you don't know
about narcissism? . . . Look it up in the dictionary. It's somebody
who falls in love with himself—to give you a quickie on it. He fell
in love with Chloe because . . . for one thing, Chloe looks something like Garbo—and so does Henry look like Garbo. Yes, he
does—especially his profile. So he fell in love with somebody who
looked like him. . . . She used to call me often—and ask me to

come up quick—and get the janitor to open the apartment—because he'd taken the key and gone out, locking her in—after first tying her up, of course. Once we stopped by there—and she hollered at us through the door. We got the key and went in—and found her tied to the bed. She'd been there for two days. She was in quite a state that time—"

"Why?" I managed to gasp. *"What's wrong with him?"*

"I called him up and asked him what on earth he was doing— tying his wife up like that," Irene went on to explain. "He said he had to—it was the only thing that worked. I asked him what she had done, but he wouldn't tell me. All he would say was, she knows. You ask her what she does with her hands. . . . Well, he wouldn't tell me what she did—and neither would she. Don't look so depressed."

"All right, I won't. Only tell me quick—is there any more or have I had the works?"

"Uh-huh, but that's only his private life. He wouldn't do anything like that to a patient! He's actually a very gentle soul. He writes poetry, too—lovely poetry."

"I'll bet. Whole thing sounds great. Nice guy to meet on a dark street. Good old Ramsey."

"Don't feel bitter toward him. That's just your transference—" By now the word irritated me like the sound of a nail scratching against a steel file. "Take it easy. Don't look so depressed."

CHAPTER NINE

. . . . . .

ON THE PARTICULAR NIGHT I HAD PLANNED TO SEE TONI AND "DISCUSS things," I telephoned home and was surprised to find a party in progress. I thought little or nothing of the tight, constricted sound in Toni's voice, until the information she was giving brought me up short.

"I flipped on the new show," she explained. "Couldn't even read my lines. My throat closed up."

"But I thought you were all cured of that."

"Yeah, I thought so too. I'm back where I started—after all that time—and money. Maybe there is no help as long as we have to live in this terrible insecurity. Look, honey, this is all very complicated. Hurry home. Something terrible happened to me tonight —I lost my part on the show—but something wonderful happened too—"

"What? For God's sake, tell me something wonderful."

"Phil Paige is here—you know, he's the director of *Abbott's House*. He saw the whole thing happening. He was very sympathetic. Remember what I told you about Phil? He went to a Marxian doctor. He's *cured*. And he's making an appointment for me right away."

"A what?"

"A Marxian. They relate your libido to the state."

"What state is that?" I asked, slightly flabbergasted. "I'd like to get out of this state."

She giggled, hysterically I thought; then, "Hurry home, and Phil will tell you all about it. Listen, honey, this is *the scientific approach.* We'll be new women. It's the real McCoy."

The party had been going on for some time, judging by the looks of the edibles. The ham Trafinia had baked was bared to its bones, the casserole of spaghetti nearly empty, the White Rock cartons piled up by the fireplace. Through the noisy crowd, a stout girl was dancing alone, waving her arms and baring her shoulders toward first one group of men, then another. She was not attractive, but she caught and held my attention, almost against my will. She seemed in a kind of trance of self-admiration, and her large light-blue eyes had an almost hypnotic effect.

"Look at that!" A small, intense-looking man was explaining the girl to a group of her watching subjects. "A narcissist in action—the moment of flight. You won't see a sight like this in a month of Sundays. As much sex appeal as a drainpipe—but she loves every pound of that white fat. I tell you, never pity an ugly woman."

"It's amazing at that," an older man commented. "With all these pretty girls around, that one is getting all the attention."

I listened now, my attention caught by the word *narcissist.* A new word to me, maybe a new kind of being. That was what Irene said the doctor was.

"Doesn't even need a man," the small man went on. "Married to herself."

"I knew a girl like that in Honolulu," a serviceman was saying. "Never did exactly like this darned girl, but I did everything she said. She wasn't even pretty but she loved herself so much she got me feeling the same way."

I heard Toni calling.

"This is Phillip Paige, Joyce." I was now face to face with the hero of the evening. "Now Phillip, you tell her about Dr. Eisman."

A tall, downy-cheeked, bald-headed man—his head resembled a peach wearing glasses—was extricating himself from a clinging girl, as Toni whispered, "He used to be a fairy, remember? Now this Dr. Eisman has turned him into a man." I whispered back, "How do you know?" And she replied, "He just got married, silly. His wife is going to have a baby. *He's happy.*"

Toni looked pale. I was just handing her my lipstick when Phil

7 9

Paige came between us and took over. "Toni looks bad, hah? Had a rough time, but we're going to get her straightened out. Poor kid's been at it for three years. She hasn't been touched. I tell you—oh well. Just didn't get to the right one. There's all the difference . . ."

Phillip, who appeared to be burning with his story like the Ancient Mariner, went straight to the sofa, pulling us down beside him, poured drinks, and began. "The only real one, Eisman. Lives in the Bronx."

I asked, "Why does he have to do that—such a long way to go?"

"Why? Bright question. Why does Dr. Eisman live in the Bronx —when all these other witchmen are crocked up with Park Avenue? Listen, you two, if I never tell you another thing, listen to what I say right now. Because Dr. Eisman gets cures, that's why. He's not selling something—so he doesn't need the phony wrappings. Glamour, impressing the customers, sales appeal—when all the time what they're working for is sickness in perpetuity. This Eisman, he's out to get people well—not half-well and half-sick, so they'll keep coming back, but well."

"Tell her how he does it, Phil," pleaded Toni.

Red had come in. I saw him wending his way over to us, motioning to me to be quiet, he wanted to listen, and settling himself behind the sofa. Phillip went on, taking no notice of the newcomer, his long arms stretched out before him in a semi-circle, as if reaching to hug some unseen figure.

"Dr. Eisman is a great man—he's the new medicine—it has to come but we mightn't live to see it. He'll never be popular, he'll never make much money, but he proves his theories. Take this war now. He sees it for what it is. The beginning—first punch— Round One in the big destruction. We don't know what we're fighting for, and that's one nasty little item in the crackup problem. We haven't got any security—nobody has—"

"Except the Russians," Toni corrected.

Red, I saw he'd been drinking and that he was getting angry, started to interrupt. "Why aren't you in the war, Mister?"

"Paige is the name," Phil replied, without even looking to see who was speaking. "I don't know who you are, and it's none of your goddamned business, but since you ask, I'll tell you."

"Yeah, go ahead. You didn't get psyched to avoid the draft by any chance?"

"No, but it's a good idea." Phil was unruffled. "I was turned down by the draft board, after careful scrutiny of my anatomy, on three counts. Improper vision—homosexuality—and flat feet. What else would you like to know?"

"Look, Red," Toni was deadly serious, "we happen to be very much interested in what Phil is saying. Joyce and I are both in hot water. If you want to fight, why don't you go over by the fireplace?"

"They're just hollering," Red snarled. "I'm so sore about this stuff, I don't want to just holler. I feel like strangling people."

"Great!" Phil turned and looked at him. "Why don't you get the dancer? She was made for the front page of the *Mirror*."

Red turned to glance at the dancer, and remarked, "She wouldn't even know I was doing it. I'd like to strangle the leaders of this great big trying-to-change movement."

"Why?"

"Because it's a lie—and people like Joyce and Toni are suckers for it—"

Toni whispered to Phil, "He's just a scared businessman," but the quarrel went on just the same.

"That violence you feel comes from the frustration of the work you do, Colonel. Great breeding place for hate, business. And now this nice mechanical operation you've got in the Pentagon, covering up for the boss men, gets under your skin."

"How's that?" Red snapped.

"I say you have no position in the society you have to live in— that's why you're mad. You ought to try the Park Avenue psychiatry. Might release you for the Madison Avenue pitch."

"I'm doing all right where I am, thanks."

"You can't be—and stay human. You're not superman. You want what everybody wants—and can't get. You don't like having no cooperation from your colleagues—you don't like all the competition. You don't like having no place to go, and no hope of anything better."

"Most of us end up making more dough than you hams. What's the matter with money?"

"Nothing, only you can't all get in. The space is limited. The rest sit around waiting till their guts crack. It's all this having to be important and rich that gets people sick."

"What do you want?"

"To feel good, that's all. To know I can make enough to take care of my family and myself. To like some people, love a few—that's about it. The minute I found out that was what I really wanted, and that I could get it, I stopped being afraid—and hating people."

Red was about to answer, when the dancer came by, twisting and turning in time to some ceaseless self-playing trombone, until Red, on whom she was now concentrating, taken by surprise began to respond with dumbfounded amazement and follow her like a hypnotized bear.

The crosscurrents were getting confusing. The pint-sized man who had first called the dancer a narcissist, Cy was his name, had migrated to the sofa. Apparently an expert in military analysis, loaded with sensational exposes, his knowledge of terrain, pincer movements and counterattacking task forces, delivered in a casual, bored baritone, was as sedative as a stream of cool water poured over the flaming confessions. Red, meantime, had picked up the dancer's scarf and was keeping step with her, so the military analyst turned to me.

"Don't be too hopeful about Dr. Eisman," he began, in the same bored voice. "What you see before you—in Toni, Phillip and hundreds of others—this blind craving for help and direction, rebirth as they call it—is the natural result of the non-working democracies. My dear girl, here's the why of the war. They can't make it. They're not hard enough or dirty enough or evil enough, so they're pushed off to the side, which is where most people are anyway. They feel lonely and helpless, and they crave authority. Any strong voice in a storm. And that's what makes the dictatorships possible."

He was speaking directly to me now, and lowering his voice. "Phil thinks he's found the way out. Oh, the doctor's a good guy—but Phil can't make it."

"He seems to think he can," I said, wishing he hadn't singled me out.

"He'll get along for a while—until he gets kicked back into the sick society. Then he'll be reinfected, a fairy again. You watch and see."

8 2

I moved slightly away from him, attracted by Toni's high childish drawl. "And you found out you didn't *need* the theater—and all those abnormal goals, didn't you, Phil? You found out you could work with your hands—just like thousands of other workers—and that changed your sexual feelings, didn't it, Phil?"

CHAPTER TEN

· · · · · ·

GUIDANCE, HELP, THAT WAS WHAT I NEEDED, BUT WHERE TO FIND it—that was the problem I faced the following morning as I watched the rain splashing against the windows. I had just begun to discover that the finding of a doctor who knew how to cure an illness of the mind was no easy matter. Every friend offered his or her particular doctor of the moment, but in thinking them over—Matthew, Toni, Irene, Phillip—I decided against seeking aid from any one of them, as pictures from the night before came to mind against the backdrop of the disordered place.

Trafinia hadn't arrived. Toni and Daphne were either asleep or out, so I started cleaning the place myself. I worked quickly as I mulled over the situation, glad that it was Saturday and stimulated by the physical activity. Arriving at Toni's room (she never cleaned it; both girls seemed incapable of any cleaning or cooking) I had to slow down, as the cough medicines, chest salves, sleeping tablets, vitamin capsules, liver extracts, and all manner of boxes of white powders and bottles of colored liquids demanded dusting and arranging. Toni was out, I knew, as a dozen or more pairs of shoes were scattered on the floor, and her bed was covered with dresses. These finally arranged in order and the bed made, her clippings next demanded attention. There were advertisements from newspapers, photographs of movie actresses, stories of prominent actresses and society women who had won divorces, usually from socialite husbands, with the figures of their settlements underscored, lists of health foods, pills, ointments, personal cards, telephone numbers and canceled checks. The stories of the socialites were stuck together with clippings from the *Daily Worker,* usually citing American atrocities.

Toni's trouble, her conflicts and confusions, lay sprawled out everywhere, yet it was all somehow admirable and touching, for it represented struggle and fight.

I was just piling clippings of collectors and collectivists in order when Toni burst in, resplendent in mink coat and make-up, obviously fresh from an appointment.

"Hi, honey. Don't throw anything away, *please.*" She fell down into the one chair, and took off her shoes. "I've just come from the most important appointment I've ever had."

"Congratulations. New job?"

"It's more important than that. I'll tell you all about it. But first I've got to fix my checkbook. You know how I am—deathly afraid of banks."

"What about that hidden thousand you always keep? Did you spend it?"

"No, but you see—I went into the bank to cash a check—and the man at the window acted kind of funny. I asked him to give me my balance and he kept me waiting—not nice at all the way he usually is. There was a piece in *Variety* saying I was being replaced on the show—do you think he knows? I guess he does, but I don't care any more now. I met Phillip for coffee and he introduced me to a very interesting man—but I don't know—I'm not ready to begin a new affair."

The telephone rang, the new man was already on the phone, so it was some time later before I heard her big news. She had been all the way up to the Bronx to see Dr. Eisman.

"He's wonderful. Oh, if I'd only discovered this man three years ago, I'd be a new woman today."

"What did he tell you?"

"Well, eventually, I've got to get out of the theater. He feels that if I work with my hands, if I give up these crazy drives I have—to be important, to become a famous actress—stuff like that—I'll make a very quick adjustment. You can't find a strong masculine man among these people in the theater and radio where everything is competitive and full of hate—"

"But in a factory you can . . . ?"

"It's highly probable. He says he's had cures that way. Right now —because of the war—it's pretty easy to get work. I called up

Helena Larkins. That plant she works in makes special electrical equipment for the armed services. She says they need people like mad. I'm going out there Monday and meet her foreman. Why don't you come with me? They need women for the night shift."

I said I might, I'd been thinking about it anyway and suggested her not wearing her mink or any of those dresses with the sewed-in brassieres, also not to wear a dress with no brassiere.

"That's already part of my past," she said, speaking slowly. "The need for glamour. My last doctor, Dr. Mannheim, he was only building it up, making it worse, keeping me in tune with the big selling deal that goes on about everything. He was deliberately bringing out my sick points so I could succeed in a sick world. That's what Dr. Eisman said. But the healthy part of me broke loose. That's why I flipped on the show."

"And just about now, how are you?"

"Oh, I feel like a new person already. Now look, you go straight to the telephone and call Dr. Eisman. Here, I'll give you his number."

She fished it out of her bag, wrote it down and handed it to me. It seemed for a minute as if I were repeating some situation in the past in which people were feeling wonderful and handing around the number of the doctor who made them feel wonderful. I said, "Thanks, anyway. But I do have to make a call."

This one was going to be strictly on my own, done coldly, with no one's advice. I went to the telephone. . . .

I made an appointment to see my physician, Dr. Allen, at six-thirty. Coming back, I found Toni still in the same chair, her shoes beside her. I had the queer feeling she didn't know I had left the room.

"As soon as I give up these abnormal goals," she was saying, going on exactly where she had left off, "that's when all my tensions will go and I'll become a part of the real world. Then I'll have a genuine life and real sex and real orgasms. Dr. Eisman says it might seem dull at first but there's no other way. . . ."

At six-thirty I was in Dr. Allen's waiting room, exchanging occasional glances with the six others who had come in ahead of me. I felt for the first time in my short search for help that I was on the right track. Was it really six months ago that I . . . yes, it was . . . six full whole months!

After all, what I had might have physical origins and be amenable to physical treatment—a highly unpopular and unfashionable notion, one that could easily cause social isolation if not complete disgrace to its adherents. True, just the same. I might be suffering from malnutrition—some part of me was starving all right. Or insufficient oxidation, a pulmonary affection—either of these would be reason enough for that sense of smothering. Or my glands might be off or I might have a tumor on my brain.

My time came at last and Dr. Allen, a gracious, inquiring man with lively eyes and an infectious smile, listened as I mentioned my symptoms. He nodded at the unpleasant words—anxiety, insomnia, apprehension—as if at old friends. I told him about Ramsey, and seeing the knowing look—he had evidently heard other stories of this kind—I felt slightly better about the sticky episode.

"Now before we start figuring out the mental picture, let's give you a physical checkup," he said.

As I undressed in the cubicle, the prospect of his discovering some horrible disease bothered me considerably. Something I was born with, I thought, or, worse still, born without.

An hour later, after Dr. Allen had examined me very thoroughly indeed, I sat down at his desk, fully clothed and in my right mind, to await the verdict.

"Well, what is it—cancer?"

"Nothing so simple." But he was chuckling.

In a word, the verdict was good health as far as he could see. I had a strong heart, good lungs, and normal blood pressure.

"What about brain tumor?" I suggested hopefully, but since I showed none of the symptoms he came quickly to the point.

"Now about your mental difficulties—anxiety, insomnia, frigidity, that kind of thing. . . . Of course you know thousands of people are going around with the same things you have—and even worse things."

"But how do they stand it?"

"I guess most people think it's just life and let it go at that. Anyway, most people wait until whatever troubles them breaks out into something they can *see*."

"Like what?" I asked, thinking maybe that blood specimen . . .

"Oh like heart trouble, ulcers, skin eruptions, liver trouble, arthritis, tuberculosis, hypertension. But I don't think you can hope for anything like that. You don't even seem to be nervous. For some reason your unconscious doesn't seem to like disease."

He chuckled and I chuckled with him. The conversation slowed down, and as it did, The Problem stirred restlessly like an animal chained in the corner. Dr. Allen looked down at his desk and talked of what he thought I needed.

". . . A thorough searching investigation—that only analysis provides. You can find an analyst or I can find one for you. The only thing required is money. . . ."

I was getting what I came for. I brushed aside the obstacles and bore down on the basic question. Did sensible people, like Dr. Allen, believe in this stuff? Was it true, as Toni explained, that once the drives were torn down, the patient was reborn? And if so, how soon could he find me the man for the job?

I don't remember what Dr. Allen said, but I know what it sounds like now, and even then a crazy rhyme blew into my head. "If you will start the cure, my dear, A doctor we can find. The Freudians are in the lead, the Horneyites behind. If you would hurry with your birth, there's still another way: French-Alexander are the boys who do it quick, they say! . . . A Freudian or a Horneyite? Or, wait, a William Allison White! . . . Depth therapy at fifteen bucks, Or lighter stuff for ten. . . . Or shucks, there's more. . . . Before you get the score! . . . If these don't suit, try the Marxians. Not Martians—No, Marxians. . . . Why they will dent your libido. . . . Reorient your bent ego. . . . You'll find your gent in the Politbo. . . . And change your scent to old Skid Row. . . . You'll be content with a sweaty beau. . . . And live and love in a two by fo'! . . . Let the flag unfurl. . . . For the brave new whirl!"

Yes, it sounded a whole lot like that. In fact, after comparing the Freudians with the Horneyites, the William Allison Whites—"Practically anybody can get in there who has a college degree and gets in with the right people"—with the Harry Stack Sullivans, and this one with that one and that one with this one, the whole thing sounded completely crazy, and it was nearly eight o'clock.

"I know a man," Dr. Allen said, "from daily contact at M Hospital. . . . He's a new psychiatrist there—in private practice as an analyst." This was the only one he knew whom he could recommend. "Shall I call him up?" he asked.

I said, Yes, and Dr. Allen called and spoke with the analyst. "He can take another patient," he informed. "You are to call him tomorrow."

It was dark night outside when I left with the name and telephone number of Dr. Rudolph Simon, thinking to myself as I looked for a taxi what a nice businesslike name it was.

I came home early on the afternoon I was supposed to call Dr. Simon and arrange appointments to start analysis. After all, I might be going overseas—that job had come up—I'd hear about it any minute. I thought of Ramsey—and then of Chloe. The acne on her face, those red horns coming up. I saw it all over again—the rope, the bruises, the turkey sandwich—and over it all was the tall shadow of Ramsey, the case-forgetter. I am looking slantwise at a wasteland, I thought, an isolated plateau where lurk these dark, ghostly creatures. And asking, Help me, Doctor, asking of these shadows.

I sat there, letting the minutes slip by, until Daphne came rushing in, in her beautiful new winter coat and laughing so hard she could hardly speak.

"Toni—" She finally gasped the word. "Toni went to Lockheed."

Here at least was something definite. I felt good as I asked, "What happened?"

"Had her picture taken. I ran into the photographer on Madison Avenue. He told me—she was trying to get them to stop the noise." It was kind of funny, but at least she did it, I thought, as Daphne continued, between guffaws. "Imagine her—in that tight black dress —going to apply for a job in a plant. It got torn—on one of the machines—and, oh yes, she couldn't stand the noise. It kills me."

I found myself laughing too until Daphne finally got to what was on her mind. She wanted to have the place all to herself on Thursday because Sir Harry was introducing her to someone, and wouldn't we take our names off the door—just for the night—so they would think it was her apartment, and could she have the maid. I agreed to everything, but she stayed on, as if trying to read my mind.

"You oughtn't to think of any more doctors—especially that Marxian doctor Toni's raving about. Don't go near that man, Joyce.

You need to meet new people is all. Don't listen to Toni. She's crazy. Sir Harry says, a girl like you, sensitive and all, you're just not meeting the right people."

"Oh yes, the right people—does Sir Harry know where they are?"

"Of course he does. Royalty, the diplomats, that's for you. He wants to take you along with us—next Thursday. You come, too— it can change everything. The British feel different about things. They're wonderful people. . . ."

I believed her, too, and felt grateful for her kindness. I was just thinking, among these wonderful people Daphne knew, I might even find the nebulous all-giving one who would know me and whom I would know, and then Devman would be soothed and stop his awful howling, when Daphne interrupted the reverie.

"And you know, if everything goes right, dear, we ought to look for a new place. You'd see what would happen if we just got out of here. Most of your trouble comes from this place *with these awful vibrations!*"

I nodded as I reached for the telephone and dialed Dr. Simon's number.

CHAPTER ELEVEN

· · · · · ·

ONE BRIGHT COLD AFTERNOON I TURNED THE CORNER AT MADISON
Avenue, hell-bent for Dr. Simon and the cure. The lobby of the
building seemed endless, with columns everywhere, several sets of
elevators and one of those over-eager doormen.

"Dr. Simon." I tried to make it sound casual, embarrassed by this
eager-beaver who, I felt, could see my trouble standing out a mile
high, and of course knew all about the odd goings-on in Dr. Simon's
office.

"Number twelve," he said. "First floor—in the rear to the right."

The front door was open as Dr. Simon had said it would be, so
I went in. After a while the inside door opened and I found myself
facing a fattish man with a heavy growth of black hair, a dark
mustache and somber brown eyes. "Hello," he greeted me in a deep
voice, then showed me into the inner sanctum, motioned me to the
one empty chair and settled himself heavily behind his desk.

"Now you just tell me anything you want," he said, opening his
hands in a wide heart-shaped motion.

Soon I was clicking off my symptoms, beginning where I thought
I had left off before. From time to time he nodded and seemed
generally sympathetic. Anyway he laughed at my jokes and that
made it easier. I noticed he had exceptionally long teeth and large
ears, and as the minutes wore away and he hunched further down
in his chair, his mouth half-open and breathing heavily, he began
to resemble a big Newfoundland dog.

He said very little, and what he did say was in the nature of absolutely safe generalities, but they seemed interesting to me. "It's understanding we look for," was one comment; another was, "I see."

The time went by on wings and before I knew it he was saying, "Suppose we make another appointment." He had said almost nothing, but I liked him. Then, with the mention of the word "appointment," he began looking into his engagement book and as he did he began talking more than he had in the entire time.

"I have to go to the hospital—I have to be at the clinic—You'll have to be patient—You may have to wait—Yes, you'll have to wait—" I said all right, I'd wait, and tried to get him out of that engagement book, as I quickly saw it made him irritable, but he kept looking at it and talking as if he hadn't heard me. "Tuesday I have to be at the clinic—Wednesday I have patients all day—you'll have to wait—you'll just have to wait—"

The poor man is under pressure, I thought. That's because he's so competent, everybody wants him, and imagine my good luck in having him treat me.

"I think I'll be able to see you again a week from Tuesday."

The Yes leapt out of my mouth. Now wasn't that wonderful? And he'd said such a friendly good-by, I could see he liked me too, smiling and letting me see all those nice long teeth.

I had taken a new job writing a daily column in someone else's name. Always able to work well as long as what I was doing was for somebody besides myself, I found the work easy and fairly exciting. This hiding behind other people, or being a ghost, and then blocking up when it came to my own work, or else destroying the finished thing, had caused me enough trouble. Now, I thought, that nice Newfoundland dog uptown is coming across the ice to rescue me. Why, I could practically see the brandy keg around his solid neck.

Things were looking up. The celebrity, Horace Lemon, whose column I was writing was the precise opposite of me in everything nameable. He wanted fame, I wanted obscurity; he wanted to show off, I wanted to hide; so the situation worked out well for us both. Another way of describing the relationship growing between us would be, I wanted to be free of my trouble whereas he had turned his into a thriving business. For some time, his many recurring physical ailments had kept him from getting around as much as a daily column often requires, but he didn't mind letting someone else show up in his place, nor did he care who did the actual work as long as he retained the fame.

It was easy to see why Horace Lemon was famous and popular with people of all kinds. An enormously fat man with a big pale plain face, pale brown eyes, and thin light brown hair, he was always laughing and showing his dimples, and his air of childish gaiety and delight was contagious. There were no strangers to him. He instantly received a completely new person whom he had never in his life seen before like a long-lost friend. He would burst upon four-star generals to whom he had just been introduced, movie celebrities or presidential candidates, invite them to his home and claim them as his bosom friends.

Sometimes we would meet for lunch or dinner at "21" to discuss the week's work, and I noticed he alternated in his treatment of me. When celebrated table-hoppers approached, he was loath to introduce me, even when the hoppers were male and indicated curiosity. "This dear child here," he'd say, the general idea being I was some vague friend of a friend who didn't quite belong in the charmed circle. Whereas when he was left alone with me, I, too, instantly became his bosom friend.

"Well, here we are, dear thing, here we are. Alone on a desert island—with this nice big fat phallic symbol of a column to bring the big boats in," and he would roar with laughter.

The work and the relationship resulting therefrom fell quickly into a pattern, and caused no pain on either side, and this was fortunate. I saw things dimly those days, but now and then the veil would fall from my eyes and I would find myself looking into the naked face of life. Sometimes Horace Lemon would languish suddenly at the table as his pale eyes, now empty of laughter, turned on me pleadingly, and I would know that for some reason he was afraid to be alone. I often saw him to his door and standing there, the mask of gaiety fallen from his face, his body drooping forward, he resembled some great swollen frog strayed from its familiar bog, panting to get back to the water it needs to live. Often as not, a nurse would be waiting for him, start removing his clothes for some treatment he needed, and talk to him as to a child, "Tsch, tsch, we've stayed out too long again—looping up the food—gotten ourselves all tuckered out." And hurrying away from the scene, I would wonder

9 3

which of us was better off, I who was trying to unload my trouble, or he who was living off his.

The appointment with Simon came through at last, and I arrived at his inner sanctum, removed my hat and coat and sat down in the chair beside the desk. Dr. Simon sat still and looked at me. He was waiting for me to lie down on the couch, but I didn't want to do it. Instead I looked around the office. There was a stained-glass window to one side resembling a church window, which cast a soft blue light across the carpet leading to the foot of the patient's couch.

"Do I have to lie down on that couch?"

"Yep."

I could tell by his face that he wasn't going to say anything further. After a while, I went over and lay down on the couch. The minute I did, I felt uncomfortable, I wished I'd tried the other a while longer, but it was too late to retrieve now. Fortunately I had brought along cigarettes, so I lit one and felt slightly better. I could hear the doctor pulling his chair up behind the couch, and soon I could hear him breathing heavily. I looked at the church window, and then at my feet. I was afraid.

My mind, flooded for days with things I wanted to say, was empty now, my hands and feet began to feel cold, and *It* was there. The terror. Minutes passed, but only the sounds of my smoking and his heavy breathing could be heard in the room.

Then, suddenly, he spoke. "What are you thinking?" I was glad to hear a human voice. "Nothing—but thanks for asking. It's as if my mind had been blown out." My mind, I thought, but the trouble is not in my mind. It's in my chest—or it feels sometimes as if part of it is lodged there. I've got a lion in my chest, clawing away, I thought. But I couldn't say any of this. It just didn't seem to connect in any way with my voice.

"What are you thinking?"

I didn't like him breathing there right behind me, maybe I'd better tell him that. "I don't like this lying down here," I said instead. My voice sounded funny. Then I made it, "I don't like you sitting there behind me."

He made no comment. I felt alone and scared in the place, and his sitting back there wasn't helping any. Well, be that as it may, I was here to get cured, and the method was to talk, say anything that comes into your mind, even if your mind pulls up and separates like the waters of the Red Sea—or was it the River Jordan? You've got to get started, I told myself. Say something!

"Your window—it's like a church window," I managed.

He made no comment. I thought of the church window in the Methodist Episcopal Church where my parents had taken me on Sundays when I was very young. I had felt scared and uncomfortable in the church. The minister seemed tall as a giant, everybody was serious and quiet except the minister—who was serious and loud— and what he said was very frightening. I heard him many, many times, but I don't remember a word he ever said—except one. *"To him that hath it shall be given, and from him that hath not, it shall be taken away . . . even that which he hath."*

My brother looked at me then, as if to say, that means you, but I couldn't be bothered with him at that moment, I had far more important matters to hand.

Like myself, and what was going to be taken away. The minister stared straight at me while I sat on the edge of the slippery seat, my eyes locked in his. That was me he meant all right, I knew it even then, and he was pretty sharp because he knew it too. He must have seen it on me. *I didn't have it. I was born without it. And that was why I didn't have anything else. A loving home, for instance, with nice people inside.* But that wasn't bad enough, to be born without it, now I had discovered something else that made it much worse. People could tell if you didn't have it. And they were going to come and take away even that which you (I) had. God himself was after you if you didn't have it. The minister had just said so.

I listened in terror and fascination, while outside the sounds of the summer's day, full of happy people calling to one another, came to me like mocking music. The song of the people who had it. Out there, and everywhere in all the vast great world, were those who had it. The grownups in the church, and the children, too, everybody, they all had it. Only me, I was the one, born without it. And now I had been discovered. And things were even worse than I thought. Even the dinner I was looking forward to, the roast I'd smelled cooking in the oven this morning as we left for church, the dessert I'd spotted waiting on the kitchen table, no, not even roast beef and hot pies could help now, when they were coming to take it all away.

"What are you thinking?"

"I think it must be very difficult, if not impossible, for people to tell what they're thinking. It came and went so fast." There, I'd spoken. "I was thinking about the minister in the church I went to—back home when I was a kid."

I lit another cigarette. Maybe I'd better tell him how I felt. "Doctor, I think I could talk more easily sitting up. Would that make such a terrible difference?"

"Yep."

"For the first few sessions, say until I got the habit—and then maybe I could take the couch in easy stages . . . ?"

"It would probably be harder that way."

I was going to say, nothing could be harder, but I didn't. That was just a comment, that wasn't free association or whatever it was they were after, it wasn't what I was thinking at all.

What was I thinking? I tried again, but I couldn't think about a thing. I tried to relax, but I couldn't do that either.

"Well, time's up now."

I scrambled to my feet and that very minute I saw everything. "I haven't got it, Doctor," I said. "Give me another few minutes and I'll tell you."

I went back to the couch. "I haven't got it."

"Got what?"

"I don't know. It's something I haven't got that everybody else has—and that's the cause of all my trouble."

I heard him scratching with a pen on paper. "I was born without it. That's why everything has gone wrong. I know I'll never get it now, maybe nobody ever gets it, if they're not born with it. It's as bad as not having your head or—or any other appendage. Only it's worse than any fleshy appendage because . . . suppose like you lost an arm or a leg, you could *see* what you had lost, and get a plastic one and get by with that. But this thing that was taken away from me—or that wasn't given me—is *where you can't see it*. It's where you can't even get at it. . . . There's no hope if you haven't got it. . . ."

I had told somebody. This strange man with the long teeth, the doctor, now he knew, and he was writing it down. He kept at it for

9 6

quite a while, I had the impression he was a slow writer. Then I slunk into my coat and went out the back door, glad for the anonymity of the cold, indifferent street.

After some weeks, in my desperation to find health—even if I had to give it to myself—there were times when I lost all connection with silent Dr. Simon, and the explanations I made went out into the air, against the church window or, sometimes, they seemed to flatten out against the wall. "This thing I was born without," I was telling it now to no one, "is more like a key—maybe a key to a door. And this key is what lets you in where—whatever happens, it's warm . . . and where you find out who you are . . . *because the people in there know you.*" I'd had a dream the night before, something about being smothered. He made no comment about this, either, but now I knew he had no comment to make, so I went on in tune to his scratching away on his pad, and I often had the idea he was writing a letter about me to somebody, though of course I had no idea who it was. "Most people are born with this key, this clue to their identities, but I was not." Sometimes I would ask, "Have you any idea what it means?" and sometimes he would answer, "Not yet." Or I would ask, "Can you say anything about that—that might help me?" and he would reply, "There's nothing to say." And the train that was too fast to catch would come flying by, and I would think—of him, and of me, and of the train. And ask—of him, or of the unseen people in the world—Have you, for instance, ever been a piece of unclaimed baggage, left in a cold, dirty railroad station, with no label on it? No, of course not, you never have—forgive me for asking the question. But, you see, that is what I am—with this difference, I am alive.

"Time's up," said Silent Simon. "See you tomorrow."

The time was not up with me. I discovered an inviting bar nearby and often as I left, always with the sense of leaving someone I didn't know, I would feel the need for a lift to continue the process I'd started to its logical conclusion. I would go into the big noisy place and order a drink. And go on with what I was feeling. Still like a piece of baggage—but after a drink or two, now with a label on it.

Alert, watchful, waiting. Somebody is coming to claim me at any minute—somebody good, the right person who will know me on sight. I can't read my name but The Claimer will know for *he has put me down here*. The minute this feeling came I stopped drinking, paid my bill and went on home.

The following Friday, in the midst of my going on about something else, Dr. Simon announced suddenly, "I think your dream about the smothering may have something to do with this fear you have of being thrown down somewhere." I had completely forgotten the Monday dream by then, having had others by that time, and other problems, too. I wondered vaguely why he chose to mention it four whole days later, and why not at the time I had mentioned it, but that must be, I assumed, for good valid reasons of his own. It was kind of disconcerting, but so was this therapy disconcerting, and after all with a doctor like this, a wonderful man who was so busy and so much in demand, anything he did must be the right thing. . . .

I talked, and the weeks wore into months. I told Dr. Simon all about the problems in my current life—the ghost writing, the interest in the wrong people, the terrors on all levels. He answered either with silence, or with safe generalities. During the week he scratched away on his paper, stopping now and then—during my silences—to ask, "What are you thinking?" Sometimes the train of thoughts had been coming and going but when I heard his voice, making the old bark, the entire train would disappear, and I'd force myself to grab at least part of it and pull it down into speech. He apparently knew no way to make things any easier, and whenever I'd deliberately ask for help he would either reply, "There's nothing to say," or he wouldn't answer.

I told him that lying on the couch, with him sitting behind me, greatly increased my apprehension. "It's dangerous—or feels that way," I said. "Can't you help me figure that out?" But he replied with silence. I began to understand I wasn't going to get any help from him—except on Fridays, his "speech day" I called it, and by then I had forgotten the problems I had brought in on Mondays. . . . And in the interim, I went on trying to work them out alone.

I had a dream in which I was walking down the aisle of a church.

Down where the pulpit usually is, a coffin was standing upright. As I came closer, I saw the door to the coffin was open and I walked up some steps and entered the coffin, then stood looking down at desks at which people were sitting. As I looked down at them, I saw to my embarrassment that they were looking up at me as if they expected me to tell them the answer. They rose in a body and started coming toward me, to try and force the answer out of me. As they came closer, I became frightened that they were going to lock me in the coffin, and I turned around, looking for a door or exit of some kind in this upright coffin.

I must have found one for the next thing I saw was the minister coming slowly down the back of the church, but he, too, was looking at me angrily for not knowing the answer. I tried to scream, "I didn't say I knew the answer!" The door to the coffin was closing and I was smothering, but I could still see the minister coming nearer and growing bigger with each step.

Eagerly I told the dream to Dr. Simon who promptly reacted by scratching with his pen. What did it mean? Devman was in there screaming something at me, but I was not able to decode his message, so after Simon finished writing I asked him if he could help me. He didn't answer, so I repeated the question, and when he didn't answer the second time I found myself getting angry.

"What's the matter with you? I know you're not asleep because you just sucked your teeth. Aren't you going to say anything about that dream?"

"There's nothing to say," he said.

"Now look, Dr. Simon, I've been coming here lying on this couch for nearly five months. I've gone on and on about myself, told you most of my troubles—I'm afraid of being murdered, I was born without something, I can write other people's stuff but not my own, I'm doing myself out of everything. I've told you about my mother, my father and my Uncle Joe—and all you've ever said is, 'What are you thinking?' 'It's understanding we're after.' Or, 'There's nothing to say.'" His silence made me all the more angry. "Then when you do break down and say something it's always on Friday—about the things that troubled me on Monday—so I've forgotten what the hell they were, anyway."

He made no comment. I went on, "If that's what they told you in analytical school—just to sit there and breathe heavily and write things down—you could have gotten that much without going to school. I might as well be staying home talking to the wall."

Now he'll say something, I thought. After all, I've insulted him. I was wrong. He said nothing.

"Dr. Simon, I feel this dream has meaning—in relationship to my troubles—as I've related them to you. Can you help me with it?"

"What do *you* think the dream means?" he asked.

I didn't know, but suddenly I heard myself talking. "I think the dream is about you and me, dear. You're going to school to learn analysis—that's you, and God knows how many other doctors down there, but the church window says it's you, that's for sure. I'm the poor sucker who's walking into the coffin while you're trying to pass your examination. Only you don't know the answer, and you have the nerve to ask me for the answer. Neither of us has it, only I'm honest. Before the coffin closes over me, I try to scream, *I never said I knew the answer."*

We were both silent after that; then he asked, "Where's the minister come in?"

"Oh, that's easy. That's you. Another version of you. The minister in my past told me, 'To him that hath it shall be given, and from him that hath not, it shall be taken away, even that which he hath.' And, brother, that's exactly what you're doing. You're taking away from me even that which I hath—my time and my money."

He started that scratching again with his pen. He was taking notes real hard on this one.

"Ministers and analysts are both phony," I went on, disregarding the dictating speed I usually employed when he wrote. "They're both making like wise men, pretending to know the answers. One is offering the ritual of religion, words, but without faith, the other is offering another ritual, but it's words again. You don't even give any words. But if the patients or the congregation should rise up and demand proof, demand the answers, you'd both be out of luck and run for the nearest coffin."

Silence. "What do you think of my interpretation?" I asked. More silence. Then, "What do *you* think of it?"

"It's not what I was going to say—but come to think of it, it's one interpretation, and it's not too bad."

"Well, time's up," said Simon the Silent, but I hardly heard him. I had started to laugh, not knowing what I was laughing at. I found out later, much later—but that is getting ahead of my story.

CHAPTER TWELVE

. . . .

I WAS BUSY THOSE DAYS COVERING ALL KINDS OF APPOINTMENTS IN the acquisition of news to feed the column—parties, luncheons, interviews, besides the war work for Russian Relief, Aid to Britain, visits to hospitals—so the home life Toni, Daphne and I shared was whittled down to an occasional conversation between baths or late at night. I could sense that something was happening to Toni. As slowly as my life was progressing guided by Silent Simon, just so quickly was hers going forward with Dr. Eisman, the Marxian analyst. Even Daphne, who took a dim view of anything connected with Toni, had to break down and admit Toni was not the same person as the one we had known some months ago.

"I'd never believe it if I hadn't seen it with my own eyes!" she commented. "That one, working in a factory. I tell you, Joyce, now I've seen everything."

Toni was indeed working in a plant, where the lathes and milling machines clattered away twenty-four hours a day, seven days a week to speed the war production. Toni, who didn't know an electric mixer from a vacuum cleaner. *And* earning eighty-five dollars a week! Her face looked pinched, she'd lost weight, a result of the odd hours no doubt, but she was in good spirits and seemed in fact on the crest of a wave. When I came to clean her bedroom—we were out of help, Trafinia having also discovered factory work—the warehouse of make-happy pills and female aids to living were pushed into corners, though the *Daily Worker* was still running neck and neck with the society pages. But something new had been added. Big books about dialectical materialism had found their way into her bedroom, with *The Function of the Orgasm* ahead of them all.

A new kind of man came home with her these days. There was Kip, a good-humored if rather miserable-looking machinist who wore a diamond tie-clasp and seemed to know a great deal about cams. And Eddie, a small rotund joyous Italian. And Jim, and Whitey and Clark, all of whom appeared enchanted with Toni and the duplex and ready for anything, but whom Toni, at Dr. Eisman's suggestion, was holding at arm's length while she—and they—attempted to "build up a good relationship."

One night, I met her at the door as she came home after midnight; we sat down for a cup of coffee and I heard the news.

"This is it, Baby."

"You mean your present life?" She nodded. "After Eisman—let's call it A.E."

"Everything is new. You can't get into reality by thinking—or even by feeling. You have to do things. Now take these men I meet. They work. They're real. They're not afraid of life because they're living."

"And how about you?"

"I'm living—for the first time."

I still couldn't quite believe that such a thing could happen so quickly and corrected her with, "You mean you're ready for the leap into reality?"

"No. Ready, hell—I've leapt. Brother, am I glad I left that capitalist!"

I dreaded to hear this, thinking of myself and Dr. Simon, but I listened, feeling envious of her achievement, and wondering, as she talked on.

"I was a sucker for a money-hungry capitalist businessman—who happens to be a doctor. I spent three years living my life in a goddamned test tube—and if he had his way I'd be spending three more. Only I couldn't because I lost my job and I didn't have any more money. And what did he do then? Tell me to get some more."

"But that was realistic, I'd say. You do need money."

"I need security—which is different from money. They're making a business of *unhealth,* I've found that out. Most of them have no social conscience—and no other kind of conscience. They have no vision of life ever being any better than what it is now."

"Wait a minute now." I kept remembering how she had sold me on the whole idea, talking of these doctors as gods, capable of reshaping people, giving them a new chance, a rebirth. "You used to talk about Good Relationships, Good Working Conditions, and that Good Old Sexual Fulfillment. All that came from your Freudian doctor. How can you turn against him so?"

"I found out what his idea of good is. Having Good Relationships means being able to get along with the double-crossing bastards you meet on Madison Avenue. The Good Working Conditions means making money, no matter how. And as far as Sexual Fulfillment is concerned—love—that kind of thing—that's one of their worst lies."

"I don't believe that. It's not a lie. It makes good sense. We can't change the world. We've got to adjust."

She shook her head. "Don't you understand—that the world is sick. It's dead. Don't you get it? Their idea is to change your disease so you can fit into a diseased society—and get more diseased—and grow old—and die. *And that's the cure.*"

I couldn't buy this: Toni had changed too quickly, she might change back just as quickly, too. Nevertheless, the conversation presented some confusing issues.

"But it's understanding you're supposed to get," I threw in, thinking dimly of the quiet Dr. Simon with all those sheets of paper he had in his desk.

"Yeah. Brother, that kind of understanding you're better off without. Look, Joyce, don't you see—you can never fit into that sick world—like that Dr. Mannheim was trying to fit me."

"Why not?" I even envied her old Dr. Mannheim—he at least was trying to fit her somewhere, whereas Simon didn't even seem to know where I fitted.

"Because you have a different goal. You want to be well."

"But if you get understanding, you do get well, don't you?"

"No. You can understand from now to doomsday but you'll never get well until you get out and do something that is well."

"But *understanding—*"

"Understanding *what?* Your mother and father were out to do you in—and that's why you are the way you are. You can fully understand that and still be sick. Look, Dr. Eisman gave me the only understanding that really made sense. He made me understand why I was sick and getting sicker."

I doubted all this, I doubted Dr. Eisman, at this minute I doubted everything, but Toni had changed. Her face looked different without make-up. I thought of those hours she used to spend mornings "building up her face," going late but beautiful to appointments. Gone. And the sounds. The high "I can't talk to you now, dear," on the telephone. The high heels clicking through the apartment, running down the steps, the doors slamming, as Toni went rushing, rushing. Gone. Now, all quiet. Even the smells were gone. The bathroom left steaming—Toni was forever bathing, deodorizing and perfuming herself. Toni, and any space recently occupied by her, had a special odor, the Toni smell. Now, to sit near to her and smell nothing gave me a feeling she had really gone away and this was a new human being, a changeling sent by Dr. Eisman in place of the old Toni.

"I know now why I was lonely—and frigid sexually," she was saying. "Because I was surrounded by hate. Dr. Eisman showed me that. Our society is so competitive and full of hate most Americans are incapable of real sexual fulfillment. The greatest lovers are in reality the greatest haters." I didn't get that, but she went on to explain. "Take the sexual athletes all around the place—men and women, too. I was getting to be one of those—trying to make it— thinking I was getting hot. When all the time all I was—was lonesome. A small icicle in the Great Glacier." Yes, this was something new all right—part of a glacier, not just a glacier all alone. "Take us now, people like us, we're not alone really, we only think we are. It's not just us that are sick. We're part of the great national sickness." I didn't believe that, but . . . "We have a national unconscious that is frozen and guilty because of our unnatural desires and goals."

"Now wait a minute, Toni!" This was too much. "You're not going to tell me a country as mixed up as America—with all kinds of people from all kinds of places—can have a national unconscious?"

"Oh yes it can—because we have a national consciousness—and it all wants the same things."

"What is our national consciousness?"

"To be utterly happy and beautiful, rich and glamorous, eternally young and gorgeous, remarkably smart and . . . That's what we're being sold all the time and that's what we're buying."

"All right, let's get off that. How is Dr. Eisman making you well?"

"I'm away from the sick world of theater and radio. A worker. When you get with healthy people you begin to get health. Courage is all you need."

"Well, I don't know. I can't believe I'm the way I am because of the society. I think it's because of my past."

"Suppose you break with your past—then what will you do?"

"I don't know. Find another world, maybe. I'll take my chances."

"You'll have to find a new way of life—and if you find that you'll be well. The crack didn't just come to your door. Think of all the people who can't even find their way to doctors . . ."

"Yes." I was slowed down here. "I do think of them—"

Even Dr. Eisman hadn't found the answer to that problem . . . and meantime I still didn't fully see how the American pattern was affecting me. I pulled her gradually back to the more immediate problem.

"And do you think you'll find your love among one of these workers?"

"Oh, of course. Any day now, but I'm taking my time. I'm growing steadily more solid."

"You haven't met the right one yet?"

"No, but I will. Any time now. Listen, this is what's *dramatic*. Dr. Eisman says, *The man arrives the minute the girl is ready, and not one minute before.*"

Then Toni came down with a cold. I noticed her attack and recovery were accompanied by certain signs of the old panic. She called around frantically, looking for work, and apparently got some appointments for radio commercials before she was well enough to go back to the plant. She always surrounded her activities with a great air of secrecy, but one night I happened to hear her walking around in the apartment, making an awfully funny sound over and over again. It sounded like a very young child, or possibly an animal, either eating or murmuring or both, I couldn't tell. Chlurump—chlurump—chlurump, it went, over and over again.

"What on earth are you doing?" I asked.

"Nothing important."

"But what is it? It's the funniest sound I ever heard "

She stopped long enough to look at me. "What does it sound like?"

"I don't know. Like somebody—or some creature—devouring food, I guess."

"Oh, that's wonderful." She laughed. "That's real great."

She closed up like a clam after that, and shut her door, so I thought no more about it. Next morning I turned on the radio to hear the news and caught the same sound in a radio commercial. Chlurump . . . chlurump . . . chlurump, came the voice and, fascinated, I stayed glued to the radio. Chlurump . . . chlurump . . . chlurump . . . Zzzzz . . . zzzzzz . . . zzzzzz. Then soft music, "The Afternoon of a Faun" . . . then some softer chlurumps and zzzzzzes . . . and then Toni squealing, "Oweee." And talking, "That tasted so good . . . I am a silkworm . . . I have just eaten my breakfast . . . a tiny bit of a fresh delicious leaf . . . I feel so good . . . because soon I will spin a thread of the finest silk in the world. . . . It's Martel's silk . . . for those pure silk Martel ties. . . ."

I laughed and promptly forgot about it all day, but that night I asked her about it. "Toni—if you were chlurumping just to be a silkworm on a radio commercial, why did you have to be so secretive about it?" She stared at me, without answering. "I'm not prying into your affairs. I'm curious why you think you have to hide things so, that's all."

"You heard me on the air?"

"Yes."

"Wait a minute. This is important. How did you know I was going to be on?"

"I didn't. I was listening to the news."

"Wait a minute, Joyce. Somebody must have told you. Who was it?"

"I swear nobody told me. I was listening . . ."

"Well, I guess maybe I believe you. How did it sound?"

"Okay. You made a fine worm."

"You didn't tell Daphne?"

"No."

"Well, please don't tell her. Wait a minute. She didn't hear it, did she?"

"No. She was asleep."

"She's never asleep, that one. Well, so you liked it, huh?"

"Absolutely. Your wormhood is assured. But why the secrecy?"

"Look, you're very foolish, the way you tell things when people ask you—give them information. I try to keep everything a secret. I have to. I don't want anybody to know where I get my work or what kind of work I'm doing."

"Why? What would happen if they did?"

"The whole thing would go to pot. You mean you don't *know?* There's maybe two hundred girls could do that part—probably more. Well with, say, maybe five hundred people wanting to be the Martel silkworm—five minutes with their tonsils, two hundred and fifty smackers—fifty smackers a minute to be a Martel silkworm, *I'm going to tell somebody what I'm doing?"*

Toni appeared mildly surprised that I didn't take more precautions, but as she talked on, I began to wonder. Did my trouble have still another face? The compulsion to believe in people—was there such a thing? Yes, there was: I knew because I suffered from it. A vague aura of goodness surrounded every human being, that was what I saw with the first glance, but behind that mask was the raw irreducible face, often shattered and debauched and evil, and this was too frightening for me to examine, I pretended it didn't exist, but all the time I knew it was there.

"I have to be secretive for all kinds of reasons," Toni was saying. "It's not just competition. People grabbing bread out of each other's mouths—that's bad enough. But I have to stay as far away from all the other forms of hostility as I can. Every step of success stirs up all this *hate* and that's pretty scary. That's why you're so scared of success."

"Have you always been this way—secretive about everything? I mean—since you were a kid?"

"You bet since I was a kid. My mother believes in the evil eye. She thinks if people find out she's prosperous they'll put the evil eye on her. I remember she used to hide it even when she collected unemployment. She still does. She tells us they wouldn't give it to her, she didn't work enough weeks. Whenever she collects money from anything she says she's so broke she had to borrow—and then she becomes extra tight, so we know she's got money from somewhere."

I listened, fascinated, for Toni, with all her problems, represented a kind of living reality to me—especially as I thought of the bad break I'd had as a child listening to Christian lies like "Love your neighbor" and "Do unto others" and God will reward you.

CHAPTER THIRTEEN

· · · · · ·

IT HAD STARTED OUT TO BE A GAY EVENING. PHIL PAIGE, WHO WAS
Toni's escort, knew a little place uptown; Red said it used to be good,
so that was where we headed. We were all disappointed at first, finding ourselves in one of those big, noisy, dark, eating-and-drinking
emporiums with a bar and booths in the front, and tables in the back
where people sat listening to two Negro musicians playing at two
pianos placed back to back on a dais under bright lights.

It was a long time before we got anything to eat. Meantime, the
place was thick with smoke and uniforms and faces, talking, talking,
talking. Red had been talking to me, I'd told him things I hadn't
meant to and he'd done the same. A comedian was singing under the
spotlight now.

> The waiter hollers down the hall,
> Ya gits no bread with one meat ball.

The drinkers clapped and laughed at this funny sad lyric. Next
the singer switched to "Old Black Magic." Red went right on talking
during the singing. He was going to an analyst now named Dr. Priest
"to get over me." "The science is made for people like you, Dr.
Priest thinks," he said. "Your prognosis is good, very good in fact,
if you get to the right man. It's too bad he's got a dumb bastard
like me for a patient—and therefore of course he can't take you. . . ."

I wasn't particularly listening to him. I was still seeing the little
man in the lyric, sitting in the big restaurant afraid to order from the
big expensive-sounding menu and asking for one meat ball, while
Phil discussed the lyrics for Toni.

"Listen to the American love lyrics. All about the unattainable.

1 1 0

The people in love ain't going to get nothing but trouble. The women are going to get left alone or beat up and, brother, are they sad and is it good!"

Phil seemed to know a great deal about practically everything, could express himself clearly, too. I remember wondering why he always antagonized the other men. Red quietly detested him, and even David, the plump, intelligent, young student doctor who was in love with Daphne and occasionally accompanied her somewhere— when the British and all else had failed—was mildly irritated by him. "It's because he sees the awful American mother-worship," Toni whispered. "After all, he *was* a fairy, and look at him now. You see . . ." Daphne put in. "Yes, look at him now—going for *you*." But Toni continued making her point . . . "Whereas the other men —David and Red—are still vitally interested in the unattainable."

The party began breaking up, but Red and I stayed on, drinking and talking. The girl who isn't there, I thought, listening to him. Just as I was crazy about Dr. Ramsey, the man who wasn't there. Not the real Ramsey, of course—I had his number—that wife-tying, patient-forgetting old match-stain. And now, here I was the same way about Silent Simon . . . but not the real Dr. Simon, the fat quiet old oak . . . but—somebody he was pinchhitting for. Somebody lost way back at the beginning of the trip from nowhere to here. "I must kiss you," Red was saying, "I have need of it," and I was thinking, at least he can kiss the one who isn't there, whereas I . . . I took another drink.

I noticed the man sitting by himself at the next table—a big black-haired man with sharp eyes who kept watching us. Later on when the place was gradually emptying out,—and I was coming back to the table from the Ladies' Room—I saw this man walking behind me. I stopped to let him pass, but he didn't. Instead he said softly, "Hello, Joyce. How about having a drink with me?"

"Thank you, not now," I said, and moved to pass, but he stood in front of me.

"Look, I think you need to talk to somebody, don't you now? We two aren't strangers . . ."

"But you are a stranger. I've never seen you before."

"And may never see me again. Ideal for a conversation."

"Well, maybe in theory," I said. "Not in reality. Strangers are usually pretty dull."

"We aren't strangers though. I've been listening to you—and talking to you—for a long time." He moved closer and tried to guide me toward the bar. "You know me, and I know you. I'm more your kind than the redhead. He's not your kind, he never could be."

That was when I noticed Red—he must have left the table when I did—standing not far behind us. I saw him through the bar mirror, watching and listening in fascination, and I hated him. Why doesn't he come and get me? Why does he stand there watching? Watching while the stranger touched my arm, harder than before—and listening while the stranger spoke. "I've been waiting for you for hours—maybe for years—" His voice was slightly foreign. "You've been waiting for me too—I know."

I started to answer him, but just then Red burst in.

"So you're the guy she's been waiting for?" He looked the man up and down, and the man looked back, but neither spoke. It was all in a matter of seconds. I stood there, staring foolishly at Red. Don't you know? Don't you understand, something is happening to me, I'm afraid, I need help. What was this he was saying—No, it couldn't be, he wouldn't—but it was. "Well all right, Mister—if this is how the lady wants it."

Red went off without saying good night, and I was left standing there in a vague, stricken mood, but now anxious, feeling suddenly alone and unprotected.

Trying to shake off the slow cold fear that was breaking over me, I felt myself following the stranger to the bar. Then, sitting there, I became slowly conscious of a certain new sense, almost of—was it relief?—in the knowledge of yielding to the old unconquerable inevitable. It took the form of relief from all personal contact with Red. Those soft mushy good-night kisses I dreaded; at least I had turned my back on them, and it was like turning away from all the soft safe mushy bogs of the world, and going into the forest with my eyes wide open but unable to stop walking straight on into the face of my peril.

Why? What was I doing here—in this strange man's apartment? Listening, watching, with his eyes holding mine, not answering. Staring helplessly at him like a bird—or a child—a very young child—staring, hypnotized by the sudden move of some big strange animal.

We had come here in the company of another couple—that Burt and Ruth somebody, friends of this Chet something. Now suddenly I saw they had gone. I wanted to go too, I'd better go quickly, I thought, but I felt frozen to the chair, unable to move, while this Chet went on talking in his low-leisurely, slightly foreign voice. "Don't look so worried, dear. Nothing bad is going to happen . . . Nothing but something you want."

The enemy had struck, was still striking—I knew it, and rallied for the fight. "Please—I've got to go—Help me!" But my voice sounded funny, half-gone, breathless and pleading, and as I stared up at him his fingers tightened over my hand. "You don't really want to go, you know you don't. You don't know what you want, but I know," he said, as he lifted my hand and put it back on the table.

I wasn't drunk—no, I couldn't blame it on alcohol, this sudden absence of will power. I wasn't out of my mind. I saw what I was doing, I knew. I saw the place clearly, too. The heavy ornate room, with the stained tapestry over the mantel, had a certain brooding quality, even out there in the kitchen that showed through dark-green old-fashioned portieres strung on a wooden pole. Back there would be the bedroom. I could see it all. And him, this Chet. Not old, but not young, the kind of face that could never look young because of the way he smiled maybe, an old, hungry, joyless smile . . . Just as the furniture, the table, for instance, inlaid with mother-of-pearl, had never looked new.

"Have a brandy. Here, this has authority." He poured glasses for both of us. I sipped some of it and set the glass back on the table. I was still staring, suffering from this awful vague paralyzed sensation, as he got up and came over to me, and I could feel him pulling me to my feet. As he came close I felt some new sensation, a certain wild excitement toward this stranger, this man who was somehow danger-ous . . . but it left me immediately as I felt his hands inflicting pain.

I was awake now, out of the hypnosis, and genuinely terrified, as I began to struggle against him. My voice was normal again, I screamed, but it was too late . . . He was smiling, that queer wild hungry smile, as he lifted one hand and slapped me full in the face. I twisted and fought, but he had a tight hold of my arm with his other hand. The glances I caught of his face as he slapped me again and again told me quickly how dangerous and warped he was. His lips had widened out away from his teeth, and his teeth and gums lay bare in a terrible wolfish leer. I was screaming in pain and terror when his

1 1 3

telephone rang. This presented a problem. He wanted to answer the phone; he tried to pull me over across the room, but I caught hold of a chair and that made it next to impossible.

"Don't try to go. If you do I'll come after you," he said, as he went through the kitchen. "I'll find you too, and you'll be sorry—so you'd better wait."

But the minute he disappeared I grabbed my coat and bag and went tearing out of the door and down the stairs into the street. I ran panic-stricken down the block and around the corner, my coat and bag still in my hands. There was a hotel around the corner, I could easily make it there before he could get down the stairs, and even if I couldn't, I was safe in the street. Then I was in the lobby, walking in the opposite direction, away from the desk toward a telephone booth, the first handy dark place I saw where I could pull myself together.

The first thing I thought of as I tried to cover the swelling on my face with make-up was not of Chet coming after me, not of how I looked, and not even of what I had done and what had been done to me. It was of what I had that had not been touched—for all these months with the doctors. "This thing I have is worse than I thought. I daren't go on this way. I've got to be cured of it, no matter how. *And I will be.*"

CHAPTER FOURTEEN

. . . . . .

ONE COLD DREARY EVENING TONI CAME IN AROUND ELEVEN, FLUSHED from recent dancing at one of the canteens for servicemen, in the company of a French sailor. She was usually fairly secretive with her special beaus but Daphne had told me of this one. Daphne and I were both surprised when she brought Alphonse upstairs and introduced him to us, then left him to go downstairs for drinks which she served to us all before the fire. Alphonse was a tall, lithe young man with bright red cheeks, merry brown eyes, and a very winning smile, and while he spoke little English, what he did say was interesting enough to make us wonder where he had picked it up.

"We Frenchman, we say, Love is in the skin," he confided, after the first drink. "I tell to Toni, 'I love you,' and she says, 'Why, how you know,' and I say, 'Because I love your skin.' "

Alphonse further confided that before the war he had been a waiter and part owner of a bistro in Paris which he had left to join the French Navy. He seemed worried about his family—fortunately, his mother and father were in Honfleur when the occupation troops entered, but of his brother, a loyalist rebel since the occupation, no word had been heard. "Alfi is afraid he might be dead," Toni whispered, "or else being worked to death at forced labor. He's devoted to his brother. He gets awfully depressed sometimes." But what Alphonse said did not sound exactly sorrowful. "Philipe, he is héroique—mystique—Hélas —qui peut dire? Mes amis, the life is *here now*. No other life I know. Only in this minute—" He lifted his glass and every worry in the world seemed to disappear in the allness of his bubbling spirits.

"Isn't he attractive?" Toni whispered, as she watched him. And later, when Alphonse had finally and reluctantly departed, I had to admit he was, for he left a rosy picture in the place. He put his arms around anyone who came near him, and offered himself in a casual but friendly caress.

"He makes me feel good," Toni told us. "He is healthy—mentally and physically."

It was easy to see the special charm Alphonse held for her. A huge warm animal vitality flowed from him, radiating out to all who came near him. He was happy, he felt good, his life was a bottomless glass of good fresh milk which he somehow wanted to share with anyone who happened to be thirsty; yet he was far from coarse in his behavior, and there was a discreet tenderness about him.

"Women are crazy about him," Toni told us. "And that kind of scares me. I noticed you liked him—didn't you, Daphne?"

"Oh, sure," Daphne admitted. "At least he isn't crying in his beer. And he's interesting. I like Frenchmen, *generally*."

"Why?" Toni demanded.

"Oh, they know more than Americans. Even a French sailor."

"He's only a sailor for the duration. In civilian life, he's a restaurateur. He's got friends all over. You should have seen the rich bitches going for him at the dance. Old hags, of course—but loaded."

We asked her how Alfi had reacted, knowing her fear of competition.

"That's what's so nice—he was very aloof with them. Acted like I was his girl, and these were just acquaintances, strangers—that kind of thing. I guess maybe it's good in some cases, a man's attractive like that, and he's had lots of women. Dr. Eisman says he doesn't have to conquer, maybe, because he feels everything is his anyway. Isn't that funny—I should like a man like that?"

"Of course there'll be a language barrier," Daphne told her. "You'd better start learning French. I think maybe you'll make it before Alf gets on to English."

"Oh, sure, but I think we can overcome that. The point is, he's real. He's healthy. Don't you think so, Daphne?"

"Yeah," said Daphne, as she went off to retire—only to show up in my room later for a final comment.

"Healthy. All that girl thinks about is, is a man healthy. He hasn't got a head cold maybe, or—small pox. But how's she know what else he's got—or hasn't got? One thing I'll bet he hasn't got is money."

During the following weeks Alphonse became a fixture in our apartment. He was there whenever Toni was home, and much of the time when she wasn't. He would drop in, bringing a pint of brandy or some new dance records, and sit waiting patiently for her to return.

I wondered what they talked about during the many hours they spent together—by now they were inseparable—but since Toni was obviously much happier than she had been before, it seemed foolish to demand conversation. It looked to me as if she had hit the jackpot at last.

Once, noticing that she received Alphonse in an old pair of slacks and with cold cream on her face, instead of her former magnificence, I asked her why she was letting down so much.

"Alphonse is a waiter, Joyce," she explained. "And workers and their wives don't need glamour."

"Don't they?"

"Well anyway, if they do, I don't want us to be that way. I don't want Alphonse to love me because of my glamour. I want to be as plain as possible around him—so he'll see the real me. I have trouble enough with him in that direction."

"I thought he owned a restaurant—didn't you say he was a restaurateur?"

"Yes, he is—part-owner with his family. But he works. He waits on tables."

One night we heard how Alphonse had insulted her. Toni, always a sufferer from colds, had taken the precaution of wearing extra-heavy, old-fashioned winter underwear, otherwise known as "woolies." And it seems Alphonse, always on the alert, having glimpsed the revolting underwear, had promptly brought her a present of a pair of black chiffon panties. She had discussed the situation fully with Dr. Eisman and both had agreed it was time to stop Alphonse before he went further with his dirty capitalist longings.

"The next thing he'll want me to be his mistress instead of his wife and partner," informed Toni.

While Daphne and I both thought Toni was showing a very spartan attitude toward poor Alphonse, this tendency of hers to become a girl scout was certainly a new twist. Still we had to admit Alphonse was taking it with good grace, unless of course his knowledge of English wasn't good enough to let him know why he was being scolded. He played the adoring suitor for her hand, waited humbly for her to say the word. All told, it began to look as if Dr. Eisman was indeed a magic man.

Came the day, the long-awaited day, when Dr. Eisman told Toni she was "ready." Having proved herself as a worker—she'd kept her job at the plant for three months—the reward of sexual fulfillment was at hand.

If, as Dr. Eisman said, Toni was "ready," it was nothing to what Alphonse was. Having been kept waiting lo these many weeks for his beloved to emerge from the Marxian test tube, and having meantime declared his love in every bar on Third Avenue, now to be told at last that Toni "consented" and that they would "go away together" on an analytically approved pre-nuptial honeymoon, Alphonse's ardor knew no bounds.

"I hardly can wait," he confided to Daphne and me, adding with eloquent simplicity, "I do anything to make good. And later I show her a side of me she never will forget."

The "anything" included the immediate purchase of a much more elaborate set of black chiffon underwear with many blue rosebuds, but this time the "good relationship" between them having been established, Toni said it was all right. As she showed me her pre-nuptial gifts, I found myself feeling exhilarated and tremendously interested. Something was happening, and I was a part of it. Even if nothing, or almost nothing, was happening to me—at least life could be reached this way, via the test tube, and here was Toni proving it. I found myself envying her, and yet at the same time rooting for her. Maybe Alfi wasn't the "final man"—but at least he was real, a flesh-and-blood man one could see, and he and Toni were going to be married. Something entirely different from sitting around with doctors, waiting for the thing to happen. But the doctors were responsible for it, and therefore . . .

In the next few days the problem of where Toni and Alf were to go for their honeymoon became a major conversation piece in the apartment. Even Daphne, she who had opposed the "mating" and was entirely opposed to this "expensive probing you girls go in for," felt the contagious enthusiasm, and started helping out. We three talked about it all the time, "the place" seemed that important. Forgotten was the war, psychoanalysis, Dr. Eisman, Dr. Simon, the evils of our corrupt society, the terrible futility and money-worship after the war, *and* the neurotic effect of glamour, as four simple words emerged, posed first by Toni and quickly picked up by Alphonse, echoed through the duplex. "Where will we go?" Alf didn't know or care. "The point is *when*," he would say. Or, "Why is it so important?"

It was true, places in the country were hard to come by those days, but after quite some telephoning, one morning I asked Toni, during an interlude of calls back and forth to country places for reservations— mostly famous places I noted, that had been turned over to other purposes—"Why is it really so important? Wouldn't any hotel do— say some hotel in the city?"

"You don't understand, Joyce," Toni's eyes were wide with seriousness. "I thought you would but you don't. Alf and I are beginning something. I've been trying to make him understand he has to provide for me—and protect me. A girl like me, I'm used to nice things and I want to go to a nice place—for something as important as this."

I did understand, or I thought I did, but I kept remembering Alfi's recent desperate words on the phone, as of two hours ago. "I don't know no nice plaze in America. I know nice plazes in Paris—in Honfleur in Calvados—in Deauville—but I don't know no nice plaze over here—in America—in New York. You girls, you should know hundred nize plazes—what's matter with you—I pay—I pay anything for my Toni?"

He had something there. We girls, what was indeed the matter with us? But the situation wasn't getting any better for these mental meanderings. In fact, it was getting worse, and Toni was beginning to get depressed. Daphne and I packed her bag—walking shoes folded over the chiffon underwear and these over the new winter socks— while Toni watched silently. We had several hotels we hadn't called— these Toni had told Alf to call "on his own"—and now Daphne and I both urged her to make the reservations herself.

"Look, dear, Alf feels strange on the American telephone. Can't you have any sympathy for that?" I asked. And Daphne added, "Why do you insist on making the poor man suffer?" But, we soon discovered, we were on the wrong track. The more we urged her to make the reservations herself, the more we pleaded, the more logic we used, the more adamant she became.

"I will not have another man leaning on me!" she protested. "Alphonse is a man. In any country. He's not a baby. He must take care of things like this. A wedding yet, and he can't make reservations for his bride at a hotel!"

"But he's ready to take you anywhere you tell him to take you."

"Stop it. I told him this morning not to call me until he had figured the whole thing out for himself—and for us. I told him not to call me until he had found the place—and if he couldn't find the place not to call me again in his life."

I noticed he hadn't called her for a number of hours—five was an awfully long time for Alf to leave Toni untelephoned, and now it must be ten or more—and fearing the worse had happened, and Alf had somehow given up in despair, I suggested she call him.

"What are you suggesting—that I show him how to remain a baby?"

"No, not exactly—just call him and say hello. Just make sure he's still alive."

"He's still alive, all right—the dopey sonofabitch. But if he can't find the place, he might as well be dead."

She picked up a new toothbrush she had bought for the honeymoon and threw it on the floor.

"But you're supposed to be starting out tomorrow morning," I said. "There's not too much time. He'll be leaving soon, you've got to go back to your plant—we're both waiting here to help you get started—"

The telephone rang just then; Daphne went to answer it. "It's Alf," she informed, hollering from the dining room.

"Tell him I've gone to bed," Toni told her. "And look, Joyce, I know you mean to be helpful, but I wish you'd go. I'm really going to bed. After all, a man who can't find a place to take a girl should be left alone. I'm ready—for a v-v-v-aginal orgasm—and everything that goes with it—and if he can't even find the place—"

She was weeping, but she slammed the door.

CHAPTER FIFTEEN

. . . . . .

SATURDAY. THE MINUTE I AWAKENED I KNEW WHAT DAY IT WAS.
Toni's wedding day—I wondered what time it was, looked quickly at
the clock and saw it was after ten. The telephone was ringing. I put
on my robe and ran to the steps to call Toni.

"It must be for you," I hollered toward her. "Hurry, it's probably
Alf."

She stuck her head out of her bedroom.

"I'm not going to answer it. Our plans are all made."

And before I could say anything more she had closed the door. I
went promptly to the phone, but by the time I lifted the receiver the
caller must have hung up. I had planned to help her finish packing
and, I felt certain, continue the discussion so abruptly halted last
night, but her refusal to answer the telephone had me stopped, and
when she came in for coffee she elaborately avoided all mention of
the impending event. Then Daphne joined us, but as she tried to make
helpful suggestions the atmosphere became unbearably tense, so we
soon broke up the party.

"It looks like Dr. Eisman's wedding is out the window," Daphne
commented, laughing. "I'll just keep the present I got her. You'd better
just forget about it, too. . . . Don't know what you're so interested in
it for, anyway. Nothing can happen—it never could—that was obvious from the start."

But I was interested in it, and I found myself hating Daphne for her
snickering, cynical attitude. It didn't make sense to try to explain it
to her, she couldn't possibly understand what I hardly understood
myself. I was by now deeply interested in what this queer, subtle doctoring could do, and here right under my nose was a life-sized guinea

pig, my friend Toni, leaping smack out of the test tube and into the arms of love. It was action, living proof that something could come out of all these words, these trips back and forth to doctors.

I had an appointment, but even after I had dressed, I was loath to leave. Toni had, meantime, taken a long steamy bath, then retired to her bedroom where she sat stolidly smoking cigarettes and reading. When I peeped in on her, I saw among the pile of big books on dialectical materialism two new titles, *French in Five Days* and *How to Run a Restaurant*. She was still uncommunicative, but I found myself lingering too long for comfort in the overheated, smoky room.

"Are you sure you're all right?"

"Of course I am. Don't worry about me."

But she looked pale and nervous, sitting up in bed with the heavily packed, open suitcases on the floor beside her, staring out like an open question-mark.

"What will you do if Alf doesn't show up?"

"He will show up."

"I think so too—but how do you know?"

"Because he's healthy. Alf is psychically sound. He's male. He's not afraid of love."

"Yeah, well—then it'll be all right?"

"Only an unsound man with a mother fixation backs out on a woman. As Dr. Eisman says, The American men don't really like women—as women. Thank God he's a Frenchman. He likes women." She smiled, a secret, secure little smile. "He'll show up all right."

The spectacle of Toni sent a challenge straight to the core of my being. So far I had felt slightly envious of her achievement, yet proud too of the impending victory: she was my friend, and like me she was shooting with loaded dice and, it appeared, about to win anyway. Nothing must stop it now, I determined, as I drove uptown in a taxi shared with Daphne, trying not to hear the abysmal logic she kept pouring out.

"That Alf—he can't make reservations anywhere. You heard him say ours is the only telephone number he knows how to call. Don't you get it—she's forcing him to find the place because she knows he can't do it—and that will keep them both from going anywhere. She's only got two more days on her leave from the plant and one of them is gone already. I promise you, darling, Dr. Eisman's wedding party *just can't happen."*

I had no real reason for coming home at five o'clock, but after trying the number four times and finding it continuously busy, I hopped into a taxi and came on home. I went straight into Toni's bedroom. She was gone—but obviously not on her honeymoon. The suitcase was still open on the floor. I placed on her bureau a bottle of her favorite Arabian Nights perfume, and was just scrawling good wishes when the bell rang. I promptly pressed the buzzer and just as promptly it seemed heard loud eager footsteps leaping up the stairs.

There, before my eyes, stood Alf. Hatless, coatless, breathless, and almost speechless, but rosy-cheeked and smiling.

"Halloa. Is my Toni in there?"

"No, but she'll be back. She's been waiting for you."

"This I know. Wal, I have found the plaze."

"Wonderful—" He started to go. "But why don't you wait now and tell her about it?"

"This I cannot now do. I have taxi—" he pointed to the window. "I am buying. Tell to Toni I telephone p.m. and come here. We go then. Good-by."

He started down the steps, but I hollered after him, "Where is it? You have to be sure about reservations today."

"This is sure. And beautiful."

"In the country?"

"Oh yes, the country. With trees, hills, water, everything—just like the Bois de Boulogne—"

"But how will you get there? You want me to get the train reservations?"

"No, no, dear girl. My friend Salathiel—he will loan me his jalopy. He show me the plaze. He go there all time—parfait pour l'amour. Salathiel—Georges Salathiel—he have his honeymoon this plaze—and he says, don't worry, it is good luck. Eh bien, at seize heurs et demi— Daphne, you, Toni, Alphonse—we celebrate. Chez vous, et puis, chez moi. But I must buy things now. 'Revoir."

I had followed him downstairs; he kissed my cheek and ran through the door. The last I saw of him was just as the taxi started up when he leaned forward, and I saw he was surrounded by boxes.

Daphne was wrong, and Toni and Dr. Eisman were right. I left a note informing Toni of the good news, and, relieved and happy, hurried out to keep an appointment. As my taxi pulled into our street much later that evening, the first thing I noticed was the dilapidated old jalopy parked in front of our door, and I knew that Alphonse had been true to his word.

Upstairs, the scene that greeted me was even more cheerful. There I found Alphonse, Toni and Daphne seated in a happy circle before the fire. A magnum of champagne was on the table, and the three were sipping from the green champagne glasses we hadn't yet used. Alphonse leaped across the room the minute he saw me and quickly pulled me into the group.

"Ah, Joweece, my sister," he exclaimed as he quickly kissed me on both cheeks and poured champagne into the waiting green glass for me, then quickly filled the other glasses. "Congratulations," I told Toni as I sat down on the sofa beside her. "Oh, thanks, dear—" Toni's voice sounded so low, the excitement must have made her hoarse, I could hardly make out what she was saying—something about the bottle of Arabian Nights perfume I'd given her being "spectacular."

"Now you can open my present," Daphne announced. She pushed such a huge box toward Toni I knew she must have buried the hatchet. This time Daphne, a crafty one with a dollar, had gone all out. Toni opened it gingerly, with Alphonse standing and watching behind us. She lifted first an old discarded college pennant of Daphne's marked, "Something Old." Next, a very pretty town suit, Toni's size, marked "Something New." Then a pair of red earrings, the ones Toni was constantly borrowing, marked "Something Borrowed." And last was a large and very bad photograph taken of the three of us sitting in the apartment, labeled "Something Blue." We were all surprised and delighted at the generous good humor Daphne had shown, but then, this obviously was going to be a good-humored evening, with Alphonse hovering above his Toni, and the French expressions, *magnifique, hélas, mon héros,* and *coup d'état* mixing with the *okays* and *wonderfuls* and *snafus,* as the magnum of champagne was lifted again and again from the ice bucket and ever more amiable toasts were raised.

The apartment was littered with paraphernalia prophesying a most athletic wedding, what with the bicycle, ice skates and blankets Alphonse had parked downstairs, near the sterno stove. I remember wondering about this, deciding quickly Alphonse, who always brought a certain incongruity into our atmosphere, was the perfect catalyst for Toni, and he knew best. Toni was taking it all straight, sitting smiling and complacent with her wide-eyed, serious, life-is-a-desperate-business look and talking in a low voice. Alphonse, like a streak of sunlight showing us all up and yet changing us, his white teeth flashing in and out, his dark skin, his blue eyes creasing with laughter under the heavy eyelashes, his eyebrows arching impertinently as Toni explained, in answer to vague misgivings we felt about the athletic week end, knowing Toni never even walked if she could find a taxi. "He's an athlete, dear—aren't you, sweet one?"

"Oui," announced the bridegroom. "I beeld Toni up. She needs fresh air more than many people." He had also brought along his camera to take pictures of the happy couple.

"It all comes with the dinner." Toni was delighted with Alfi's plan. Yes, everything was all right, including the Packard convertible, vintage 1935, that Alfi had been loaned by his friend Salathiel. "Everything is now," Toni whispered. "Health is catching, too—like sickness. I can't even remember the men in the theater—all those experiments. All right, of course, to have men like that if you know you're in it for health-seeking and growth-making—but it's in the past. A breath of the real thing, and it's forgotten."

She was getting drunk. With the magnum now finished, we had been toasting the couple with brandy. It was nearly midnight before Toni and Alf were finally settled in their convertible, complete with bicycle, skates, stove, camera, blankets, suitcases and various unopened parcels, and we heard Alf's voice, bursting with the special philosophy of life he was foisting on his paramour, booming in the street. "I tell to Toni, yesterday is gone—like anshan history. And the futshur, this you cannot touch. All you can see is this minute—that is all that is. Come here, you girls, slip me some skin."

We kissed them good-by, then Daphne and I went back into the apartment, heaving a great sigh of relief, made ourselves some coffee and finished up the appetizers for a midnight snack.

"How on earth did those two ever find each other?" Daphne kept asking me. "Some magnetic pull is the only explanation. The two most impossible people in the world—for anybody but each other. How on earth . . . ?" But we were both too tired to figure out the answer and went promptly to bed.

I fell into a deep sleep that seemed to last for hours. I remember waking with a start. I had the terrible feeling the door downstairs had opened and closed, someone must have come in, but I was still sleepy and somehow it didn't matter as much as it should. It was getting light outside, and anyway I thought I heard Daphne coming out of her room; she'd go down and see what it was all about, I thought, as I snuggled back in the bed.

I must have fallen asleep again, but after a while I heard sounds— footsteps, voices downstairs, then very loud sounds like furniture being moved out—or in—or around the room, I couldn't tell which but certainly the door opened and closed more than once. Someone was tapping on my door. . . . There was Daphne, looking down at me.

"You'd better come downstairs," she said.

"What's the matter? What's happened?"

"You'll see. Hurry. I've put the coffee on."

I grabbed my robe and went down, prepared for anything but what I saw, in the semi-darkened room. Toni was sitting on her suitcase, all wrapped up in her coat, hat and muffler, wiping her nose with a pink silk chiffon handkerchief. Alf, also complete with overcoat and muffler, was walking around, arranging bicycle, skates and other athletic objects in a corner against the wall. There was nothing so surprising in their reappearance. I decided something had happened, the hotel had been filled so they'd had to return, but there was a certain something—maybe the expression on their faces, maybe their abject silence—that wasn't quite natural. Something terrible must have happened. I went over to Toni.

"What's the matter?" I hated to ask her. "Are you all right?"

"I don't know." Her voice was very hoarse.

"Why don't you take off your coat now—and have some coffee?"

"I can't. I'm freezing." Then, in a terse whisper, "Wait till you hear."

"But you had reservations, didn't you? Couldn't you get into the place?"

"We never even got there."

1 2 6

"But what happened—did the car break down?"

"Oh, God, Joyce," she moaned, "it's been a nightmare. We kept riding around—all over the same damned road."

Alf, who had elaborately avoided entering the conversation, turned suddenly from intense preoccupation with his bicycle, and interrupted.

"Not for so long. Maybe one hour, maybe two. I don't know the road."

"I thought he didn't know where he was going. But he did know —that's what's so awful. He had all the directions—written down in French—from that friend of his. He did know—oh God, how he knew!"

"Well then, did you find it at last, I hope? But you couldn't get in, was that it?"

They were both quiet. Toni stared at Alf, and Alf looked out the window.

"Yes, we found it. Even in the dim-out we found it. We never got out of it."

"Out of where? What on earth are you talking about?"

Whatever it was, I knew it had some awful significance for them both, especially for Toni. Suddenly she got up off the suitcase.

"Tell her, Alf." She walked over to him. Daphne stopped pouring the coffee and watched the scene. I noticed how pale and shattered Toni looked. "Tell her where you decided to take me—pour l'amour. *Tell her.*"

Alf turned fully around, letting the bicycle fall to the floor.

"The biggest place up there. There is trees and a house where we can be like kings. Look I have bought these sleeping bags—expensive, too—"

"Tell her where!"

"Santralls Park," he announced.

"Where is that?"

"Central Park." Toni's eyes were red and fierce. I heard Daphne laughing somewhere behind me, and hated her with all my immortal soul.

"What is wrong?" Alf was shouting now. "Nobody disturb—police understand—Salathiel tell to me—they leave alone sailor in uniform —if he is quiet and behave. Tonight is my plan—we stay in the house —and tomorrow we ride to the countree."

"You are crazy!" screamed Toni. "You don't take a girl like me to Central Park. You've got to grow up."

"So what is so crazy? Six hundred acres—all empty just like Bois—and who is this kept up for—squirrels!"

The conversation ended abruptly. Toni went back to her suitcase, and Alf picked up his bicycle. I went in to get coffee and started pouring cupfuls in the dining room. It was very quiet, and I knew somehow it wasn't finished. No words were being spoken but the place had life, an over-eager, desperate something was in the air, and slowly, in the silence, it seeped into me what it was. They had started something, those two, and it had been left unfinished. I didn't know how or where, but I could feel it had been started, and *it had to be finished*.

Then somehow we were all in the dining room, sitting four-square around the table, drinking coffee. No words were being spoken—in fact the only sounds, besides the clicking of coffee cups on saucers and the hum of morning traffic starting up outside, was our breathing, which could be heard distinctly. Even Daphne, never one to pick up subtle innuendoes, was feeling it: the laugh dropped from her face like a veil, she glanced just once at me, and promptly lowered her eyes. At the earliest possible moment she excused herself and went back to bed, and I busied myself with the breakfast dishes.

When I came in from the kitchen I found Toni and Alf had left the table, and were more or less in their former positions: Alf beside his bicycle, the empty coffee cup on the stairs, with Toni sitting on her suitcase, eyeing his every movement. Neither of them had taken off their hats and coats, and now, as the steam began heating up the place, they were both perspiring. I went out and when I came in again I found them staring at one another in a kind of hypnotic trance. I stole a glance at Toni, and following her eyes to Alf's, found him staring depthlessly into hers, and I looked away in embarrassment, making a big deal about the dishes again and wondering what was going to happen. I needn't have felt awkward, however, for when I came back they were still at it.

This time I watched, not knowing what else to do. I had never seen anything quite like it, this spell they seemed to be under. It fascinated me so I couldn't move, just stood about stupidly waiting for something to break. And it did.

"Joyce!" Toni was speaking to me, her eyes still focused on·Alf's, and his on hers. "Would you do me a favor—a very great favor?"

I said yes quickly, as Toni continued, still in her trance stare and her trance voice. "Could you and Daphne go out of here for a while. . . ?"

I said, "Yes, sure, right away too." I ran up the stairs, relieved and electrified into action. Next I was upstairs, talking to Daphne, between moving about in a desperate but strangely efficient activity, against Daphne's heavy irritation and somnolence.

"What on earth are you doing?" Daphne demanded. She was sitting up in bed, watching me angrily.

"Packing your bag—"

"Have you gone crazy?"

"No, but if I stay here I will. Daphne, please get up. I'll help you get dressed."

"But what for?" She knew all right, I could tell from the next words. "Why in heaven's name should we have to leave home in the middle of the night?"

"It's not the middle of the night. It's early morning—I haven't time to explain—and anyway you already know!"

"I don't know—and I'm not going to move!"

"But you've got to. You've got to get dressed right now and come with me."

"I will not. I won't move one inch until I know what this is all about."

She lit a cigarette. I went on packing, and talking. "I think you know. You can't possibly say you didn't see what was happening downstairs."

"Oh, I saw all right—but that's no reason I should move out of my place."

"Yes, it is." She was frowning, so I tried another attack. "Don't you understand what we'll be doing if we stay here?"

"No, I don't—and I don't care. But since we're playing guessing games—all right, I'll bite, Mr. Bones, what'll we be doing?"

"Interrupting a mating—"

"Well for God's sake. Is that all? I'm staying right here."

"Oh no you're not."

"Why?"

1 2 9

"Because if you do—Toni—I mean, they can't complete the thing."

"Alf can."

"Look, it's not just Alf's—it's Toni's mating. Toni's worked for a long time for this orgasm—and she can't have it with people around the place."

"Then let her stay unmated. She's been that way for thirty-one years—oh, I know she says it's twenty-six but I happen to know it's thirty-one. She's been that way for thirty-one years—and a few more hours can't make much difference."

"It can too. It can make all the difference in the world. Daphne, get up, please. Look, to stay here is like—didn't you see how they looked?"

"Yes, I saw—just like two animals tied together. Mating!"

I went on, mumbling. "Not an ordinary mating—but something special—a medicinal mating—a curative coming together. Something Toni has been living for—working for like you work to pass an exam at school—and that she's about to get now—if only you'd get your stupid bones out of that bed!"

"I won't move. Why should I?"

"Because you're interfering with nature. I tell you, goddamnit, it's a mortal sin. . . . Like stopping a butterfly from—moulting—something like that. A sin, I tell you . . ."

I was just putting her brush and comb into her suitcase, preparatory to closing it when she jumped out of bed and started taking it away from me.

"Put those back. I'm not moving."

Desperate now, a thought flashed into my head.

"Look, Daphne, if you'll get out of here and come with me . . ."

"Come where?"

"To a hotel—anywhere—only come, and quickly, without any argument, I'll pay this month's installment on your coat."

The frown between her eyes eased up a little. I was just wondering if it had hit. "Oh, Joyce, you just haven't got any sense." But she was moving, moving and muttering. ". . . So that little bitch gets in heat with a frog—and what happens?—they turn us out of our apartment. What the hell do they think we're going to do—come down there and look at them? You couldn't pay me—I might never get it out of my mind. . . . Tell you, thing like that, you could take it to your grave."

But she was putting on her stockings, and seeing her start to dress I sat down and wrote out a check for $67.75 which I knew to be the monthly installment she was paying for her mink coat.

"I won't take it," she said with great dignity as she stopped pulling up her stocking long enough to grab it and look it over, adding hastily, "as anything but a loan."

The downstairs rooms were dark and empty as we traipsed through to the door, stumbling once over a bicycle and once again over a pair of ice skates, but I knew from the general appearance of things Alf and Toni had lost no time continuing the immortal act begun in Santralls Park.

CHAPTER SIXTEEN

. . . .

DAPHNE WAS ALWAYS ADDING UP COLUMNS OF FIGURES, ON PAPER
and vocally, but during our brief stay in that hotel she was at it
almost obsessively.

"Last week I made a hundred and forty-five dollars," she'd say,
usually just before she went to bed. "This week, thirty so far. Next
week I think it'll be about a hundred." It would go on and on sometimes, but the summation was always the same. "My God, that's no
money at all."

One night I came back to the room and found her in a wild mood.

"Last night when I called in at the agency, that damned Flora told
me I had a nine o'clock booking. So I'm up, dressed and ready to go
when the phone rings. The booking is changed to one o'clock. So
what can I do, go back to bed? Not when I've just spent an hour
making up and dressing. So I've got to stay in this damned hotel room
until one so that goddamned Toni and that frog can complete a
stinking mating."

"What would you have done if you'd been home?"

"It would be entirely different. If I had to kill time until one
o'clock, at least it wouldn't be in this kind of cramped space."

"Well, what did you do?"

"I walked, called people up, killed time until one. My job was
over by two-thirty. So what do I do then? Go to a movie or come back
here or call around and see what's doing."

"What else happened?"

"Nothing. I'm just not getting my calls. I've got another early
appointment tomorrow. I just loathe being bathed and dressed and
breakfasted and looking magnificent at the dot of nine—so some dirty
photographer can tilt my chin and smudge my make-up and give me

a feel and whisper a lotta horrible stuff and maybe occasionally snap a picture."

"What did you do today?"

"Stood with my back twisted out of place—wrapped up in a bitchy cloud of red fox and black velvet—with hot lights shining on me— looking provocatively over my left shoulder while my spine cracked in the middle and I darned near sweat to death."

I said I'd take her out to dinner, she could name the place, but she kept at it.

"And you know darned well she's not going to be answering the phone like she should—and giving this number to callers so we can get our calls."

"Just let her get her call and I think she will."

"Well now, seriously, Joyce—how long do you think it'll take? Because another week of this and I'll be a chattering wreck."

"Didn't you hear from anybody?"

She enumerated her calls, they sounded pretty good. "And, oh yes, that numerology man called. Wants me to change my name from Daphne to Animal. How do you like that? Animal Johnstone."

For Daphne a few days away from her normal supply of telephone calls and presents was like being locked in a dark closet. The appointments she thought she'd missed took on a crucial importance, up to and including the launching of a new perfume at a party in a Fifth Avenue building to which she was being escorted by an adoring little fairy named Dominick whom she'd been stalling on some tentative promise she'd made to let him spend an afternoon at the apartment, wearing her clothes and answering the phone for her.

Horace Lemon was ill much of that winter, and often, besides ghosting his column, I'd find myself helping him carry on his elaborate social life. I remember once, when I was helping him plan a dinner party, he told me, "Call up General X—he's in Washington." Having recently heard him confess that he had never met the general, I said simply, "I don't know him, and neither do you." He chuckled. "I don't, of course I don't, but I just heard he'll be in New York on Sunday. Go ahead now. Call him and tell him Horace Lemon wants him here for supper on Sunday. His close friends will be here—" He handed me the list of celebrities. Then there I was telephoning the general, mentioning the celebrated friends who wanted to see him, and hearing him ask the time and Lemon's address. The same stunt worked even more easily with novelists, playwrights, book-writing psychiatrists, politicians, doctors, newsmen and beautiful women, the names of the other famous people stimulating them to the point where they seemed about to leap into the telephone.

Meantime, occupied with what I could do on my own to change the situation, I had observed the obsequious and sickly characteristic of most ghost writing. Here, I decided, was a chunk of my trouble I would chop off at the first opportunity.

One morning the telephone rang bright and early, and the opportunity presented itself. A friend was asking if I could bear to forsake the life of a ghost for the life of a magazine editor. It was a famous national monthly with a special spirit of its own, and he'd just heard they could use a woman editor.

A few hours later, talking with the executive editor, I was aware of entering a new atmosphere. The place was heavy with glamour: thick carpets, a Filipino boy serving coffee or drinks in the Board of Directors room, a bar here and a bar there, beautiful bathrooms, beautiful secretaries with wise smiles, and chic lady editors. You felt that a great deal was going on here, but whether or not any of it came off didn't really matter. It was the minute, the effect, the idea, that counted. I picked it up at once, and reacted—yes, it had a special spirit, that place, a loving indefiniteness. This was no place for tension or special ambition. News was passed around on transmitters made of gold, telling a kind of golden version of reality. Even the war was glamorized, with death given a bright plastic face and a toothy smile.

The editor himself, an interesting, sensitive man, had something of the same tentative quality of the place; in fact, when it came time to tear myself away from his oncoming revelations, I didn't know whether or not I had the job, but at the same time I felt I would come to work here and perhaps still would not know. Even after I had met the managing editor and heard what my duties would be, nothing was quite believable, we were all still floating on a beautiful pale-blue sea of vagueness, yet it was somehow refreshing and somehow just right.

I came to work on the magazine the following Monday and decided quickly my first impression had been correct: if ever I saw a place practically designed for people in need of mental repair, this was it. Everybody was walking two feet off the ground in the bewitched atmosphere, yet they were all pleasant and friendly, and the sound of the golden transmitter ticking off the glazed version of modern times was soothing to the nerves.

Now then, to inform Dr. Simon—I had already told him my intention—and ask him for a change of hours. He would of course be glad. I hurried eagerly to my appointment and quickly told him the news. I expected him to say something, but he didn't say a word. I asked him, "Don't you think it's good?" and waited. After a while he asked me how much I was getting, then relapsed back into stony silence.

"Well now, Doctor, I don't think I can get here at four in the afternoon—I'll have to keep hours—and you said you'd change my hour . . ."

"You'll have to keep the same hour. I haven't any other time."

It was a flat statement. No concession was even suggested.

"But I'll take any other hour—" The feeling of making some progress I'd had on arriving disappeared completely in the overwhelming anxiety I felt at the thought of losing him. He couldn't mean it, of course. "I can come at lunchtime—or early in the morning.

"There's not any other time!" he yelled. "I've told you that a thousand times."

I waited, there was something alarming in his voice, then, "Couldn't I come at—say, eight o'clock in the morning?"

"I'm eating my breakfast then."

Softly, "What about late afternoon—any time you say?"

"There isn't any time!" He was screaming again. This word *time* always sent him into a tantrum—the word *hour,* perhaps—no, that was just as bad. What word was there that might have a soothing effect? Think fast. Oh yes, money. I could offer him more money. I did, too. He didn't answer, but he looked better. I was sitting up for this session, the talk-it-over business to hand, so I could see his face. But he still wasn't talking. After a while, seeing the minutes were ticking away, I asked the inevitable dreaded question.

"Well, Doctor, what do you suggest I do—find another doctor?"

"There is no other doctor."

"What!"

He couldn't mean what he was saying; he couldn't believe it—yet there he was repeating it.

"I said there is no other analyst—can you get that through your head?"

I was beginning slowly to come into focus.

"You mean all the doctors—the analysts have suddenly left the city?"

"If you can find one, I'd like to know where. They're too busy, that's all. They just haven't got the time."

I began to see him for the first time as he was. A very ordinary, cranky, negative human being, with absolutely no warmth or insight of any kind. As to what happened to me his patient, he didn't give one good goddamn. I felt shocked, then angry.

"Look here, Dr. Simon—" I was screaming now, "don't you dare to sit there and tell me—or any other person in distress—there are no doctors to be had. All I need to find another analyst is the money—the time—and the telephone."

"I said there aren't any more doctors in this city. You can't find one. There are none to be had. That's all."

I stared at him, anxious but still angry, and wondering. I saw his big, tense, bloated face, frowning, irritable, and stupid. I had never before dared to believe this, perhaps in the transference situation—after all, I had told this man my confidences, I looked to him to save me, or at least help me out of the dark—I dared not face it. But not now; not any more. Because there it was. This man, who purported to be treating the subtle complexities of complicated mental illness, didn't even have good reasoning powers. He was just talking, or screaming, through his hat.

But there was something more—I saw that, too.

"Oh well, I imagine there must be a few analysts left, if you look hard enough around the wharves—but don't worry about it, Dr. Simon. You look tired."

"Well, I am."

"Don't you think maybe you should take a rest?"

There were ten minutes more, we'd pass the time talking about that. . . . "Maybe you should go away for a vacation?"

"There's no place to go." But he felt better talking in this vein. "Mrs. Simon has been calling everywhere—we can't get reservations."

"What about Canada?"

"The trains are too crowded."

A silence fell between us. There was just nothing more to say. I looked at him, I wasn't angry any more, just quietly dumbfounded. This lifeless heavy lump of protein, I had been looking all these months to him to help me, to try and unlock the strait jacket in which I was living, and all the time *he hadn't even seen it*. All those generalities and those platitudes and those silences—I had thought they were a clever façade—a smokescreen to hide from the patient the clever thinking psychiatrist at work—they represented his mental output, they were the real man.

There was something unbelievable about it—I mean what I was saying to him, as I sat there looking at that church window I'd stared at, lo, these many months. "Well, I hope you find a place to go, Dr. Simon." And him saying back to me, "Well, if you ever do find another doctor, I hope you'll let me know." And what was I thinking? All those words, falling on his ears, the nightmares, the chunks and pieces of my pain, the unlabeled suitcase, the dream about the closing coffin—to him. Unbelievable, yet it was true. And now another hour was gone. There it was in numerals on the face of the little green leather clock, 4:55. No fooling that clear-eyed baby. At least you make sense.

Things were getting kind of quiet again, the way they did around Dr. Simon. "But isn't it supposed to be unwise—for the patient, I mean—stopping an analysis in the middle—changing horses in midstream?"

"Yep. That's what they say. But I've told you . . ."

"All right, all right." I handed him a life-saver. He took it and put it in his mouth. "Wintergreen, good for the stomach."

It was time to go.

As I walked on down the street and turned the corner at Madison Avenue, I knew I hadn't finished—hell, maybe I hadn't even begun. I knew I was leaving a negative, ungiving man, but what I knew mentally was entirely different from what I was feeling. My parents had been negative and ungiving, so there was nothing new in the situation—in fact, something familiar and therefore desirable. Dr. Simon didn't want me as his patient; they hadn't wanted me either. I felt angry, rejected, bitter—but it was familiar. I was losing something very valuable: a familiar situation. I felt exactly the way a child feels. He knows his parents are pretty bad, he knows they don't love him or want him, but they're the only parents he has. The outside world looks black and threatening. He'd better stay where he is. Besides, if he's so awful even his own parents don't want him, what untold terrors may not await him out there?

I still had this child, Devman, and now he was screaming in my ears. *The big fat oaf, let's go back and kill him!* Oh no, there's a law—anyway, you know I couldn't kill anybody. *But I could. I could stick a knife right now in his big fat stomach. I'd like to run back there right now and jump up and down on his balls.* Now, now, you know we can't do things like that. Oughtn't even think about them. Dr. Simon is a nice man. A doctor works hard, why he's tired, the poor man. What else would you like to do?

It was a mistake to indulge Devman—but it was fun that night as, on and on for hours, and for days later, he entertained me with scenes of Dr. Simon and me, meeting on an equal level, and having it out. The favorite drama was when Dr. Simon appeared as my lover, courting me violently. We were alone together in my apartment, and things were high and wild. Only, just as the heaving Dr. Simon was about to consummate his passion, stark naked and beady-eyed, Devman appeared and pushed him out the door. As the naked man stood there in the hall, embarrassed and bewildered, Devman leaned over the transom and screamed, *There's no glamour here, it's understanding we're after.*

It was the only satisfaction I got, these fantasies of revenge, because obviously there's no way to get even with an analyst, any more than you can get even with your parents. I tried to tell that to my child-self, this Devman, as he kept on deviling me with these revenge dramas. I even quoted Goethe to him. "Against the superiority of another, there exists no weapon nor remedy save love." And what did he reply? *That's okay for Goethe, but not for this here kid. I've got a jackknife . . .*

Came the inevitable depression, the feeling that Dr. Simon was right to turn me down, the whole thing was my fault, I just didn't have it, and of course, he knew. I thought of talking things over with Toni, but as fate would have it, the changes in my life—new job, good-by to Simon—had occurred during her mating season. The mating had taken longer than either Daphne or I expected. For three days we kept calling home from the hotel where we were staying, and hearing Alf say, "Hallo, my sisters . . . Please stay away just a little bit longer—" Daphne took a dim view of the entire matter. "Look, he can keep up that don't-call-me-I'll-call-you all winter," she warned. "I don't care what you do, I'm going back tonight."

When I returned to the hotel after my farewell visit with Simon, true to her word, Daphne was packed and ready to go. "Something must have happened," she informed. "I called Alf and said we were coming back."

"Is it all right?"

"I guess so. Hurry up and pack—we'd better get back there."

"Why? What did he say?"

"He says he hasn't seen Toni."

"You mean he's there in the apartment by himself?"

"I guess so. Hurry up. I have a premonition."

I said, "So have I," and threw my things hurriedly into the suitcase. We paid our bill downstairs, took a taxi and drove silently home.

I don't know what I expected to find, but, whatever it was, it certainly did not foreshadow what was there. We entered our apartment from downstairs. Daphne pushed open the door, peered in and motioned to me. I wondered later why we were being so quiet, practically creeping back into our own place. Nothing was changed downstairs. It looked dark as always, with only one light from the lamp near the stairway casting an ominous amber glow over the carpet. We came in and closed the door quietly behind us. There was not a sound in the place, the grandfather's clock in the dining room having stopped ticking a while back.

I pressed the switch near the door, the lights went on in the living room, lighting up the front half of the place. It was then that we both saw Alphonse—but not the way we had expected to see him. He was lying stretched out across the floor beside the table, which was piled high with soiled dishes and glasses, as after a feast. He was lying so still we were both afraid to approach.

We both called, "Alphonse!" The prostrate figure moved, a head shot out, and we sighed in unison with relief. He wasn't dead, this

1 3 9

was not a murder scene, but there was something unnatural and terrible in the way he was moving and the way he looked as he got to his feet and came slowly forward.

We were both upon him now, talking fast. "Where's Toni?" I asked, and Daphne, "What's been happening here—we have a right to know." Alphonse didn't reply, but he pointed to the bedroom.

"In there?"

He nodded. We hurried through the kitchen to the bedroom. I turned the knob but the door was locked. Alphonse was standing behind us now.

"She lock the door," he moaned. "She lock the door in my face."

I knocked loudly on the door and called, "Toni—what's the matter —is something wrong?"

After a minute a small tight voice answered. I could hardly believe what she was saying.

"Make him go, Joyce. I won't open the door until he's gone."

"All right, I will—but what happened?"

"I'll tell you later. Make him go."

For the next few minutes, we both first pleaded, then ordered, and finally threatened to call the police—before Alphonse finally consented to leave the premises. The minute he had gone, I ran to the door and told Toni, "He's gone," while Daphne watched from the window.

"Are you sure?" wailed Toni. "Make sure—or I won't open the door."

"I swear he's gone," yelled Daphne. "I saw his car turning the corner."

Toni opened the door. She was wearing a bathrobe, her hair was disheveled, her face looked very pale and her eyes were red.

"I'm sick—very sick," she said. "Here's the doctor's number. Please call him—right away."

The doctor hurried down to see her when he heard that her temperature was 104, examined her, promptly called the hospital, and ordered an ambulance. Poor Toni had come down with pneumonia. As we hustled about following the doctor's orders, and making her ready for her sojourn in the hospital, she lay in her bed, talking in a whisper.

". . . All his fault. He's a fiend."

"But what did he do—we thought you were happy?"

". . . Happy? Yes, I was happy . . . until he tried to destroy me."

"But how, dear? Maybe we should have him arrested—make a complaint."

"But we'll have to know what he did," whispered Daphne.

". . . Tried to kill me. Tried to destroy me . . ."

"But what weapon did he use?" asked the blunt Daphne. "If you want us to make a complaint . . ."

"He knows what weapon," she gasped. "Been using it on women for years. Broke every promise. I'm frightened of him—I'm terrified he'll come back."

"But he's gone. He can't come back here."

"That's illegal entry," said the legal-minded Daphne. "He wouldn't dare."

But Toni was still moaning her fears when the ambulance came and we helped her on the stretcher. "He'll never go. He'll never be gone. Things will never be the same."

"Jesus, what do you think the guy did?" Daphne asked me as we waited for the appointed time to call the doctor and find out how she was. "He looked like such a harmless thing—and so in love with her. I don't know. I just don't get it."

"I don't know either, but I was thinking—maybe—it's just possible . . . but—Oh no, it couldn't be *that!*"

"What? For God's sake, it's too late to talk in riddles."

"I just remembered the terrible thing Toni told me her ex-husband did. He was a fiend, too. According to Toni, the sonofabitch stayed all night."

CHAPTER SEVENTEEN

. . . .

I MET HIM AT A PARTY AT IRENE'S. A MIDDLE-AGED MAN, GOOD-looking, with a charming way of speaking. Everybody was calling him Richard or Dicky, I was surprised to learn he was a doctor—"Dr. Richard Osborn," Irene explained. "A very prominent—and important—psychoanalyst. Head of the Institute."

The man had such a humble, inquiring, pleasant way of speaking, and such a nice sunburn, I thought he was some relaxed businessman just back from a trip to Florida. He asked if he could take me home, and we stopped off at a nice bar. Over the second drink I asked him, "Do you know Dr. Simon?"

He chuckled. "Oh yes, I know old Rudie. Why do you ask?"

I parried the question, indicating I knew him socially. "What kind of an analyst is he—or perhaps you don't know?"

"Oh yes, I know. I know everything there is to know."

"You make it sound bad."

"Not bad, not good." He shrugged. "Switched to psychiatry recently —couple of years ago, I think."

"What was he before?"

"A nose and throat man."

"What made him switch?"

I was fired with eagerness to know, and slightly irritated by Dr. Osborn's flippancy.

"What makes a man change from nose and throat to psychiatry? What do you think?" I said I didn't know, and he continued. "Maybe it's just as well you don't find out. It's not such a big jump—from the nose and throat to the head. But why are you so interested?"

I saw I couldn't get anywhere holding out on him, so I told him the story.

"Unethical, isn't it, dropping a patient in the midst of an analysis?"

"Don't be too hard on poor Rudie. He's just being analyzed himself." I was just pondering this odd fact and trying to understand what it meant—they were supposed to be analyzed first, weren't they?—as other facts Dr. Osborn was giving crowded in on me. "Heard they needed another psychiatrist up at M Hospital—and he came up and got the job. He was my assistant on the staff up there—we needed somebody to take over the ward. Next thing, there he was—making the rounds. We used to laugh at him. He'd go around from bed to bed—picking up things off the patients' tables—"

"Good God! I don't think it's so funny. These people are *sick*."

"Sick, of course they're sick. But don't say Good God. Kind of situation we're in—too many sick people and no doctors. He was so silent with you because, as he kept telling you, there was nothing to say. What he meant was, he didn't know anything to say. He knows absolutely nothing about psychoanalysis. And his control analyst is pretty busy too."

"His *what?*"

"His control analyst. You've never heard of a control?"

"No. Only on the ouija board. Sorry to be so dumb. What is it, anyway?"

"The control is the experienced analyst the learning doctor refers his cases to. Rudie kept referring your case, and all his other patients' cases, to his control. So you see, when you told him something was troubling you, or you had a significant dream—he couldn't give you the interpretation until the control had told him what the interpretation was."

"But what did he say to them—those poor sick people?"

"What did he say to you?"

"Nothing."

"That's exactly what he said to them."

I was muttering to myself, I guess. "Now, anyway, I know at last why he could only talk on Fridays. . . . And now I know to whom he was writing all those damned notes."

"How's that?" Osborn interrupted, but I smiled without answering, so he continued. "There's the time element—sometimes pretty bad. Before the doctor gets the right interpretation from the control, and gets around to seeing you again, anything can happen. Old Rudie just wasn't saying anything. He shouldn't have dropped you in the midst of the analysis—but you don't know when you're lucky. It's too bad—what happened—"

"What do you mean by that?"

"Well, Rudie's control is—*was* a fine man. Dr. Forester. But he committed suicide sometime last month—I guess just about the time you say you left. So you see there was poor old Rudie—with all those questions of yours stuck up in the control analyst's desk. All your dreams and your fantasies and you—waiting for the answer . . ." He chuckled. "Well now you see how long you'd have to wait."

But I wasn't laughing. I kept thinking how I felt about those waits.

"While I was thinking it was all me—all my fault I wasn't getting better—Well, of all the . . ." But there weren't any words.

"Yes, that's one of the very bad parts of this thing. It's too bad, too bad—this kind of thing is happening."

"And me lying there—pouring out my guts—and he had to get the answers from this—this control. And he couldn't."

"Not very well, my dear—with the old boy in the grave."

"But why was he so mad at me?"

"For the simple reason you wanted help. You wanted to get well. You wanted to know what all these things meant. And he couldn't tell you the answer because he just doesn't know. And you must have suspected—"

"Of course I knew something was wrong—but I suspected myself. Oh, I did ask him—was he going to school or something—giving me the answers on Friday—and why couldn't he get the book and keep it with him."

"Well, it's very irritating to a doctor when the patient begins to suspect he's a boob. You're ruining his god-image of himself—hurting his narcissism—"

"There's something of his I'd like to punch—but it's not his narcissism."

Osborn laughed, he thought it was very funny.

"Now, now, don't be so angry at poor old Rudie. How'd you like to be in his spot—all those people coming to you for help, screaming at you to give them the answers. You can't tell them you don't know the answers—that they may end up in their coffins if they wait for you to get the answers."

"Well, so I wasted all those months—and all that money." I had another drink, and started to laugh too, and make jokes. "And on top of it all I lost him. Lost my pop. 'A poor thing, but mine own.'"

"So did he lose his," said Osborn. "Nothing old Rudie could say could help very much—but it probably couldn't harm you much either. And your money had to go somewhere. It's better than playing the races—or giving it away to strangers. And now it's finished. The way things are—I tell you you're better off."

"That's what people say about the dead," I commented. But I was smiling. At least I'd heard something bad had happened to Silent Simon. He, too, had had some trouble, and was being made to suffer, and wait around for the answers. It wasn't enough—not nearly enough —but it was something.

The winter languished, faded, ran away and came back, colder and dirtier. Toni—she was well now—had been staying uptown with her mother, but after commuting between both her homes she returned to the duplex.

"I just couldn't stand it up there another minute," she complained bitterly. "My mother—with that Christian Science—and those diets. She thinks the yolks of eggs can cure cancer. Is she crazy?"

She was more like her old self—before Dr. Eisman and the Marxian therapy—spending an hour on her face in the mornings, then talking energetically on the telephone, making appointments with people in the theater and radio, and then tearing out of the apartment and into taxicabs. She wasn't working in the plant any more, I gathered, as I saw her emerging in fur coat and high heels and small cockeyed hats.

"I can't work in a factory—until I'm stronger," she explained one night when we finally saw one another long enough to talk.

"Oh well, you'll be all right soon and then maybe you'll go back."

"Oh no, I won't. I'll never go back. Even my doctor says that. He's too busy to see me now—but I talk to him on the phone." There was a resigned note in her voice. "I can't seem to take reality, Joyce. I'm just an inferior member of society. I'm not strong enough to fight and work with my class—so I'm back where there's no real security."

"I don't think it's that bad. After all, when you make money, you make much more than a factory worker."

"You don't understand about that. There for a while—working in the plant—I felt real happy and secure. Now it's all over."

"What about Alf?"

She went a shade paler. "I haven't seen him. I hate him. Please don't mention him to me—*Please*."

"All right, of course I won't if you feel that way. But—I often wonder what really did happen."

"I'd rather not talk about it. I'm not ready for love—or health. It was too much for me. I couldn't face it." She stood up. "Every time I think about him—I feel like killing him."

"Toni! But why?"

"He took something away from me. Besides—he did something else —something worse—much worse—oh, let's not talk about it."

"What will you do now?"

"I'm already doing it. I'm back in the theater where there's two hundred people for every part. Everybody grabbing the bread out of everybody else's mouth. I'm back with climbing and competition and hate. It's getting worse, too. And it'll be still worse after the war. Much worse. Then we'll really see the emotional plague. I'm going to bed now. I'm tired. Get money, Joyce. There's nothing else."

I went on, trying to work my own way out of my troubles, too discouraged to seek further help from doctors. I was still afraid, the mob was still at my door, and now in addition I had the sense of two failures behind me, which I chalked up against myself. I still avoided the telephone, was always relieved when someone would answer for me, saying, "She's not in, she's away, I don't know when she'll be back—" And so I walked on in the foggy twilight, and the fog was lighted sometimes with those unholy red lights from the past. Like the time Eckhart caught me on the phone and before I realized it, there he was talking to me, as to an old friend. "I'll be back in New York Saturday morning—we've got a dinner planned for seven. Junior called you, didn't he? If he didn't, I'll fire that free-loader." I sat there listening, too frightened by this pursuit technique to speak up, letting it slide.

As soon as he hung up, his stooge, Whyner, was on the phone, and he was easier. "What's the matter with old Hank, huh? Why don't you like him? So he's a pirate. Duncha know the pages of history are full of pirates? Tellya, honey, nobody gets remembered but the sadists. Line up with a good sadist and you're in." He'd come down and get me, he said, I had to be there this Saturday, and just as I was explaining I wouldn't be home, he hung up.

I had almost forgotten about it, but promptly at six-thirty on Saturday, Eckhart himself appeared at the downstairs door. Daphne generously went to answer it for me, and she asked him in. To her amazement, and mine, too, I went down and saw him. Somehow, I wasn't afraid of him. There he was, and what was he? Why, he was just a shadow. He had murdered me once, I had taken the weapon, and died. Therefore, he was disarmed, a twisted memory. *There is no second murder.* I could laugh—it was such a relief—and I did. I never heard from him again.

(Oh, if only they were all disarmed like this, all shadows, I thought, as I went out that evening. But they weren't, and of course I couldn't disarm them all. I didn't understand this, it was terrifying just to feel it—but somehow I knew. Oh yes, I needed a doctor all right to help me understand myself. But I was in no hurry about that now, not after the two I'd seen.)

One afternoon I came home early from the office to write one of those hoopla pieces about psychiatry being the new panacea. I had all the notes and information, but I found myself having such difficulty writing the piece, it seemed almost impossible. I finally did get it going, but as I typed I kept hearing a certain sound over and over again. I thought at first it was coming from outside, but once, stopping my work to listen in earnest, I knew immediately it was coming from downstairs. Footsteps, heavy footsteps. Someone was marching up and down across the carpet.

I heard Trafinia cleaning in the next room—she was back with us again—so I called to ask her, "Who's that walking downstairs?"

She stuck her head out of the door. "That's Mista Alf."

"Did you tell Miss Toni?"

"Sure I told her." Trafinia chuckled, lights sparkled in her big soft eyes and her gold tooth. "She call home and I told her. That why she won't come home."

Seeing nothing to do about it for the time being I turned back to my typewriter, working even over Trafinia's prolonged muttering.

"He been here five times today. He come eight o'clock this morning. Something on his mind. Miss Toni tell me last night to say she gone away, but he say he know different."

"Do you know when she's coming back?"

But Trafinia didn't know, and eventually I got back to work. Then, as the footsteps were still pounding away, the telephone rang.

"Joyce!" Toni sounded frightened. "Is he still there?"

"God, yes."

"Walking up and down?"

"Um-hum."

"Well take this number and call me here when he goes."

"All right." I took the number. "But maybe he won't go."

"He will. He has to. His ship leaves tonight. Then he'll be out of the country—and I'll be free of him."

"Ships are still running both ways. He might come back."

"I know what to do. I'll pretend I don't know him. Oh, he's evil, Joyce. You don't know what he's done—and what he's capable of doing. He's *dangerous*."

"No I don't know—you've never told me. Suppose he comes upstairs—what will I say to him?"

"I'm away—on the Coast. A movie contract. Anything. Only, listen, honey, be very casual with him. Say we're giving up the apartment— if you're afraid. A fiend like that could hang on, you know—and . . . exploit us."

This was a new side to the picture of Alphonse. Was it possible I had failed completely to see this part of him, I wondered curiously, as Toni continued.

"There are things people just *don't talk about*—" I could hear her drawing in her breath. "And this is one of them. That waitress found murdered in the vestibule uptown last week—well if she was alive she might not like talking about it. Now do you understand?"

My ear hurt from the way she banged the receiver. I lit a cigarette and thought about Alphonse, the way I remembered him, in contrast to the wild man walking up and down below. Long white teeth, dimples in red cheeks, skates, bicycle, an evanescent sense of joy. Alf, straight and shining as a rain-drenched sapling—what dark waters had come between that Alf and the heavy marcher downstairs in his lone tramp?

By the time I finished my piece and dressed to go out, the footsteps had stopped. Tafinia had left. It was nearly dark, and I was alone in the place—with only him down there, if he was still there, as somehow I suspected he was. A stranger—not the Alf I'd known a few bare months ago. The situation gave me the creeps.

I couldn't wait any longer, yet I hesitated to go downstairs. Suppose he was, as Toni indicated, a dangerous person, a fiend who had threatened her. In that case, we ought to call the police. Meantime, I had to get out of the house and into the street. I planned to bypass him by leaving from upstairs—I hated to leave him in the place but there seemed nothing else to do—but when I went to open the upstairs door I found an item I'd overlooked—the breakfront, weighing a couple of tons and bursting with dishes, silver, books and bric-a-brac, was carefully braced against the door for safety from other fears. There it was staring me in the face.

Now I would have to face Alf. I cursed the day I'd had it placed against the door, gritted my teeth and went downstairs.

Halfway down the steps, I stopped. The place below was in total darkness, with only drifts of light coming in from the street. I listened, but I couldn't hear a sound and, frightened, I hollered out, "Alf, are you down there?"

Two tense sounds hit my ears, both at the same time. Someone springing up, and a voice speaking.

"Yes, Joyeece, I am here."

"Turn on the lights, please."

He moved. The place flooded with light. I came on down the steps.

He was leaning against the wall. His mouth looked strangely set, as if he hadn't smiled in a long time. His face seemed longer and older than I remembered, the look of youth had dropped off, leaving rage, bewilderment and anguish.

"What's the matter, Alf?" I asked, trying to hide my fear of him. "Why are you waiting here like this?"

He crossed the room in a step.

"You know why. She called and told you. I wait for Toni."

"What do you want with her?"

"She know. We have not finish. She is afraid."

"From what she says, maybe she has a right to be afraid."

"Oh yes, she have the right. This is true, she has the right." He grabbed my arm. "Where did she go?"

"I don't know. I think she was going to the Coast."

"Where is that Coast?"

"California. Three thousand miles away."

He dropped my arm.

"You'd better go now, Alf. There's no sense waiting around here."

"When I finish—then I will go."

"No, *now*."

He lifted his head and stared at me.

"Why?"

"Alphonse, I'm trying to get this thing straightened out. You didn't do Toni any harm, did you?" He kept on walking. No answer. "Did you *threaten* to do her any harm?"

"I did."

"You did what?"

"I did already the harm."

"What harm? What did you do."

"I am assassin. Ha-ha. Your friend Toni, I have killed her."

I didn't believe him, and yet . . . But no, it couldn't be. Only an hour ago I'd spoken to her on the telephone. She was alive then and waiting at her mother's place. She did say there was no one at home— he might have gone out and then come back—but somehow I felt he hadn't done that.

"My dear Joweece, don't you understand how the thing go? She love me a little while. All right, the love is the death. So she die." He was walking again. "You American people all are talking about the love. Love the neighbor, love the ice cream, love the soap! Why do you keep on talking about this love? Because this you do not have! You do not even know where is, the love."

"Ah," I sighed with relief. "Well, where is it, Alf?"

"Joweece, it is not in the head. It is not in the talk. It is not in the books. It is not with these doctors. It is here." He hit the side of his stomach. "I make my Toni to feel this and she is hating my guts."

"You two must have had a lovers' quarrel—" I was thinking out loud. "And Toni's had a shock of some kind. I begin to see . . ."

The first man to give her this thing she had wanted so much, I began to think, had almost deranged her. Yes, that was it, of course. Love, sexual fulfillment, both of these unusual experiences coming bolt together, created a cyclone. And this masculinity, this maleness Alf had, why that quality alone was fairly disturbing: the upright honesty of it staring right into a woman's face.

Out loud I said, "Why is she so afraid of you? And you, Alf, I must say you've been behaving very strangely. Telling me you've killed her—when of course the opposite is true." For it had hit me suddenly: what he had done was to bring Toni straight back to life.

"Her trouble. This theeng she have—what she go the doctor to fix —I have assassinate him."

I looked away, not wanting to hear any more. There was something wrong about this peeping directly into their hearts—but Alf couldn't stop now.

"That why she is afraid. That why she say I may kill somebody. She believe that. This little girl, my baby, I make her warm. She cannot live this way, she can live only in the cold. I am sad. Oh, how sad this make me!"

He sat down suddenly and sobbed like a child. I walked toward the door, remembering my appointment, but I couldn't go out. Instead I came back into the kitchen and got him a drink which he drank down like water.

"Joyeece, you are like a sister to me. Some day I coming back to North America. Maybe I take you both back with me to France. You tell to my Toni—this doctor—she don't need him no more. Taking the money from this poor baby, this is wrong thing. These doctors— what they do this girl! She think I don't know but all this time I know, I know. It take more than a doctor to make over the woman. It take a man."

I got him another drink and pushed it toward him. He drank it down and wiped the tears from his eyes.

"Ah my little Toni, she is heartbroken—that what make this cold thing in her. I tell to you, my sister Joyeece, you cannot vomit up the heart like a nickel you have swallow. Maybe you come back with me to France—you and my baby. In Paris, I tell you, my home is your home. You are my sister!"

I was about to get him still another whiskey when Daphne burst in and, seeing the emotional scene going on, hastened discreetly toward the stairs—but Alf spied her and caught her by the arm.

"Come back, Daphne. You, too, my dear—you both are my sisters." He put his arms around us. "I take you all back to France. It don't cost you one penny—only the fare. My home is your home."

He kissed us both, then shook hands and then somehow, slowly, we were seeing him to the door. Was it possible he was leaving at last, I wondered, as he kept stopping for one more word?

"Good-by. I have to go because I must—even without seeing my Toni. I have leave something in there for her—in her room—you tell to her so she find it when she come back. She don't need no more this doctoring, you tell this to her. She have to wait and then maybe she start to live again, maybe not. Dear girls, good-by."

The minute the door had closed behind him I remembered my promise to call Toni, ran upstairs to dial the number she had given and told her the news.

"Has he really gone?"

"Yes. Daphne is at the window now—watching him getting into a taxi."

"Oh he's always taking taxis—but he always comes back."

"He can't now. He says his ship is leaving in a few hours. You're safe to come home."

She said she would and I hung up.

"Well thank heavens that's over," Daphne remarked as she came back from the window. "He's really gone—at least I saw his taxi turn the corner. What are you looking so sad about? You just got a nice new home in Paris."

"I wish I wouldn't keep getting homes from homeless people."

"Aw now that's not nice, Joyeece." Daphne thought it was funny. "Alf is so sincere. My home she is your home. He'll have everything ready. Which bush do you want in the Bois de Boulogne?"

CHAPTER EIGHTEEN

. . . . . .

AND TIME PASSED. AND I WAS FEELING BETTER. THERE WAS SOME-
thing soft and consoling in the rolling, silvery ocean of life at the
magazine office. Everybody had a problem but everybody was glamorous, chic, brave and quietly untruthful. It was easy to hide out in this
prettified army of other hider-outers. Personal ambition was lulled to
sleep. The big man who owned the shop made all the important de-
cisions, the rest of us were only shadow-boxing, and we all shared together the peaceful anonymity. It was like being a member of a family
of ghosts.

I felt better for weeks. Maybe *It* has gone, I thought. Gone, never
to return! Maybe the hope I had cherished, that one day it would go,
just disappear the way it had come, was justified. I thought back, and
remembering the ease with which I had dismissed Eckhart, of whom
I had been so terrified, I concluded the miracle had happened at last.
Quietly. A wave of new hope swept over me. Now I could begin to
live, and make plans. I would be careful, of course.

It was in this mood of secret joy that I went one windy afternoon
up Fifth Avenue to interview R.J. A prominent man this, whose name
was often on the front pages those days. The minute I entered the
apartment I recognized him from the newspaper photographs. A big
man, broad-shouldered, with a quick smile, a ruddy, weathered face
and alert, uneasy eyes. He seemed friendly enough, perhaps a mite
more bluff and hearty than the occasion warranted, but ah, he was a
family man, his daughter and her husband were on hand, so I could
relax. Drinks were served, I asked him the questions and he gave me
the information I had come to get, and I thanked him and started to
leave, when to my surprise he, in fact the entire group, insisted upon

1 5 3

my staying on for dinner. I hadn't planned on staying any longer, I had most of what I wanted—a few more anecdotes might be useful but these I could get from the files, but apparently his daughter had misunderstood, or he had misunderstood. In any case, they were making it rather plain that they had counted on me to remain for dinner. It didn't really matter, so I let myself be persuaded to enter the dining room where a plate had obviously been set for an extra guest, and before I knew it the meal was being served and R.J. was giving me the rest of the story.

The party was fairly stiff. R.J. was tense, I noticed, his daughter and son-in-law threw in some light patter, the dinner was only fair, and everybody seemed relieved when it was over. I was just apologizing for having to leave when I noticed his daughter and son-in-law appeared in a great hurry to get somewhere and left the table without waiting for me to finish, only to reappear a few seconds later in their hats and coats. They threw their father and me a hurried good-by, explaining that they were already late for the theater, and left. "And now I hope you'll excuse me for running off, too," I said to R.J., as I started out of the dining room again, "but I really have to be getting on."

"Good Lord, you're not going to leave me here by myself!" he was saying. I heard a door close somewhere in the back of the place: apparently the cook had gone, too. Nobody likes a tense man, I thought, as I hastened by him. He got up and tried to block my passage out of the dining room. I assumed he had meant this as a joke so I laughed loudly as I made for the hall closet where I knew his daughter had hung my coat, got it and was now ready to say another quick good-by and go for the elevator. This time he stood in the lobby, blocking my way to the door.

No, I thought quickly, not this man. It wasn't possible—no man as famous and important as this one—no, of course not, it couldn't be . . . but there it was happening right before my eyes—and I was struck dumb with the old cold fear. Like an insect threatened by an enemy, I retraced my steps back into the room, and stood still, waiting. He moved away from the door toward the sideboard. I started toward the door again. I nearly made it to the closet when he caught up with me. "You wouldn't leave me alone now. I knew you wouldn't."

What on earth was he doing this for? A man of his intelligence and international reputation—how would he dare! And what was this he was saying. . . . Why, it was crazy! "Just what I wanted—a nice clean educated girl. Come on now, don't go home, let's have some fun. Fellow like me—gets tired—tense—you know what I mean. You're going to help me out—I know you are. You wouldn't run out on me now. You wouldn't do a thing like that. I know you wouldn't. Come on, baby, give us a kiss!"

I don't know what I said. I remember the terrible sense of the panic rushing on, the feeling of danger, of *murder* in the air, and my mouth dry and speechless. And then finding myself caught, cornered, empty of will. That's all I remember of myself because—I wasn't there any more. And the rest was him. This big tense man lunging and pushing, with his heavy breathing and that wild silly adolescent pleading. "Don't go way and leave me like this. Nice clean wholesome girl like you . . . just what I need. Girl that won't do anything to me . . . won't tell anybody. Nice educated girl—a man can feel safe with . . ."

Then I remember drinking—downing the highballs he kept pouring, it was the only active thing I did—hoping, vaguely at first, then more definitely—hoping to drink my way back into my will power and to regain my voice. But the drinks were like drops of water on desert sands. The only parts of me the liquor awakened were small thinking parts of my mind. Can't he see there's something the matter with me? I thought. Doesn't he see I'm not speaking—I can't talk—I'm frightened—I'm sick. I looked at him. Doesn't a man as big and important as you know anything? . . . Do you want to sleep with a paralytic? . . . Don't you have any pride? Not chivalry, just low-down animal pride, something a lion or a dog might have. . . . Yes, a dog. A dog looks for female dog in heat—but he wouldn't have sex with a crippled dog . . . or . . . or a dead dog, would he? Well can't you see, I'm not here, you big blind silly man. Oh I must tell that to the next doctor— if there is any next doctor. And as for you, do you want to have sex with a corpse?

The whiskey lifted my mind up to the question but it didn't give me back my voice. The most awful part of the symptom had come on, being unable to speak, and the famous man was in a hurry. Then somehow the whiskey blurred the scene over with an unholy fuzz. It would be terrible later, I knew, but it had to happen. That was the only way I could get out of the paralyzed state—giving in, yielding.

It was being killed in a way, but it was the one way to avoid being killed, and it would bring me to! And now, that being the case, the sooner the better. . . .

"Ah, that's right," the famous man was muttering and beaming and grabbing all at once. "A girl like you, nice and clean and normal, that's what a tense man needs to get happy."

I moved slowly at first, waking up in that big strange bedroom. The first object I saw was a long rectangle of gray light that stretched back and forth on a background of thick purple carpet. I moved slightly as a taffeta bedspread hissed and sneered in my ears. A clock was ticking somewhere in the place. I looked around, desolate but curious to locate the face of that damned clock, and then at least I would know the time, but the minute I did I was sorry. The gray light had moved further, falling over the other twin bed not far from mine and flashing the bitter truth into my eyes. No! . . . Oh no . . . I didn't . . . not with that . . . but there it was. . . there we were . . . and the two beds with their pale purple taffeta spreads and curved tops, looking vaguely like two coffins in the light of the early day.

No sense to sneak back and hide under the covers. The room quaked with the heavy snoring of the man over there in the other bed. I'll get away from you quickly, quietly, I thought, you blob of flesh with red smeared on your mouth and, oh yes, all those other things I had to hear about—political ambitions, loneliness, and so on—but first I will have to find out where I am, and then, one by one, my clothes, the time, and the elevator. This time I sat up, and the taffeta bedspread hissed again as it settled like a snake at the bottom of the bed. *Look at you in this strange place, you've done it again, you've gone and done it again, and now what?*

I looked all over the room for that damned clock—past bureaus, chiffoniers, men's clothes, my own clothes, or what seemed vaguely to resemble my own clothes, chairs—and found it at last, a small grandfather's clock standing on a cabinet in a corner. The big black and gold face stared out—indifferent, but not threatening. Five to five.

Next I tried snuggling back in the bed for another minute but the bedroom kept intruding. The lavender chaise longue by the window, a single small lace pillow nestling in the seat, the shining silver set on the chiffonier, the big roaring face there in the other bed. What a horrid, overdressed, mocking room! There it was, looking back at me like some big complacent, critical woman, with purple veins in her face. It didn't matter, she didn't matter. The whole thing was over now. I was still alive, that was what always surprised me. Alive, not dead, not murdered. Still alive.

Fortunately, there was no one in the apartment—besides the sleeping man and me—I knew that the minute I started to move around. I found my clothes, dressed quietly, with great speed and efficiency, and made my way through the empty apartment. No one will see me leave, I thought, as I went quietly into the self-service elevator and let myself down. A sleepy doorman looked up from the switchboard as I came out of the elevator and took the long, long walk through the lobby.

Then I was in the street, fresh with the cold gray dawn, walking on alone. The question beat at me, Why? Why? But I pushed it back with, That's for later. The mass of confusion and humiliation seemed to grow bigger with each step. I remembered feeling glad I'd bought the expensive alligator bag I was carrying: its bright red was the sole cheerful note in the long gray street.

All right, so it happened. Devman had struck again, and I was his creature. All right, so it was against my will, against everything in me that was carrying me forward, and that wanted to live. Now what? I hurried my pace, in the hope of rushing away from the questions, but there they were. How far have you gone in all this time? How much have you moved The Thing—in all this time—and with all the struggle? I looked up at the great rolling gray clouds of the new day, then back down the avenue. I knew the answer. Not one inch.

What were you saying last night—in your head—when he came at you? Remember now—just before the whiskey covered the whole thing over with silver fuzz? . . . Oh yes—something about *sleeping with a paralytic*. That's it . . . maybe that's a clue, and maybe someday that clue will lead you directly to the scene of the crime . . . maybe then you'll know why. . . .

As I went down the windy, cold street, pictures came and went and came back again. The big, tense, famous adolescent, aged fifty, with those uneasy eyes. The daughter and her husband leaving suddenly—had he asked them to go? The empty library with the whiskey being poured, poured like water. "Nice educated girl—a man can feel safe with . . ." Maybe he knew—yes, maybe somehow he knew about my trouble. And, oh, those awful sneering taffeta bedspreads, and the cruel white bathroom, and you, *me,* sneaking out, leaving the scene of the crime.

The crime, *the crime.* . . . Was it possible, was it barely possible, this is how murderers sometimes feel—those who kill against their will out of some tremendous compulsion coming from another stronger will? Yes, it is possible, and I know how they feel sneaking away—for I, too, have killed something, the part of myself that I hold most dear —and now I must walk along with the corpse, looking for a place to hide it. I walk with you, the killers. I am an accessory to the crime. I know you, and you know me. But the corpse I carry can't be cut into pieces and thrown into the river—here's the twist—because it happens to be me, my very own self.

Now for any restaurant where I could sit still and hide my wound and drink coffee. Life was beginning to move around me. People. Three servicemen walking together, a couple in evening clothes, a cruising taxi. Too many eyes.

I slunk into the first open restaurant, found a nice dark corner and ordered coffee. It was better in here. A young couple, a marine officer and his girl, were breakfasting at a nearby table, holding hands, laughing and talking. I could see the man's eyes focused on the girl's face and just the side of her cheek breaking in laughter as they talked. How pleased and interested they looked, so alive, with the music of their gay murmurs filling the corner. Beginning the day together—engaged, maybe. I watched them for a while, anything to escape from myself. My, but they had things to say to each other!

"Just married," the waitress informed me, after she put down my coffee. "Can't you tell from the looks of them?" I said I'd thought that, asked her how she knew, and she said they had told her, adding, "They're higher than kites—on coffee." I didn't answer that. I felt like crying, breathed in deeply and stirred the coffee. Shortly afterwards, I met the new bride in the Ladies' Room and there we were powdering noses together. A pleasant girl with a soft voice, admiring my red alligator bag. It was true, what the waitress had said. She was talking away about it to me—a perfect stranger, but it seemed natural for she was in love with the whole world that morning. There she was, showing me her ring, and talking as to a friend. "Jim wanted to take me shopping today—but I hate to use up the time in stores—" They had their troubles, too. He had just lost his father, and now he had been alerted. The time was precious.

I found myself watching them again as I went through the revolving door into the street. Somehow I wished I were going to be with them— at least to know them for a while and share in their happiness, perhaps even console her when he went away. It had grown very cold. The red alligator bag felt cold as ice in my hand. I thought for a minute, I'd like to do something for the girl, and then suddenly I found myself emptying the insides of the red bag into my coat pockets. There, now it was nice and empty, new and shining, too—perfect for a wedding present. I slipped back into the restaurant, found the waitress and gave the bag to her with instructions to give it to the girl and hastened out again.

Through the glass windows I saw the girl look up with the bag in her hand just as I was getting into a taxi, her face all lighted up again in that characteristic smile she had—and I waved good-by. Well, now I was a part of them, the happy people, and I felt better.

I must remember them, I thought, as the taxi went past familiar streets and buildings. There, in that building, was the office of my erstwhile agent, Lorna, who didn't call me any more . . . and there was the bar where I'd gone with Red that night when . . . and there was the street I used to turn to go up to Silent Simon's . . . and that was the street I turned down to go to Ramsey—those damned doctors to whom I'd gone with such hope. I didn't care either, I couldn't care now, as tears of rage, bitterness, helplessness and remorse washed all the scenes and faces mercifully into a great red nothingness, and I was alone with my curse.

CHAPTER NINETEEN

. . . . . .

"YOU DON'T HAVE TO LOSE TIME WHEN YOU CHANGE DOCTORS. Especially when you do it so *soon.*"

I was sitting in Irene's kitchen, listening as she talked on.

"Now Dr. Vespers has been an analyst for nearly thirty years. He's not in the same world with Simon, not in the same *world.* He was analyzed a long time ago. Besides, he knows about your case."

"How? How on earth does he know about my case?"

"Because I called him and told him—the minute you called me."

"Why did you do that?"

"I wanted to find out if he could take you. And he said yes, he could. You could start right in with him where you left off with Simon."

"How could that be? What would happen to the rest of the story?"

"Oh I think Dr. Vespers would catch on to that. . . . You'd better do it, Joyce. You'll have to do something—and there's only one thing to do. You know your analysis with Simon wasn't any good—and besides, it was interrupted right in the middle. Now you can't go around with your Id half in and half out."

"How's that?" I had heard about this, but it wasn't completely clear. "What was that about my Id?"

"Your Id. Don't you understand—you left your Id with Dr. Simon. You still haven't gotten it back." She was laughing. "It's like being half dressed—going out in the street with your clothes left back in the closet at home. You're not all there. You can't keep on like that."

"In my job it doesn't matter. I do the work, and nobody knows. Nobody else is all there either. In fact, I think I'm more there than some of the others. Has somebody got their Ids too?"

160

"Maybe. . . . But let's not think about them. You'd better think only of yourself."

I watched her get up quietly and pour us each another cup of coffee, then come back to the table and light a cigarette. I knew why I was watching her: somehow it helped me avoid making a decision. She wasn't looking at me, I could see she was avoiding my glance.

"All I have to do is call him," she said, very softly, still avoiding looking at me. It was quite a while before I finally got around to answering her.

"All right," I sighed the words. "Go ahead, please."

She reached for the telephone and put it beside her on the table.

"And another thing," she was saying, as she dialed the number. "He's not far from your office. You won't have much traveling to do."

Two days later, during my lunch hour, I went to see Dr. Vespers. I had time, so I walked. I didn't expect much from Dr. Vespers. I was going to him out of necessity—much as some hungry person who knows he must eat or die, who would like to eat a good dinner but cannot travel the distance required to find a good restaurant, turns in at any old lunch counter and quietly devours a leftover sandwich.

It was probably just as well. I had no faith—neither in the doctors nor in their so-called science nor in myself. If there had been any way of not going, and remaining *comfortable,* I would gladly have settled for that, but obviously there was not, so I went.

I went to Dr. Vespers. I was weary, and I met a weary man. I had known that much about him, even from the first telephone call. He gave me his lunch hour with ease. After Simon's obsession about his time, this man seemed extraordinarily relaxed and incredibly pleasant as he said, "You won't mind if I have my sandwich brought up to the office?"

I had no emotion as I rang his bell, and only a mild curiosity. Here I go again, I thought. This time it's half-hearted but maybe . . . who knows?

Vespers had a suite of offices in a hotel. The door opened as soon as I rang and a middle-aged woman with a nervous smile received me and took my coat. She said to sit down, the doctor would be right out, and went back to her typing. I had barely sat down when Dr.

Vespers came out—he was just saying good-by to another patient, yet he managed to smile at me as he passed. Then he came over and spoke. I saw a little man with friendly light-green eyes and a sad smile, and I heard a pleasant voice. He introduced me to his secretary and then opened the door to his inner sanctum.

Before I knew it, I was talking to him very freely—about Simon the Silent, and Ramsey the Forgetful. I remember saying, "They're not a very pretty pair of boys," and him laughing. "Pretty," he chuckled, "have you ever seen a bunch of analysts gathered together?" I hadn't, so he explained. "If you ever went to a psychiatrists' convention in Atlantic City—and saw them all together under one roof— you'd never go to another one as long as you lived."

I got easily into my horror story. This man was different from the other two. He was genuinely warm and human, for one thing. He was not a phony—that is, he was not hiding behind a false face. He was a sad man, disenchanted with life, with himself, and with his science— and so was I. He was not bothering to hide it, either, and at the same time he was kind and I sensed he was sophisticated. Of the three doctors I had now visited, he was the first who talked in an easy, natural way, the first who smiled often and occasionally broke out into laughter. With the other two it had seemed almost a point of honor to keep a long face and stay on the lugubrious aspect of the situation.

I noticed his face was tanned, as if he walked now and then in the sun. It would be easy to call this old boy Pop, I decided.

During the very first session we "got somewhere." I told him, quite frankly, "I like you, Doctor," and he asked the inevitable, "Why? Do you know?" I said, "Sure. You're people." And he, "What about the others—did you like them?" "Definitely not. I was emotionally involved with them. But there was absolutely nothing to *like* about them." (Unless one has a fancy for the eating of porcupines.)

Literally before I knew it, in the first week, the film of life started unwinding again, only this time it was going in a different direction, guided by the gentle, tired hands of Papa Vespers. "Now let's go from near to far," he suggested. "Let's start with the near men. Ramsey and Simon. And see what we can find out."

Oh, this sad little man, he made the therapy so easy. Why, it was almost pleasant. It didn't matter in the least whether I lay down on the couch or sat up, he said, so I sat up. Now, he asked, did I see anything unusual about the situation with Ramsey and Simon? Getting emotionally involved, being excited and afraid, with two such patently undesirable types of men. "Is that a common characteristic of yours?" A challenging point, I thought that over. I was certainly afraid of and often attracted to undesirable types of men, but I had been smart enough not to marry one of them, also to make sure the attractions were not indulged beyond the point of "getting it out of my system." So far I had been lucky, but there was always the chance the day might come when my luck would run out.

"This is commoner than you think," he commented. "You'd be surprised if you knew how many women feel attracted to these dangerous types of men. Sexual slumming. Sometimes very fine girls—and beauties, for some reason—"

One day, talking of this, he said an amazing thing. "This type of maladjustment is the easiest to cure."

"Why?" I shrieked.

"Because—since you want to know—this kind of emotional freeze is the most superficial."

"What does that mean?"

"It's the nearest to the surface in the unconscious."

I began to see myself and my disease in a new light. Why, my case wasn't hopeless after all. Instead of being down at the bottom of the bin, I was way up there on the top rung of the ladder, capable of being pushed off into real living with the lightest touch—the slightest reassurance of safety. Jesus, I'd better warn him. . . .

"But there's something I haven't got. There's something I was born without. Maybe these others you mention got cured because they had it—"

He chuckled. "They all thought they didn't have it."

"Oh, but they only thought it. I *know* I haven't got it."

"Well, child, when you're cured, you'll know something quite different about yourself. By the way, do you know what it is—this thing you were born without?"

"No, of course not. That's part of the conundrum. But I'll tell you this much. It's *not* a penis!"

"How do you know?"

"I don't know how I know—but I know."

Cured, I thought. He says I can be cured. I didn't quite believe him, but it was good to hear the words.

How was it possible, I wanted to know, as we talked on through hour on hour. Going from near to far. Now the present, my terrors, my current life, and now the past. Now the general—the other sick people in the world, now the specific, me. Here was a man I could talk to, and who could—God be praised! Nirvana!—*talk back*. I could hardly believe it at first, but there it was right before my eyes. The cure, coming in quietly, unheralded, just when I thought I had lost the race.

No, what I had wasn't hopeless at all, to hear him talk, and the talk was like balm to my tired head. Why, most American women felt a secret attraction to monsters! The paralysis was the result of an unconscious attraction that I couldn't face—not yet—but we'd get to that.

Gradually, I began to feel better. As I told him about my cruel father he would listen with sympathy and understanding, but even toward this he replied with consoling and healing information. I would listen, argue, get mad, and go away feeling better. I thought about him very little, but when I did he seemed to make sense.

By now Dr. Vespers had become relaxed and cozy with me, and I with him. He would have his lunch during my sessions, and as I listened to the crunch-crunch of the toasted tuna-fish sandwiches from the drugstore downstairs going through his choppers, I would find myself trying to choose pleasant words to describe my blues so he wouldn't lose his appetite. He noticed it and said, "Why don't you say what you really think?"

"All right, I will," I said. "I wish you'd finish eating—so I won't have to watch what I say. There's something about murder that won't mix with toast—"

"Go ahead and complain, child," he chuckled. "I shouldn't wonder if you thought my eating was a terrible thing—with what you're going through."

Every way I moved I felt his sympathy—or empathy, to use their overworked word. A deep, subtle change was taking place. Whereas with Simon the Silent, left alone with my miseries, getting no help and only a negative, essentially unfriendly therapy, my past life had nevertheless come alive, the figures moving and life-size and threatening, exactly as if it was still taking place, here, with this pleasant, wise and kindly man, everything was quiet.

I felt as if some powerful current had stopped. The whole world went still, and I with it.

CHAPTER TWENTY

. . . .

I HAVE CHANGED, I THOUGHT. EVEN IN LITTLE THINGS, I COULD SEE
the change. Like receiving an engraved invitation to dine at the
Blackwoods. I remember Toni looking it over greedily and saying,
"Joyce, you're in. She knows everybody. I wish I got invitations to
places like that. You're going, aren't you?" And me saying, "Of
course." And starting immediately to talk of what I was going to wear.
And thinking, Why a short while ago I would have been in a
conflict—afraid to go, and afraid not to go. "I used to be afraid of
her eyes," I told Toni. "That couple of great big black saws coming
at you—with the make-up all over them. Now I know Adiline Black-
wood has an overdose of the power drive. A castrater, but so what?"

"Social climbing is a reality, dear," Toni allowed. "A recognized
pattern of our society. When you are invited to a place like that it's
always for a purpose—but that's all right."

It was, too, a fact not to my liking, but now I knew, to want to be
liked for one's self is infantile.

"That's the child craving love from parents—a fantasy," Toni
explained. "And if you wear that dress, I know you're getting cured.
No masochist in the entire world would dare to go out in that dress
—but it's terrific on you."

We went on talking, and my, how much we knew about ourselves—and everybody else! I was wearing the dress without even
thinking about it, even though now I knew the Remarkable Person
I'd been expecting to arrive all my life would not be there. That was
just the child looking for grownups—so Dr. Vespers said, and so
I now repeated, and believed. "And now it's all different, isn't it?
Jesus, how much we've learned—and in so little time—haven't we?"

I remember especially that conversation, as it seemed the high-water mark of what I regarded as my recovery. It happened on a Saturday afternoon. We were all three at home—Daphne and Toni were both taking baths—and suddenly Toni wasn't running the water any more, so I poked my head in at her door and found her making up her face with liquid suntan.

Everything was always new with Toni, and this was no exception. She had been undergoing a new analysis for six months, she had a whole new version of herself and her history, and she had a new man.

"I understand things about myself at last," she was saying. "Oh well, it took me five years to get to the Horney therapy. Now I see why I did everything I ever did before. Dr. Horney has completely departed from Freud, you know—and my doctor has studied with her. In six months with Dr. Balman I know why I went for Alf and then threw him out on his ear—as I've done with every man in my life. I've been living with an idealized version of myself. I thought I could do everything—but I wanted to have a vindictive triumph. I thought I could be great and free, pick men up and throw them down, and rise to glory that way. I couldn't see that the way I was going—in my search for glory and complete fulfillment— was against my own best interests. . . ."

I could see she was rolling again. As usual, she was way ahead of me, she understood herself completely, and had taken steps into a new kind of life, whereas I . . .

"You see, darling, the reason I was putting such emphasis on sex— and having an orgasm—was that Freud was all wrong. He thought everything was libidinal—just as the Marxian analyst thought every- thing was economic."

"What does this Balman think?"

"Oh, he's a Horney man. He *knows*. It's the search for glory. Oh brother, have I got it! Only I was moving against people—moving away from people—now I see it all and I'm a new person. I'm moving toward people. Now here's what's so funny, Joyce. When you start moving toward people, you automatically move toward the right people."

"Who are you moving toward?" I asked.

But it was a long time before I found out. His name was Ludwig, and he was a businessman. "He'll never be the rage of Moscow, honey," she admitted, giggling. "Wait till you see him." I had met a man, too, and now that Red was in his "cruel era," I had been seeing the new man. His name was Alex . . . and since Alex and Ludwig were both converging upon us the following night, Sunday, we agreed it might be interesting to make a foursome. After all, we both had something to celebrate. Getting well, at long last.

"It won't be as exciting as you think," Toni cautioned. "It's just reality—and you feel different is all. You just do things and live—and get what you want is all. But there's something kind of cool about it, I'm warning you now, Joyce. It's not exciting."

Now Toni could give and receive love—and success, and she had Ludwig. I didn't quite understand the tremendous departure of this new therapy, but she did seem calm and contented. I thought of my own sweet kindly little Vespers—he wasn't a strict Freudian, he said—and . . . Well, anyway, we were both coming out of the dark—and at the same time. I looked forward to Sunday and the celebration. No matter what she said, it *was* exciting.

That Sunday I knew I was cured. I had the magic key and with it I could open any door, think my way out of any dilemna. *By their fruits shall ye know them,* and the fruits were words.

I had the key to myself at last and, strangely, it was the key to other people, too. That Sunday for the first time I turned and twisted it again and again, trying it on the human situations that came up, and finding the doors springing open. There were the answers, straight and clear. I could see them coming brighter and clearer with the minutes. Later, as friends began dropping in, I saw them with new eyes. Whereas in the past I had been frightened and confused by the mystery of human beings—why oh why did they behave as they did?—now I had only to watch and listen, and sometimes slowly, sometimes quick as a flash, the answer would come up. I had walked a long time in a dark gray street, I was still walking in it too, but now, merely by thinking, I could see neon-lighted signs flashing overhead. And each person, who before had been nameless and therefore frightening, carried a bright tag of identification which showed up in the dark merely by one's listening, watching and thinking.

Toni and I doubled-dated. She wanted me to meet her tycoon and . . . a group sometimes creates a family feeling which can be productive. "Ludwig is interesting, Joyce. He owns his own business —in Astoria. Real estate. His income tax gets published on the front page just like movie magnates. Anybody who can make that much money is bound to have something healthy about him. And he's going on radio with his product—little houses—and . . . this is reality." Reality is cold and dull at first, Toni explained, but after a while you get to like it—like a cold shower. "I haven't been seeing Red, he's in a state of aggression and attack," I told her. "I think now he's decided it was his mother after all who did him in and he's therefore trying to get it out of his system by attacking all woman-kind—which is quite a trick. Anyway I can't relate to him in this mood, as we analysands say." So I said all right to Toni, I would be glad to share reality with her and Tycoon if she would share same with Alex, my new admirer. I thought it might work out well because Alex loved to meet tycoons; the minute I mentioned Ludwig's name to him he went out and looked him up so he'd be ready with the palaver.

"What is Alex like?" Toni asked, and I replied, "He's the hero of *How to Win Friends and Influence People.*" You had to see Alex to believe him. Physically he was large—tall and plump, with soft dimpled hands. "He is photogenic," I went on, "or he thinks he is; anyway he is constantly having photographs taken and passing them around like candy. His face is soft, with shiny skin that al-ways looks clean and rosy, not exactly as it would after a shave, more as if he were still adolescent and didn't need a shave. He has a small rosebuddy mouth and big soft brown eyes. His expression is sentimental; I thought at first it was as if he were watching a baby, but at second glance you're not sure he's looking at anything, maybe he's thinking how he looks. Expression, glances, are important, and this could be depressing until you remember. It's primary narcis-sism, the baby look, and knowing that is so consoling."

"Alex is a good boy," I explained, "he's practically a boy scout." "What does he do that's good?" Dr. Vespers once asked, and I had replied, "He goes down to the Bowery Christmas nights, looks for bums, takes them to dinner and tries to talk them into a different life." It was true. Imagine a publicity man being nice like that. There was only one trouble with these jaunts of Alex's: he kept looking at the people he was trying to help, and every now and then—he told me this—people got up and ran away. I thought it was all in his glance, because I often felt inclined to hurry along when he turned it on me.

"I am trying to like a good man," I told Toni. "Alex is good to his mother, he's good to his sister, he's good to his father, he's good to his kid brother. He worships success, fame, money, big shots— he honestly thinks big shots are good—and he wants to save the others, the have-nots, only his pitch is wrong."

"Now, Joyce, don't start to hate him."

"But he stares at them as if to say, You poor have-nots, you just come on over here and eat those nice big double-meals I eat and you'll get nice and good like me. This would ordinarily annoy the hell out of me, sometimes it still does, but then I pinch myself and I remember, I must relate to a good man. Alex seems to like me so I'm practicing on him. I wish I had somebody more interesting to practice on."

"That will all come," said Toni.

Alex arrived promptly at seven. He was always prompt and he always said, "Hi, dear." While I was greeting him I thought, uncharitably, I've noticed most men who have this no-shave look are stupid, but I quickly turned my head and found the answer in the back of the book: *This yen for the extraordinary is infantile.* Next, Alex showed me a folder he had brought along about himself. "I just wanted you to know what I've done," and I calmly looked it over. I found it was bursting with rather formal letters from big shots—bankers, brokers, congressmen, a few stray senators, mayors, authors, corporation presidents, and their relatives. Most of these letters were from people thanking him for sending their sons or daughters or wives or sweethearts something or other, or else saying they too were pleased to have met him, and would be glad to discuss something or other with him at some future date, if he would get in touch with them after their return from Florida, Paris, or Hawaii. Awful. I said out loud, "Gosh, you seem to know a great many celebrities," and grabbed at the sign. *Oral optimist.*

"It's all in being thoughtful, dear," Alex explained. "There's something everybody needs and can't very well get for himself. Now if you can just quietly find out what it is and then supply it—why—" I said, "Yah, what happens then?"

"Why then you've not only done something kind for somebody and helped him, but you've helped yourself, too. You've put yourself in his mind."

I was just thinking: Dialogue with good people is lousy, remarkable revelations like this go on ad infinitum, and was pushing for the next sign, when the bell rang and Toni's tycoon arrived.

Toni's tycoon—his name was Ludwig Sachtel—turned out to be a whole lot of man—dead-ringer for Santa Claus, with his round face and thick carpet of hair, black and white, and blue eyes as hard and smart as a couple of ice cubes. He was only slightly illiterate but very energetic and good-natured. Yessir, a big bruiser, with a nice loud, persuasive voice; I felt a tremor of excitement . . . until I remembered and quick came the neon-lighted message: He's probably a schizophrenic. . . . I backed away and gave ground to Alex. Toni was still dressing, so I had to play hostess. This wasn't difficult because while Alex waited impatiently to flatter the tycoon, leaping in at every opportunity, tycoon was busy flattering me.

"Toni told me she lived with a very lovely little lady but—well, seein's believin' assa fella says." Things like that. Alex watched him as he paid tribute to my brains, of which he knew nothing, the furnishings which weren't even mine, "I know good taste when I see it all right," and then on to my purple dress with the epaulets, an awful creation that even Daphne the economical hated so much she handed it over to me for helping out with her coat installments, and that somehow turned out wearable. Then Alex started on Ludwig. "Mr. Sachtel, it isn't every day a young man like me gets to meet an older man in your position . . . And if you wouldn't mind, I'd like to ask your advice about . . ." I noticed Tycoon wince at that "older man" crack but he gave Alex his full attention. "Why certainly, boy, go right ahead!" The two of them swapped business stories. Ludwig was well in the lead when Toni finally came out, wearing a black number that fitted her like a glove, and quickly changed the atmosphere.

"Well, look at my little English gentleman!" exclaimed Ludwig, throwing his huge arms around Toni. "How are you anyway, fella?" Toni, who was being passive and feminine, a state which consisted of little besides smiling, occasional agreeable mutterings, and sipping from her drink, seemed to find nothing unusual in his endearments; but I did. In fact as the evening ripened, we were sitting in the restaurant after an excellent dinner, and Ludwig kept calling Toni *Richard* or *Dickie,* and asking me, "What do you think of my little British gentleman—fine little fella now, wouldn't you say?"—the sign went up . . . Mother fixation . . . Not a good bet for marriage . . . Latent homosexual leanings—and toward Toni of all people. Naturally these neon lights are never to be read out loud, and as I saw them, I thought, I may of course be wrong, she's been reading these signs for a much longer period, Toni is further along than I am, or it may be the wrong sign appearing as a result of alcohol; but I was probably right.

Alex kept bringing people he seemed to know only casually over to the table and introducing them to us. He would speak exactly like a man dictating one of those pompous business letters people write to sell things. "It gives me a good deal of pleasure to be able to say—" or "I know a person of your unusual talents and vast experience—" I watched, fascinated and slightly repelled, until I remembered a former neon sign, *oral optimist,* and that made me feel better. In fact, explaining him later to Toni, when we were alone together in the ladies' room, I answered her question, "What does he do?" quite easily. "He flatters everybody with the same words. He calls up all kinds of celebrities or writes them notes—important men he has met casually—and says these incredible things to them and somehow or other he gets to know them, and ends up being good friends with some of them. He'll read a book and then sit down and write to the author. If he gets a brush-off answer from the writer's secretary, he'll simply write again and mark it 'personal.' Maybe he wears people down, but eventually he gets to know them. Here's what's funny, they seem to like it. They must like it because he knows scads of famous people. In fact, he is often asked to parties just to supply celebrities." Toni seemed unbelieving. "This fat boy—he really knows these people—he isn't just name-dropping?" I told her he did, and she thought it over with interest.

"Narcissism," she agreed with me, "I wish I had more of it." And told me something I thought worthy of note. "He's not an exciting man but he thinks he is, and that makes him exciting, Joyce. He'll make good, honey. I've noticed the same kind of thing in some awful plain women. You see it at parties all the time—plain Janes going up to handsome men and talking and flirting like mad. I couldn't dream of doing it, but they can. They just go up to anybody and smile and flatter the man with this same kind of chatter, and next thing you know they have a new friend. And now you take a really beautiful dame like Garbo, who really deserves to have confidence, why she and dozens of others, I guess—well they're shy and uncomfortable about themselves, they want to hide. I tell you nobody should be envious of beautiful dames. Ugly dames with narcissism are much better off. Same goes for men." It's pleasant when two cures can compare the answers, and coming back to Alex, Toni commented, "Business is hard and competitive. I think Alex is nice—and as to his being fat, you can reduce him. And suppose he is dull, well after all this is reality. You know, Joyce, Reality is dull."

I kept on being fairly contented that evening, even though something happened that in the past would certainly have knocked me off my pins. Senator W, a VIP whom I knew, was seated at a table with some other Washington VIP's in the corner of the restaurant and, knowing that I knew the Senator, Alex began pleading, "Why don't you speak to him?" He kept this up every five minutes for a full hour, with me explaining each time that I had no intention of going over to the other table, nor of sending a note to the Senator via the waiter, nor of following any other of Alex's frantic suggestions. We were just about to leave—Alex was by now at fever pitch to bag the big man—when the Senator and his group got up to leave before we did. He spied me as he was passing near our table—and Alex got his wish. The Senator and his group all came over and sat down to have a nightcap with us, and of course Alex got his chance to do his stuff all over again, and the Senator took it big. I felt that nasty revulsion coming over me at Alex's fawning behavior, but I put it down so hard it didn't culminate into a full crescendo until much later.

This was when Alex, lingering over his good-night, said he had an announcement to make, and went on to make it. "You know, dear I didn't know how much I loved you—until tonight, when I saw you with the Senator." It was a while before the sign came up on this one, but it did—I tell you, these neon-lighted signs can get you over some dark roads. The need I seem to have to be loved for myself, and not because I know a Senator or any old sonafasenator, is just "infantile wounded narcissism." Alex has a right to feel good because I know some VIP's who can help him in his business, people all want others to give them something.

This is reality and, as Toni says, reality is cold and dull at first.

It was all of that, I decided, as I went to open the window before jumping into bed. The first day of the cure—and tomorrow, another chance to turn on the nice new lights. This is a rough ride all right, but no more flying blind when you can hear the voice announcing speed and altitude, sudden drops and bumpiness at any hour of the day or night.

But questions stirred uneasily. This system of answers I had found —would it last? How much would it help when a storm came—and the plane ran into real trouble?

I opened the window quickly. A cat moved at the sound, I caught its face in the light, aghast with skepticism and terror, looking up at me like my old self.

CHAPTER TWENTY-ONE

· · · · · · ·

MOST OF THE TIME I ENJOYED MY SWIM IN THE WORD LIFE. I often felt secretly superior to all the others who had never taken the plunge—and often inferior, especially those times when I met people who appeared to be living without all this referring back for the answers, and sometimes, not often, there appeared one who seemed to have worse troubles even than mine.

Such a one was the young Russian we met at one of the dancing bistros Christmas week. Toni knew him from somewhere, they nodded to one another as our party came in, and I noticed him immediately. He was sitting alone at a table in the rear of the crowded restaurant, moving his head back and forth in time to the gypsy music that was being played. There was something intensely pleasing about him. A thick-set man, with an extra large head and bushy reddish-brown hair and wide-open gray eyes, he might have been a farmer dressed up for a night in town.

"He's amusing—and bright as a dollar—but I can't make out what he's doing over here—" Toni was watching him and smiling as she whispered. "A captain in the Russian Air Corps—or maybe he *was* a captain. He's all around—you keep meeting him in the strangest places. I thought he came over on a mission, but now he seems to be here all the time."

"The young men from Moscow," Sir Harry commented. "Hundreds of them around." "But how do they get in?" Daphne asked him. "Who knows?" Harry shrugged. "What's more interesting is how they got out—or shall we say, when and why they left." He was about to say more, when the Russian suddenly appeared at our table and the atmosphere was instantly charged with a new buoyancy.

His name was Serge Orloff. He spoke in a thick childish accent and as he answered our questions, bursting into lighthearted anecdotes about how the Russians reacted to the Americans, such a gay roguish expression came into his face he won us all over so we wondered what we had ever done without him.

Between anecdotes, Toni told Serge all about his native land . . . "Wonderful over there. That's where I want to go—after the war. Russians don't crack up. The state is their good father—so they have no neuroses."

"That right," Serge replied in his special brand of infantile English. "They not live long enough."

"The state is the only possible good father," Toni continued, "and that removes all this crazy longing for parents."

"The state also remove the parents," said Serge.

"What does he mean?" Toni whispered to me. "He must be kidding. I wouldn't like it if I thought . . ."

But I liked him. He could dance, his conversation was fun, and I had the tantalizing feeling I had met him somewhere before. I began to feel alive in a new way, as if a current had suddenly been turned on that a short while ago had seemed dead, so dead indeed that trying to get it going now looked like trying to light a fire with wet newspapers.

There were certain aspects of his personality that might have troubled me had I been in the mood to notice them. He avoided answering Daphne's, "Where are you living?" but when it was repeated, he replied, "I live with friend." Later, "I stay here short time —then I go to Detroit—and then to California." I noticed he seemed on the alert, ready to run and hide at the first signal, but this might be because he was an alien. ". . . Getting to be a great national type," Sir Harry commented, when Serge was dancing with Toni. "Uncounted numbers of them here illegally—why, it's almost a new generation. The ex-Communist, the man with an ex-life. Took desperate courage though—wangling their way out of Europe and into America. Think of the headaches and the bewilderment, and all the dead people in the background—and look at him there jitterbugging away as if nothing had happened—"

I liked Serge more as I began to sense his mood, that combination of the need to confide, and the sense of fear, perhaps of real danger. But it hadn't gotten him. He ate all his food, drank all his wine, and laughed often. Besides, a certain blind spot had come up in me, so I saw and heard without complete clarity. "Let's go somewhere," he said to me, when the party broke up.

The evening turned out to be a novelty. I forgot my troubles, forgot the neon signs, forgot everything in the pleasure of discovering this nice big exciting Russian bear. I quickened to his thick, childish accent, caught his ingratiating smile, noted his soldierly walk, shared with him the sudden bursts of laughter. We danced well together, his dancing came replete with innovations more American than the Americans, more Latin than the latest Latin rhythms. Now and then, with a twist of sympathy, I'd catch a look of oncoming uncertainty, as if he didn't quite know where he was and was afraid to ask directions; and sensing that here was someone who like me had seen the crumbling of the wall, I knew I was not alone.

I wasn't surprised, just quietly delighted, when he appeared at my office the next day. I took him with me to the photographer's studio and let him help shoot photographs for the July issue, watching his naïve delight in the beautiful models being posed in bathing suits for a beach scene. I saw him again that evening. This time he was standing at the end of a long apartment in which a party was being given, and by the time I arrived, Serge was definitely the lion. At the center of a group, he was being plied with questions, and now I saw he was using the information he had about Russia to win friends and influence people. He told stories, but as he went on, the Stalinist government emerged as the murderer while the people appeared as the struggling, lovable victims with whom he was deeply identified. I began to feel better.

The following night we were together again in a sense—in the midst of an impromptu Christmas Eve party which was going on at our place when I finally got home after the office party. I lighted the lights on the Christmas tree and it made a cheery note, with logs burning in the fireplaces. It had been a pleasant day altogether, and now I was conscious of Serge there in the group enjoying himself as he talked or danced, watching me with those nice big eyes. We are already lovers, I thought. You have made things easy by not talking about sex, too . . . (Oh, those cooks who keep telling you how the stew is cooking!) . . . and tomorrow, a matter of hours, I will try out my new word-bandaged wings with you. If I can make the love flight, that will mean I'm well, says Dr. Vespers. But maybe I'll fall to the ground again, after the usual brief climb. Oh well, I've got my signs all ready in case of trouble—anyway, it will be fun, Serge knows a great deal, he will save me, carry me back to safe shores. And I forgot everything again, looking at him.

The wonderful sense of recovery was just going strong when Daphne burst in, followed shortly by Red, who had come uninvited and who managed to spill a pint of black ink into the atmosphere. He threw his overcoat on a chair and started walking up and down, taking no notice of me.

"I didn't bring him," Daphne apologized. "He came in behind me."

"Just couldn't resist having a peek at Christmas on Guinea Pig Row. Just had to see how the little patients are doing. Daphne, how's your analysis?"

"Never touch it—you remember me." Daphne slanted the words flirtatiously toward Red as Sir Harry claimed her. I noticed her eyes jumping from Red to Serge as she talked animatedly to Sir Harry, while Red wandered off toward Toni.

"Merry Christmas, Toni. You and Ludwig look kind of complacent. Young love at Yuletide and all that." I knew from the way he talked he was tight. "No more penis envy, huh? Girl like you, I thought you'd be jealous of Santa Claus."

"Not that guy!" Toni, ablaze with excitement over Ludwig and Reality, didn't seem to mind. "That dirty bourgeois myth is all yours, Red." Then, as Red poured himself a drink, she whispered to me, "He's not the man we used to know, Joyce."

The party got lively toward midnight. Sir Harry was leaning over Daphne, speaking in that aloof British whisper I'd come to know, his head inclined forward covering her as with an umbrella. Phrases floated out from them, something about "the universe in flight" and "tired light." "That Englishman—he smart with words," Serge commented. "I don't understand so good those words. I wish you to tell me what many things I hear mean." I had just started to explain, when Red, who had been standing by the fireplace, suddenly started speaking in a loud voice.

"Christmas with the wounded," was the opening gambit. "You'll

1 7 8

never get back, not a single one of you. Never. I tell you you're done for. You'll never get back with the crowd."

I saw Serge glance up at him, and then back to me, and felt a stab of fear.

"What he mean by that?" he asked me. But Toni was answering. "What crowd?"

"Leave him alone," Daphne called over to her. "Can't you see he's drunk?"

"No, I'm not drunk at all." He was staring at Serge, talking straight to him. "I'll explain what I mean. My grandmother has a farm in Pennsylvania. One summer she bought a pig from a nearby farmer and kept it all summer. When we went back to the city we all drove over to the farmer's to ask him to take back the pig, she even said she'd give it to him free for nothing. But he said no, he couldn't keep that pig any more. It had been away from the other pigs. It had become—different. They would kill it, he said. My grandmother didn't believe him. How could the other pigs know that one of them had been away? Pigs weren't that smart. But the farmer told us the pigs would know in a minute. His smell had changed. They'd kill him and eat him, that's all, because he wasn't like them any more."

(I reached now for the signs. What was it Dr. Vespers said— when I mentioned Red's attacks? *The arrogant person is compelled to seek vindictive triumph to cover up the terror of his own weakness.*)

"See here, if I'm not too personal, the story must have a point hidden away in it somewhere, no doubt?" Sir Harry sneered. But Serge whispered, "He mean the story for you." I nodded. And I am, I thought, trying to get into the river that flows, and flow with it, Red, and all your vindictive triumph can neither help nor hinder me on my way.

"Might try a bit of dry cleaning yourself, old boy," Sir Harry threw into the silence.

"I'm not trying to hurt anybody. Just philosophical fact-finding. Research. You dames better listen. If you do get back they'll murder you. You're out in the storm, that's all, and you might as well get used to heavy weather."

"Jesus, he's murder," Toni whispered. "He doesn't know what he's saying," I defended. "It's that third doctor—telling him to compete with men." Toni went on, "I wish he'd go. Ludwig doesn't get this kind of thing."

The last I saw of Red as I went downstairs for more liquor, he was standing near Daphne, obviously encroaching on Sir Harry's territory and trying to crowd him out. Daphne had lowered her eyelids and was looking sideways toward him, her mouth open, her lower lip dropping way down showing the inside of her mouth with all those expensive capped teeth. She was saying something sharp to him, though I didn't catch it, and he answered in kind. Then, next thing I knew, he was beside me in the kitchen.

"I'm sorry I've been ornery to you," he said. "It's that goddamned Daphne I really hate. I had to hit out at somebody—"

"Why can't you just leave people alone? We haven't exactly done anything to you."

"Oh yes you have. You've done plenty. The atmosphere here tortures me. I hate people in groups. You girls have a goddamn group—and I'm not in it. You seem to be having such a good time *together*—in a way that I'll never have a good time. I feel like I've wandered into some kind of a private club where I'm not known—especially to Daphne. I tell you, that goddamned Daphne drives me crazy."

"Now, Red, she can't help being beautiful—and she hasn't done anything to you."

"She has, though. She's alive, isn't she? That's doing something to me. She's one of those hard, frozen, beautiful bitches. I tell you, those frigid actress-model women drive me crazy. Can't you see what she's doing with her beauty? Every time she walks down the street she castrates twenty men."

I said I didn't believe that, people didn't castrate that easy, but I don't think he heard me.

"She's a bitch, I tell you—and what she needs is to be whipped and conquered. If only I had enough money—I will some day—but I wish I had it now. I'd buy that Daphne and make a slave of her. Brother, would I have fun. She needs to be tied to a bed and . . ."

"Do you tell this stuff to your doctor?"

"Sure I do. He says, 'Iff you want to gif a woman a little spanking—some little luf-taps on the buttocks—that is almost normal. But if you want to beat a woman with a whip . . . if you want to hurt chumone . . . that iss sick.' Ergo, I am sick. I'll be better when I have the million dollars and can express my hatred of women—and pay for it like any other good American businessman who was knocked by his mother—Look, baby, this Russian boy scout—you'll never make it with him . . ."

I was glad to get back upstairs and see Serge, Sir Harry and the others, even if it was to hear the familiar bleak code words we all spoke and understood, symbols of this new test-tube living. To find Serge waiting to talk, this time we held hands. He had such nice, hard, stubby fingers, they made his hands seem so competent. It was actually pleasant now, living this moment upstairs, after the escape from Red, the now wild and tormented.

"A place like this must seem awful to you, doesn't it, Serge?" Toni asked him, when we joined her on the sofa. "But don't worry, you don't have to stay here. You're here on a mission, aren't you?"

"Yes, I am here on mission."

"You don't have to say what it is—"

"I will. I have big mission to stay alive."

"That doesn't sound very realistic. The Russians are the only brave people—"

"I am coward. I like the life here."

"Of course—for a visit—but not to stay. What can you find to like?"

"Capitalism I like. All I want is more capital."

Toni moved quickly away from him, and later, as she was passing drinks and appetizers, I noticed she slighted him, and I chided her for it.

"Listen, Joyce, he's not a turncoat, is he? Jesus, honey, I'd hate to see you having your first orgasm with a turncoat."

"It's a little early for worry. I haven't had one yet."

"Yes, but maybe you will—and with a turncoat—and one that admits he wants money—of all things for a Russian—"

"Wait a minute now. What's so terrible about that?"

"Don't you see, he'll louse up your entire fantasy life. Wait till I tell you what happened to me. Look, if you're successful with him, and he's the first, why it's like losing your virginity—only worse. You'll never get the man out of your system. You'll be lost, darling—absolutely lost. . . ."

CHAPTER TWENTY-TWO
. . . .

I WAS UP EARLY CHRISTMAS MORNING, THE BETTER TO FINISH wrapping presents and make way for the new era. I was into it now for sure. At the very outermost edge of the test tube. Soon, a matter of hours, I'd be meeting Serge—we had planned to have an early Christmas dinner, and then come home and be together—and then for the final jump out of doctoring and into living. With Toni and Daphne still asleep, I wrapped the rest of the presents and sipped my coffee.

The room stared back at me. Outside, the El trains came roaring in, stopped and went rumbling grumbling on. The balls on the Christmas tree picked up the room with the white light filtering in through the windows. The place seemed watchful—waiting, maybe even listening. I remembered how sometimes in the past it had seemed remote and disdainful, a disapproving adult of a room; today, with the cheery Christmas tree and the embers in the fireplaces, it seemed waiting to enclose us in its warmth, and felt eager with me as I changed into my new, expensive, gold wool dress.

By now I could hear sounds coming from Daphne's room. Her radio was going, it sounded like war news, the garbled words blaring through the closed door. . . . Invasion of the Gilberts . . . Assault in the western Marshalls . . . Kwajalein and Eniwetok Atolls . . . Roi and Namur . . . Assault . . . slight resistance . . . capture! Beachheads expanding! It switched off suddenly and Daphne came running out, looking handsome and Christmasy in her blue mink coat and mink skullcap, with a corsage of holly pinned rakishly at the top of her cap

"Hi. Any coffee left?"

I heated her a cup of coffee which she sipped standing up and talking between sips. "I'm flying to Washington—any minute now. Hope I can get a cab. Christmas with some Navy people—friends of Sir Harry. He wangled the plane seat for me. You know, Joyce, last night he talked to me for quite a while about us."

I wondered what was coming—every comment interested me those days, as every person interested me. How often I'd seen Daphne standing like this, or striding in those long steps—she seemed more comfortable than when sitting down—and talking in the wind-driven voice. What I said was, "Him, too? What did he allow? Can we make it—or had we better give up?"

"It's not very funny, dear. Sir Harry *sees* everything—he never misses a move. You'd better be thinking seriously about what you're going to do."

"Do about what, Daphne?"

"About your future."

"When?"

"Now."

As I listened to the soft, elegant little gusts coming out of the perfumed dress and furs she always seemed to be floating in, I noticed how oddly unrelated they were to the real girl. Like a cloud of vapor floating over a pool. It was almost as if a ghost were speaking through her, holding her up with invisible hands. And all this queer stuff was coming through.

"We ought to begin looking for another apartment as soon as I get back."

"When will that be?"

"Tomorrow night I think. I'll call you if I decide to stay over."

"*Why,* Daphne? Why do we *have* to leave this place? What on earth gives you this idea?"

"Look, Joyce—there's something about this place that brings out funny things in people. If you don't know about it, it's high time you found out. That's what was the matter with Red last night."

"What *are* you talking about? You mean to say you think this apartment went to his head—something like that?" She nodded. "How can you possibly believe such things?"

"Because I saw him earlier in the afternoon—if you want to know. He called me and asked me to meet him—so I did. I didn't think you'd mind, you haven't been seeing him very much. Anyway, I had half an hour to kill—so I met him, and he wasn't like that at all."

A stab of pained confusion went through me. I had suspected something last night. "What was he like?"

"Oh, perfectly normal. Rather gracious, in fact. On the make, of course, but I just didn't notice. Then when he got down here, the minute he put foot in the place he changed into a devil."

"Uh-huh. And you think the place did this to him?"

"Of course. Don't you know what's going on here?"

"Yeah, the place. You don't think he was angry with you for turning him down—and that was what made him so strange?"

"Of course not. Anyway, I didn't exactly turn him down. I never completely turn any man down." She laughed, showing those beautiful, snowy capped teeth again, gleaming white against her red lips. "I said I'd give him a date week after next, and he wrote it down. It's this place, Joyce. It has terrible vibrations." I was beginning to react to the sound of the words, feeling as if I might scream with laughter. "I've begun to feel queer sometimes myself. Sir Harry says it's definitely not me—and I believe him because he knows. . . . Oh, well, I suppose it's useless, telling you about it. I know you and Toni only believe what these witch doctors tell you. But if you'd just get out of this place for a few weeks . . . you'd be surprised what might happen to you."

"All right, Daphne, maybe you've got something. But tell me, what do you think is so bad about the place—I mean, specifically?"

"Oh, Joyce, other people's thoughts are here. Other people besides us are living here. They are living here with us—and crowding us out. They are working against us."

There was a psycho sign on this one. *The woman with no sexual outlet often seeks importance on the other spheres.*

"Harry knows a house we could get. As soon as I get back we could go look at it together. I know Toni wouldn't like it, it's just not her kind of place, and that would be a good out. And then we could take it together. She'd be better off in a place of her own anyway. Well, Merry Christmas, dear. I left something for you under the tree."

There was a flash of mink and blue dress flying through the door, and Daphne was gone, taking with her the certain cool, silvery atmosphere that was always there wherever she was. I wondered about her for a minute. I was especially curious about the Christmas present. I hadn't expected anything from her, we had tacitly agreed not to exchange presents, and if she had given me one it would mean that something was expected from me in return, something more than a Christmas present. Probably the house, I decided, as I started toward the tree to find her package, just as I heard the front door opening and closing, and then someone running up the stairs and into the apartment. It was Toni.

"Where's your hat and coat?" I asked her.

"I haven't been out. I just went to the door—to see if she's gone. Has she really gone away?"

"Yes, she's gone away, I thought you knew."

"Oh sure—to Washington—big deal. I heard most of what she said. She's still on the vibration kick. Jesus, Joyce, sometimes I'm scared of her. Aren't you?"

I had to laugh at Toni's face. She did look scared.

"Oh no, honey, I've heard lots of talk like that in the Bible belt. It's common down that way. Ghosts—vibrations—stuff like that. Matter of fact, I eat it up."

"Well, all right. If you think you can take it, I guess it's okay. Now listen, sweetheart, I can only stay with you a few minutes. I'm rushing to meet Ludwig. But I wanted to talk to you before I go. Now look, today's the day—with Serge, huh?" I nodded. I had thought, naïvely, that nobody knew, that this was our secret. "Well now listen," she went on, with the inexorable kindness of one test-tuber to another. "I'm staying away tonight. Now stop—don't say a word—I've got it all arranged."

"But why—?"

"Listen to her. She's asking. Because it may take hours. And so I thought, if you and Serge had the coast clear—with no pressures—so much the better."

"That's awfully sweet of you, Toni—but I don't think you need to do that."

"Why not?"

"Well, tell you the truth, I sort of think two or maybe three hours would be enough—"

"Two or three hours—" She gasped. "For your first orgasm? Are

1 8 5

you out of your mind? It may take two or three days—if you're lucky—in fact, very lucky—and things happen fast."

"Oh no, I'm sure you're wrong—"

"Otherwise it might take two or three weeks or two or three months or—"

"But I couldn't stand to keep trying that long. We'd both be dead."

"Oh no you wouldn't. People don't die that way. They die the other way—from not trying."

"Well, anyway, I sort of thought we'd come back here after Christmas dinner."

"Don't eat much, Joyce," she interrupted. "Remember, too much food on the stomach is just no good."

It was becoming embarrassing but I went bravely on. "I'll remember. Well anyway, like I said, after Christmas dinner with Serge's friend—I thought we'd just drift back here and stay from five to, say, seven or so. And then go on out."

"Five to seven? Are you crazy? Are you completely mad?" Now I didn't know what to say but that didn't matter. "Now listen, dear, you've got the time element all wrong. For a thing like this you need time, endless time. You've got to try different things—different fantasies. Look, now say when Serge starts making love to you—what will you be thinking about?"

"Serge."

"That's wrong right from the start."

"Why?"

"I don't think that would ever work."

"Is there any law about it? I mean you don't *have* to think of somebody besides your partner—at a time like that—or do you?"

"You certainly do. Look, the thing to do is to think about your *fantasy*. You do have a sexual fantasy, don't you—something that gets you excited—practically everybody has?"

I thought about that, and remembered my fantasy—the wonderful, thrilling, cruel man who came to me in my dreams—about whom I was shy to confess. "Yes, sure I have," I admitted, "but it's somebody entirely different from Serge."

"Of course it is. It has to be. But couldn't you even *pin it on Serge?*"

I thought that over. It was quite an idea: deliberately pinning the cruel stuff in the fantasy on Serge, that is, making him do what the man in my secret daydreams did. But Serge was too short, he just didn't look the part; it would be difficult to imagine Serge picking a woman up and throwing her around like a doll.

"I don't think so," I said, at length.

"Why not?" snapped Toni.

"Because he's too short."

"Well but can't you lengthen him out? You can make him any height you want, remember. Six-foot-eleven or twelve is a good height. Just try and keep his face, if you can—and even that you can change."

"Never. Why?"

"Gee, that's bad. Jesus, honey—you don't seem to have gotten anywheres near how to make things work. I mean you're in a bad way—and especially what you tell me about Serge being so different from the man in your fantasy."

I didn't know much about this phase of the sign-punching game, and listened with both ears as she went on. "It's bad, but not impossible, of course. It would be very convenient if you could pin your fantasy on Serge. But now listen, if you can't—and you're absolutely sure you can't—why then don't even try."

"I won't. Go on."

"Just bring up your fantasy in your mind and keep on thinking about it while Serge is making love to you. Just ignore Serge. That's the whole trick—that's what I've been meaning to tell you. Now if you can just keep thinking about it long enough—and if Serge can keep up his end—the chances are pretty good. Now—I mean after all your analysis and all—eventually you'll have an orgasm. But don't be disappointed if you don't the first few times you try—or even the first few hundred times you try—with some it's even the first few thousand times—What's the matter?"

"Nothing. It sounds kind of depressing—anyway, I'm feeling depressed."

"What about?"

"Oh, all these things I have to remember—and keep trying—"

"Now, Joyce, people have been at this thing for years. Don't be impatient. And don't be depressed. There's nothing to remember except *hang on to your fantasy*. Now how do you like it best—I mean

—which is the most like your fantasy—naked or with your clothes on?"

"With clothes on, I think—but probably Serge likes it naked."

"Well then, try it both ways. Serge understands this is an experiment, doesn't he?"

"No. Certainly not."

"But you've talked to him about it, haven't you? You've told him you can't come, haven't you?"

"No, of course not. I wouldn't dare tell a man I'm like that."

"Why not? What do you think he'd do if you told him?"

"Run like hell."

"He would not. Listen, Joyce, you dope. If you tell a man you've never had an orgasm, all he says is, Great, because he thinks he can fix that little matter in just about five minutes. Well, you do what you want—but I'd tell him if it was me—like I told my Frenchman and—"

"You told him that?"

"Why certainly. And I also told him about my fantasy. You see, in my fantasy I'm a slave and the man is the king. I dream he whips me first and then rapes me—he is very tall. And I told Alphonse please don't talk so I can hold on to my fantasy—because Alphonse didn't sound like any king in the world—I mean, when he talked. But you know the sonofabitch double-crossed me. That was why I hated him so."

"What did he do, Toni?" She had never told me, and I was curious.

"He kept saying, *The King is dead. This is Alphonse, Alphonse who loves you—Alphonse is making you come—not the lousy old broken-down king in your dirty dream. Alphonse, man, your man.* And oh, I hated him for what he did to me—"

"What did he do?"

"Don't you see. He made me come—with him. After that I—I could never go back to the king. I didn't know what to do. He and the king were both in my fantasy—and that stopped everything. For a long time afterwards, for months in fact—every time I had sex, just as I saw the king again and my fantasy was going good, I'd hear that damned double-crossing Alphonse saying, *The King is dead, this is Alphonse.* So of course I became frigid again. That's why I'm so crazy about Ludwig. He's the first one I've been able to pin my fantasy on since that frog of an Alphonse upset the applecart."

"Yah. Gee—how's that?" I gasped, fascinated by what I was hearing.

"Well, Ludwig almost looks like the man in the fantasy—I mean the king. Besides, he told me—he used to beat his last wife on the ass once a week with a strap. You see, I think maybe he is my fantasy come to life."

"Maybe he is? Don't you know yet?"

"Not yet. I can wait until the honeymoon. It's highly possible that Ludwig is the real thing. I'll have my fantasy and then I'll have everything. Because that's all there is."

I said, "Well, thanks, Toni. I'll remember what you said. But honestly, you don't need to clear out. Where are you going, anyway?"

"Oh, I'm meeting Ludwig. We're going for a drive—then after dinner I told him to take me up to my mother's."

"It's sweet of you, but really . . ."

"Sweet nothing. Didn't you and Daphne stay holed up in a hotel for days to give me a chance with Alphonse? Least I can do is empty the joint for *your* bar mitzvah. Well, honey, I've got to run. Success to your chain of delicatessen stores."

"I hope they're as successful as yours."

"Yeah. Some success. I should have stood in bed. Well, Merry Christmas. Try to forget what I said now and get back on the romantic kick. If you can't make it that way, you can try the other. Well, so long now, honey. It's all in a life."

There were moments during the Christmas visit that followed when I rued that conversation with Toni, much as a convalescent from some long, dull illness who finds himself suddenly able to get out and enjoy the sights resents the doctor's instructions not to overdo it. All day long, whenever Serge touched me, I felt a vague consciousness of Dr. Vespers looking over my shoulder—and now Toni—it was becoming a multitude. (Goddamn this medical sex anyway.)

Hours later, the Christmas cheer mingled with the fears comfortably behind us, Serge and I finally came home together and lighted a fire. I was at last oblivious to the peepers, they seemed to have disappeared somehow, and was feeling no pain as I watched him making drinks for us both and putting on a dance record. "We not talking with words no more," he said, pulling me up from the couch at the opening sounds of his favorite rumba record. We played out a number of records, dancing to them all, and we were silent. Once, near the end of the third, Serge said something. "All is matter of living in present. That is secret. It have to come on you suddenly. You just wait, you don't try to do nothing. I show you."

Ah, now that was something. Suddenly I felt absolutely certain Serge knew everything, as all these days of listening to him telling of his past in Russia, his war experiences, and seeing his incredible ability to walk out of the past unharmed, flared up into sudden realization. This magnificent creature possessed the remarkable insight for which I had been searching. He was almost occult in his powers of perception. He was the man from Mars. Awkward as I had often felt, recounting my own experiences, the Bible belt as commonplace as cheap glass beside the richness of the Byzantine, it didn't matter now that I had met at last the one who would interpret it all for me. "There, you are doing it now," he said. To make absolutely sure he was reading my mind, I asked, "Doing what?" And he replied, "You came up. Living in the present."

As we sat down again, a new secret thrill in this unexpected man stirred in my spine. With the next drink I knew he would tell me the thing I had been waiting to hear: he would know what it was I had lost, or was born without, that made it so hard for me to find my way. Why, he might even give it to me, or lend it to me for a while; yes, anything could happen, he had so much hidden up his sleeve. Possibly merely the naming of it would be the secret magic that would break the spell of my denial, fix those "crossed conditions"; and after that I would know where I was going. We were staring at each other now. I wouldn't even have to speak, I thought, he could read the question in my mind; I could wait.

I did wait, too, but after a while, when the answer didn't seem to be forthcoming, when the silence was broken only by, "I like to see your hair on top your head," I spoke up. "Serge, you know, I've always felt there's something I haven't got." It sounded silly, especially coming on top of that one about a new hairdo.

"Oh, sure!" He was smiling. "What you think that is you don't have?"

"I don't know, but I was thinking maybe you know." He nodded, knowingly, I thought. "It's as if I've lost something somewhere—or maybe I didn't have it when I was born."

He was laughing, rubbing those big stubby fingers along my arm, and laughing. "Yeah, sure you born without. That good."

This wasn't quite the right reaction I expected from the oracle.

"You wait. You are here—right now—not somewhere else. That the beginning."

Now it was something to see that. He got up and put on another record.

"I dance tango when I have something to celebrate. I have job coming up in Washington. We dance now for my job."

This seemed delightful and funny. He was in love but he was also interested in getting ahead fast—an intensely masculine quality, it seemed, the indestructible male with a bare suggestion of the unattainable, in addition to being an oracle and a mind reader. And all spoken in those delicious mispronunciations, with the humor and intelligence to sense what he was saying. He kissed me lightly as we finished the dance, and succeeded in turning on the current that had seemed so dead.

Now we were talking again. I was conscious of being slightly drunk but exceptionally clear. What I saw and felt—his head, his eyes, his words, the room, the onrushing experience—seemed extraordinarily bright and clear and close, a segment of life viewed through a three-dimensional camera. The words seemed to fall into place as they came out of his mouth and to become living things. "You not happy girl. You gay, you friendly, you generous. But you have something—some force—drawing you away." Ah, there it was, he was the one man who knew me, and now he would give me the clue. So far the script had not been quite right—his answers went off somewhere, I had been conscious of disappointment—but that was just the beginning of the play called the seat-banging dialogue. Now, at any minute, the big dramatic words would burst precise and perfect from the hero's lips. "I know many American girl—but not any give away so much like you—" There, that was the stamp of his identity: he knew my secrets. "But that because everything you give have no value to you." The play was getting hot now. "Go on, Serge. Don't stop now." He grinned. "Okay, have Chesterfield. I don't say nothing bad—you understand?" I almost shouted, "Of course I do. Say anything." He made another drink and stood up, talking to me from above, leaning on the mantel. "You are tender and sweet—but you are only saluting people. Like flag raised on boat in the middle of the sea. The captain say hello but he do not stop the boat." I said, "Yes, that's right, but why won't the captain stop the boat?" He was laughing. "I got you going, haven't I? I don't know why the captain don't stop the boat. I think the captain can't stop—the boat going too fast."

It was fun to be kissing him, but I wanted to hear the rest so I moved away to take up my drink. "It don't matter now, dear girl. The boat get blown up when the destroyer arrive—and the hell with the dumb captain. He don't know nothing."

"You mean the destroyer has arrived."

"Sure. But I hate the captain of your ship. Sonofabitch been running full steam ahead for twenty-four hours. I was afraid the dynamite get wet."

I tried not to hear the vulgar wisecrack. After all, he was a peasant, he said so, and he did know how to manage things nicely, with just enough conversation. Then I began losing my thoughts in the first excitement of coming closer. It was just enough conversation, too, one more word would have been too much, and like me he didn't believe in singing as he worked. The firelight made the room seem alive, a living part of us. Here it is, I'm up with it now, it's going to be all right, and after that maybe I will go to sleep and never again dream about the tired wanderer resembling me arriving at the wrong house in the wrong street and not being able to get in.

We are coming together now, but Serge is whispering. If only he'd shut up, I thought, uncharitably. The lovely little strides I'm making up the ocean wall are impeded by the sound of a voice asking those foolish questions . . . Now he is hollering or crying in joy, something awfully irrelevant it seems to me, a crazy cry of victory before the battle has really begun. Abruptly I stopped climbing, fell down the wall, and felt the familiar "Oh God" feeling. I closed my eyes, feeling drunk and warm and sleepy and sad with the special sadness that the dead must feel as they wander among the foolish, busy, happy living and try so desperately to join up with them. Oh well, so he wasn't the one I thought he was. . . . Just another man. But if you close your eyes tight enough you won't know what you know. And from this to the merciful inner dizziness of whiskey, and down the spiral of sleep.

A riveting machine had started up somewhere. It was grinding away, and very near too, reverberating in my head. *No, oh no,* was my first feeling. They can't be tearing up the street again right outside the window: it's still Christmas, after all, a legal holiday—or is it the day after Christmas? I didn't know the answer to that, surrounded as I was by a heavy body of water pressing in on me—or was it stones, rolling dark wet stones—but how did they ever get under my shoulders and across my head? I moved and the stones faded, and I saw the wall of the room. No, oh no, no, I don't want to wake up, and I wouldn't either, if only that damned riveting machine would stop. I closed my eyes but I knew, I knew. A stranger, a big heavy beef of a stranger at that, had a strangle hold on me. He was muttering, too, "You perfect woman. . . . We going places. . . . I am on moon." Words stirred in my head. "You're not on the moon at all, you big wet fish, you are on me and I wish to God you'd move. You weigh a ton."

From this uncomfortable position the accent that had sounded adorable a while back was now embarrassingly revolting. Then, oh well, it can't last forever, he'll go back to sleep again soon and then I'll wriggle out from under him and see to that riveting machine. After all, I'm polite, even in duress, it's not fair to shove.

But he showed no signs of moving. Desperately I peeped at my wrist watch. Five past one. My God, how long had we been here— locked in this death clutch from which at this moment there seemed to be no escape? An hour, more likely five hours—oh God, oh no— well, all right—now the whole thing was coming back to me. No more hiding among those wet stones. We came home at six—I and my man from Mars . . . and now, seven hours later, here I was, my back broken, my arms aching, trying to get out from under so I could do something about that terrible banging. I moved stealthily as an Indian in a forest surrounded by enemies, one desperate wrench, and then, bang, there I was out, and without any more of that adorable Russian accent, only a nice solid snore. I was looking for my shoes, why did they have to be black when it was also black under the bed, then made my way barefooted and cold out into the living room where the riveting machine located oddly in the telephone was blasting away.

"Hello."

"Hello, dear." It was Toni. "How are you? I mean, is everything all right?"

"Fine. Everything is fine. Just ducky."

"Because if it isn't now, honey, don't be discouraged. Remember what I said, a thing like this takes time."

"Oh yes—time—I remember. But five hours is time."

"It's no time at all. After all it's the most important thing there is for a woman."

"No it isn't. Giving birth is."

"This is the beginning—giving birth to your self. Now listen, you stay right there and don't take a hate on the fellow, you hear? Don't do it now, and don't be sad."

"Who said I'm sad?"

"Sad, schmad, who cares? The point is, hundreds of women can't make the grade for years, but with all your therapy, everything's been speeded up, see? You mustn't get impatient, you mustn't get sore at the guy or throw him out or anything like that."

"Oh I won't. I'm polite to the last."

"The last! Get you. This is the very beginning. Now take yourself a slug of whiskey and go on back. Did you do like I said with the fantasy?"

"I guess I didn't get to that."

"Oh well, there's always a next time. I'm staying away—"

"I wish you wouldn't. The coast will be clear in an hour and you can come on home."

"An hour? Listen to her. I'm staying away, I said. Go on back and try it next time with the fantasy. I've tried it, and I can tell you, sonofabitch works like a charm."

And there was more.

"What's the matter? Dreamboat ain't quite the doll he was before the act? That's perfectly natural. Most women feel that way—and men, too. *Après l'amour tristesse* is what it's called. Alphonse told me that one. The French know all about these things and take them for granted. It's only us dumb Americans that get sore at our partners

194

—me, included. Now keep it under control, you hear, and don't start hating his guts."

"I won't—I'll try not to, anyway—but frankly, just this minute, they seem awful easy to hate."

"I know—but that's just the result of the first shock. Your hatred will lessen after a while. You thought he was a god before, huh?"

"Yeah."

"Well. Now you know he's just a man. Well, you try to forgive him, and in time you'll get to like him. This has to be handled scientifically, dear—not *emotionally*. You don't like it when you hear about men trying to get rid of women after they've had sex, do you?"

"No, I certainly don't. But honestly I'm not planning to drop Serge out the window."

"Well, great. Now that's the first step. And that very decision may be the beginning of love."

CHAPTER TWENTY-THREE

. . . . . .

AFTER CHRISTMAS, DOWN THERE IN THE PLACE WITH THE BAD vibrations, we three hesitated in the lull before the new year, lifting one foot to catch the music for the next step in the dance we were somehow compelled to dance straight through to the end, stopping only when the players in the orchestra put away their instruments and the watchman came to close the hall for the night. Then, before we knew what was happening in the anesthesia of the busy days, the season of expectation was over and the march had begun again.

Another winter, another year. The soldiers walked more swiftly in the dirty snow left over on Third Avenue. Daphne became suddenly busier than ever with men, only now among her gifts of rationed foods, liquor and jewelry, appeared the bright fresh faces of the new how-to-be-happy books. Among the paths to peace were nudism, health foods, deep breathing, projection of the astral body, new interpretations of the Bible, and the power of words.

Of them all the one that seemed to have taken the most effect was the one on nudism; for lately both Toni and I had seen her walking about naked in the apartment—doing her exercises and deep breathing—but occasionally causing one or the other of us to rush to the windows and pull down the blinds, as the apartment faced the street. Once, pulling the blinds hastily . . . I saw two men peering into the window, a look of trance happiness on their faces, I asked Daphne if she didn't think it might be dangerous, stirring up evil in men's minds and all that.

"Evil? If people see anything evil in the human body it just means the evil is in them." I said, "Yes, I know—but aren't you afraid? They might break in—they looked as if they were about to climb in."

She stared out at me with those big, beautiful, expressionless eyes as she went on doing her exercises. "Of course not," she said between breaths. "What on earth should I be afraid of?" I said, "Men," but she scoffed so I was half ashamed, and went on to defend the suggestion. "Not exactly men *per se*—but the excitement roused in them by the sight of all that tall, white body moving up and down." Daphne apparently didn't think this worth answering. "Eh, that—that happens every day—" So I suggested, "And of getting a *cold*."

This word caused her to stop bending and breathing.

"You know I can't stand that word, Joyce. I never have colds." She looked angry, her face flushed bright pink. "That's the trouble with you and Toni. That's what keeps you running to doctors. Those words you use. Compulsion . . . homosexuality . . . heterosexuality . . . impotence . . . frigidity . . . and colds."

"Really, Daphne? You honestly believe it's as simple as that?"

"Of course it is. These doctors have been giving you the wrong words. Negative words that take you back to the past instead of pushing you forward. All you need to do is to change those words and you'll change the condition. Words have a life and power of their own, you know."

"Words, huh? Well, maybe . . ." I reminded her she had words herself: metaphysics, nudism, vegetarianism.

"Those are good words. Oh, Joyce, you mean to say you don't understand the power of words? But I thought everybody . . . You mean to say you don't know each word has a vibration which instantly starts up a conditioning of its own?"

But the words were not all bad, I allowed. Toni, for instance, had a nice new set these days, bright enough to bring on a condition of blinding sunlight. The mention of Toni, as it often had before, ended the discussion.

"Don't mention her words to me. And that voice! And those clothes she wears. Have you ever seen her brassieres? They make her breasts look absolutely ridiculous. No man in this world believes anybody's breasts stick way up in their faces like that girl tries to pretend. And those girdles! They're pressing on her nerves—destroying her vital life force. If she keeps on wearing those things she'll go insane and have to be put away."

Although I seldom thought about it those days, I was involved in the relationship between the two girls. A tension, rising and falling, dependent upon the flood tide of circumstances in which each of them was involved. One night as I met Toni before dinner in the sober lull that comes over people after a season of expectation, when the path ahead looks gray and cold and the call to march sounds unreasonably loud, I saw it clearly, and heard it too, in the extra loud pained note in Toni's voice.

"That Daphne—she gives me the creeps. You can't tell what she's going to do next."

"Oh well, she'll soon be married. She's getting engaged to Sir Harry. In a few months there'll be a nice big social wedding—and after that they'll be living in Beekman Place."

Toni's mouth opened slightly. Her eyes were very steady and her breath came faster. "Jesus! Is she really?" I nodded. "Have you seen the ring?" I said, no, they hadn't bought it yet, and she thought that one over. She lit a cigarette and smoked a while before she spoke. "Oh well, whatever she does won't matter. But that Harry Morsby— he must be mad. Going for her is one thing. Any man might do that. Just to be seen with her—that kind of thing. But marrying her. Only a lost soul, somebody utterly desperate—why it's like a man lost in a snowstorm and he's dying and suddenly the snow feels warm—"

"I don't know if it's exactly like that. I see what you mean—but maybe they'll make a good team. He's got what she wants—a title and money—and she must have what he wants—and—"

"Yeah, royalty yet—that one," she cut in.

"Anyway, I kind of envy Daphne. She's feeling no pain and I am, or shall I say we are?"

In a minute the words burst from her. "Don't you understand? Of course she's feeling no pain. She can't feel anything. She's frozen up so tight and solid—I tell you the size of the glaciers inside that woman are frightening—"

"But she's getting what she wants. And soon there will be a little Daphne or a little Harry—and the picture will look very pretty."

"It won't matter, I tell you. She'll murder them just like she'll murder that dope Morsby. It won't be real warm living. It won't be life."

"I don't know, Toni. It looks like those glaciers operate pretty damned well for her. I agree with you she's cold as hell and can't love anybody—but right this minute that situation looks pretty good to me. I think she's lucky."

I was sorry I had said it. Toni was in a state, I could see that. Her lips were sucked up so tight, they had completely disappeared—only a suggestion of lipstick remained—and her eyes were staring off at something. Not at me, not exactly at anything, though they must have hit some point near the fireplace. And she was breathing heavily.

"Do you want a drink?"

She nodded. I felt she couldn't speak, whatever it was had stirred her that much, and went to get her a drink. When I came back upstairs, she was still staring off into space, and her mouth was still sucked in. I put the glass of whiskey near her and she reached for it and began sipping it. She drank the whole glass down in sips without saying a word. Then she spoke, still staring off somewhere.

"You're right," was what she said. But her voice was desolate and she spoke with an awful finality. "Those glaciers of Daphne's work for her—and whatever it is I have and whatever it is you have won't work. So we have to try and fix it. But Daphne doesn't have to fix anything. Daphne has no sense of guilt. She's above life—or beyond it or something. There's no way of telling. Can I have another drink?"

I started to hand her the bottle, then thought better of it—she needed to be taken care of at this point—and poured the drink for her.

"Oh it won't all be a bowl of cherries for Daphne, the way it looks now. There'll be a break somewhere. She'll crack sometime—but we won't be around to see it—that's the hell of it. . . ." She drank the whiskey and went on. "The doctors say—with these sexual athletes—the crack comes when they start getting old. Well anyway, what's it got to do with me? Plenty. I'm jealous of her, honey." Her voice cracked, and I saw she was crying. "I wish I was that way—but I'm not. I'm stuck with my goddamned fantasies."

I poured her another drink, and poured one for myself.

"Has anything happened between you and Ludwig?"

It must have been the wrong question, it made her cry more.

"When a man lives to be fifty," she sobbed, "and he's never loved anybody, he begins to s-s-s-s-tink."

She was about to explain when Daphne suddenly ran naked from her room and into the living room to recover a bracelet left inadvertently on my desk while telephoning."

"Did you see that?" Toni gasped, the minute Daphne disappeared.

"You mean Daphne's nude body?"

"What else?" I said I'd seen it, and had almost every day since the arrival of the happiness-through-nudism book. "Look, Joyce, I'm getting pretty upset about that going naked kick she's on. You're the one who has the apartment. You ought to tell her to quit that stuff or move out."

"But why—all of a sudden? After all, she's not doing us any harm, and if it helps her, I can't see any reason—"

"There are lots of reasons. I'm sick of it. Always having to close the blinds because of that goddamned exhibitionist."

"But she has got a good figure," I said, teasing.

"So what! She's doing it for a motive—don't you get that? She hates men. She's a castrater of the worst kind. A man-eating female. Don't believe she's doing it for health reasons. Her deep unconscious motive is something entirely different. But listen, Joyce, I'm telling you right now—if she starts going naked when Ludwig's here there's going to be trouble."

"I don't think she will."

"Oh, you don't, huh? Well last night I heard her walking around in her bare feet and I knew she was at it again, so I wouldn't bring him upstairs. We wanted to have a cocktail up here in front of the fire—but with that hanging around—I got him out fast. You've got to tell her to stop it."

By the way Toni was hollering, I knew she had recovered from her recent sorrow. I said I would, but we ought to have a better reason.

"I don't have to think of any reason. I don't like seeing her naked all the time myself. You just tell her I'm sick of having her ass in my coffee."

As the weeks went by I noticed a change in Daphne. I thought at first I must be imagining it—there couldn't be any change in Daphne. It was a subtle, almost indefinable business, something so elusive as to be allocated almost to the temperature of the personality. Her eyes, those beautiful hazel eyes that stared out with that wonderful emptiness, possibly because of the frown now continuously registered above them, looked actually questioning, almost worried. And she was rouging her lips and running the comb through her long hair every five minutes or so. The nude exercises had stopped suddenly. Yes, something was happening or had happened, and Daphne the invulnerable was showing a dent in her armor, no matter how slight.

She was as popular as ever. Packages in her name were continuously arriving at the place. The long-stemmed-rose man continued to send her fresh flowers every Monday. The phone rang just as often for her and devoted swains waited for the beauty to come out of the bath or to awaken from slumber. The same number of eager male faces gravitated to the duplex of an evening, awaiting her pleasure. She was even being considered for the lead in a new play, and added to her list of admirers were now the producer, the director and two actors—a fact which seemed to rouse deeply negative impulses in Toni. "Nothing will happen," was her dire comment. "Oh, of course they're all frantic for Daphne. After all, that one—five foot eight and gorgeous in the right lights and nothing inside her—well, nothing anybody can understand. But that script *Small Victory* is from hunger and nothing will happen."

"But something seems to have happened to her."

"Umhmm. Sure. Sir Harry is going back to England—I guess he's gone already. Looks like she's going to have to get along without the diplomatic background. That's tough, a girl loses her sponsor, and she's scared."

Toni had read it in one of the columns, adding that his wife, from whom Daphne had been expecting him to be divorced, was instead coming to the States for a visit. This was all news to me. The last I'd seen of Sir Harry was the night he'd brought along a Texas friend of his to meet Daphne, one Thomas Royston Richards III, a man with deep lines in his face, a certain constant rather gruesome grin, as if he were smiling over the taste of a fresh lemon, and a slow Southern drawl, who seemed to have taken a violent shine to Daphne, having been in constant attendance upon her ever since.

"I don't think Daphne's likely to become the next Lady Morsby," was Toni's conclusion. "That's why she's talking different these days, or hadn't you noticed?"

I had noticed, the one time I'd seen Daphne to talk to—she seemed to have elaborately forgotten Sir Harry, which was something like forgetting her own name. However, since by this time we were about as familiar with the Morsby's being third holder of the Baronetcy created in 1716, his diplomatic posts in Rome, Beirut and Madrid and his old family home on an island in the Thames at Cookham in Berkshire as we were with the super's arthritis, it was fun hearing something new. Now Daphne was talking about Mr. Thomas Royston Richards III, the veteran oil wizard who since the advent of Daphne had broken out in a rash of poetry and who conveniently owned half the state of Texas. She continued to see her other admirers while Richards remained in New York, dancing attendance on her with great patience and fortitude, even though she was often accompanied by other men—actors, an occasional director, an embassy secretary or some other male friend. Tom Richards included Toni and me in his generosity, was constantly sending house gifts of liquor or plants for the yard, asking in return only that we indulge his odd pleasure in lurking on the phone, asking questions about Daphne— her whereabouts, her company, what she wore and where she was going. Toni and I were both at a loss for what to say, this was a new quirk in a man, but Daphne shrugged her beautiful shoulders at the entire matter. "Just tell him the truth."

And obviously Sir Harry had not lost interest in his protégé. There were cablegrams and transatlantic telephone calls, packages and special delivery letters. All *sotto voce,* Daphne opened the packages in her room, no longer displaying their contents as she had in the past, and the cablegrams, which ordinarily she left around— Toni insisted she wanted them read—were now being torn into small pieces. "That's Sir Harry she's tearing up," explained Toni. "She had other plans for destroying that man—but he pulled out. Nothing left but cablegrams—when she wanted his cables."

Daphne continued to see Richards for whom the Lone Star State grew lonelier. She continued to see her other friends while he continued escorting her around—sometimes singly but just as often in groups with other men friends. Sir Harry continued with the cablegrams and the transatlantic calls. Daphne's frown deepened over her eyes and Toni's interpretations broadened.

"That oil man is a weirdie, I don't know yet what his kick is and

frankly I hope I never find out. Never quite dug that old Harry either
—but I can tell you it's more than his family home that's on an
island. I mean he's on an island himself."

One day Sir Harry was back in New York. He had been to
London as he had done before, this time we heard some tragic facts
delivered in his crisp British voice, but Daphne was still his darling,
and if he suffered from her shameless switch to the oil man during his
absence he didn't reveal it. He was either waiting on the phone or appearing in the apartment just as often as ever. Sometimes he and
Richards would arrive together and go out to dinner, the theater or
on motor trips with Daphne, apparently a happy threesome. "I don't
get it," said Toni. "I just don't get it." She claimed she'd seen Tom
Richards reconnoitering outside the apartment on nights when Daphne
had engagements with other men.

There were other complications. A Siamese kitten suddenly made its
appearance in the place, a gift to Daphne from Richards, that spent
its waking hours running the length of the apartment and howling continuously. The wailing meow was irritating, but a live animal seemed
somehow better than the alarming stuffed fauna the Texan kept
sending—ranging all the way from a set of tiny ladybugs to a six-foot
rabbit, a life-size bison which Daphne said cost the nature lover five
hundred dollars, a zebra, a tiger and a lion, bargains at two ninety-
five. "My God, how that man can waste money," wailed Toni who
had almost a horror of the stuffed animals. "It means she's going to
move out soon—and that's something. If she doesn't, we'll have
to get out ourselves. But it's so goofy, Joyce—stuffed animals, who
needs it? That Tom Richards has got something awful about him.
I know he hangs around outside the apartment—and I tell you it
gives me the creeps."

I didn't know what to think. Tom was extraordinarily good-natured, a mite childish for his age and given to fits of uncontrollable
laughter, but his frank delight in Daphne and the situation he was
enjoying with her was pleasant to see. "All right, Miss Smartypants,"
cautioned Toni, "you wait and see. Listen, a man spends a thousand
dollars for stuffed animals and hangs around peeping at his sweetheart—a situation like this, it's *trefa*."

Cheetah, Daphne's red-and-white cat, had to be kept out and fed
behind locked doors for fear that, in his jealous fury at the new

2 0 3

Siamese, he'd go for its throat. Daphne had lost all interest in poor Cheetah, and if Toni or I hadn't fed the animal he would have gone without food. "I had no idea you were so merciless," I said to her. "I pity any child you'd have."

She gave me a puzzled look. "You think I'd make a bad mother?"

"Absolutely terrible. The worst."

To my surprise the frown appeared as she seemed to be thinking it over. "I think I would, too," she said after a few minutes.

"Breaking the heart of an animal—that's pretty revolting."

She gave me one of her empty looks. "I just don't care about it any more—if I ever did. I don't know. . . . You wouldn't understand if I told you."

"Tell me anyway."

But she sounded angry when she spoke. "Oh, haven't you ever looked in yourself for something—that just wasn't there? Aw, you wouldn't know. You just don't know anything about it." She snapped her bag, grabbed her gloves and hurried out before I could think of anything to say. Besides, the telephone was ringing. . . .

The lovely healthy animal vitality Cheetah had waned fast. He ate less, was less affectionate, and finally, it was obivous to us all some spark had gone out of him, never to return. "If either of you knows anybody who wants a cat—for goodness sake let me know," Daphne pleaded. We didn't, and one day she announced a butcher down the street who adored her had promised to take the cat and we were all relieved. But I can still remember passing that butcher shop of a Sunday afternoon and seeing Cheetah sitting there staring out the window with that lifeless look in his eyes. He just wasn't the same cat I had known.

One freezing, cold afternoon in February I left the office to keep an appointment for cocktails with Liza. As I came into the Little Bar at the Ritz—it was nearly six and the place was filling up—I saw Liza was nowhere among the many faces and, knowing her to be always late, was just about to settle in the nearest empty seat when I saw Daphne coming hastily through the crowd.

"Are you blind?" she screamed successfully over the raucous medley of voices. "We've been signaling you like mad."

"Who's we?"

"Tom and I. Look!"

I glanced down at the back of her outstretched left hand and saw a square-cut green stone surrounded by many small sparkling diamonds and knew at once I was looking at Tom Richards' engagement ring. She didn't seem especially excited until, bustling me to the table, I caught the thrill in her voice over the words . . . "had it appraised" and then "insured" and then, almost lost in the sudden peal of laughter from a table we were passing, I heard the words "fifty thousand dollars." Tom appeared more eager and normal as the male of the species celebrating the happy occasion, and when Daphne announced in her floating voice, "I showed her the ring!" he chuckled as if he was genuinely pleased.

"Ah yes, that. Nothing like a bit of beryl to cheer a girl in the midst of a cold winter. Preservative against epilepsy, good for the eyesight, and all that. How about a drink for you, Joyce—what would you like?"

As we drank together and I wished them the best of all good things, I couldn't help noticing how they seemed more like two partners about to consummate a successful business coup than people about to be married—but then I had never quite understood Daphne, she had always been an enigma to me, and on this happy occasion the mystery appeared only to deepen. So much so, in fact, that as they talked on about what they would do and where they would go after the war, never once touching hands or locking eyes, I began to feel unemotional about the matter myself and found myself answering questions and giving advice about theatrical investments, dressmakers, and the proper number of guests and shaded menus for an engagement party during rationing. This sentience increased later when, after the visit with Liza, I joined Daphne in the taxi Tom had found for us, and listening to her talking about how busy she was going to be in the coming weeks, I felt embarrassed at the questions I wanted to ask, "Are you happy? Do you love him?" as if I had been naïve and slightly ridiculous to entertain such notions, and went swimming right along with her on the bright upper surface of things.

I noticed something else: there was a slight discomfort between us, at least I began to feel uncomfortable. With Daphne talking about nothing but herself—she always did, of course, but now it was somehow more serious than ever before—I felt myself being forced to watch and listen *against my will*. As she went on, "I'm going for a fitting tomorrow—you'll have to go with me, Joyce—it's at five o'clock now, don't forget—I can't trust myself with that Madam Laurents, she's too extreme—and after that Tom will pick us up," I felt more tired and remote from her by the minute. I was glad to get home and, I hoped, out of her tentacles, but she followed me into my bedroom and, all unaware of any mood of mine and its attendant desire for a minute of privacy, started up again. It was not until some time later, after I'd listened to minute descriptions of friends of Tom's I'd never met, including digestive tracts and financial statements, that toward the end there was a sudden flash of communication between us.

"Now you'll learn a lesson, I hope, Joyce," she was saying. "You see, if you'd done what I suggested in the first place—gotten out of here and found a new place—you might have met more of Tom's friends or Sir Harry's, and maybe something like this would be happening to you."

"Maybe it would," I said.

"And then all your troubles would be over. You'd have what you want most."

"But that's not what I want most."

"Oh no?" She was laughing now. "What else—or who are you kidding?"

"It's peace I'm after," I blurted out, and felt immediately foolish revealing this to her, and yet strangely relieved: for once that day she was looking at me. At the same time, I realized I had never actually said anything to her before, anything I meant apart from the spoken words, that is, and having gone this far I couldn't retract, but decided to finish up as quickly as possible. "It's more of an aphrodisiac to me than the Hope diamond."

She was still watching me, a minute or more was an incredible length of time for Daphne to give her attention to anything outside of herself, and shaking her head.

"I don't get you, Joyce." This time the British accent was gone from her voice, and with it the sense of the ghost speaking through her. "I tell you, I look at you and it's like looking at a wall. I just can't see through you."

"I'm not exactly mysterious. You're after something like that, aren't you? And if not, why all these vegetarian books and peace through nudism and breathe your way to happiness?"

"That was to please Sir Harry. I've had to keep ahead of him so he'd stay fascinated. With Tom, it's different. Oh I believe in it, of course—but only in a way—not in the way you mean. I'm having too much fun. That way *you* mean is just not in the books—and anyway it's not for while you're young like we are. It's for old people—people who are through and can't get anything else. And anyway, I don't believe you. Peace. You may believe it yourself—but that's not what you're really after. That's not what anybody's really after. It's a second-best—sour grapes maybe—because they know they can't have what they really want. Well I'm getting what I want, see, and that old peace can wait. And as for you, if you'd just get out of this place—and away from Toni and people like that—you'd get what you wanted, too. Don't you know—you've got everything, you goddamned fool!"

I thought that over. It was the most generous thing she'd ever said.

"Thanks, dear. But you see, without this peace, I can't know anything very much." She was shaking her head again. "But I see you don't believe me, isn't that right? You think I'm lying, putting up a sour-grapes front. Because I'm not marrying a millionaire and getting an emerald to boot, I'm pretending it's not what I want. You stopped believing me the minute I mentioned the Hope diamond—and said I'd rather have peace than have that."

"I don't know," she said, and she did look a bit confused. "All I know is, I'd believe it a helluva lot sooner from somebody that had the Hope diamond."

I said, *"Touché!"* We laughed, and the conversation was finished.

Yes, Daphne was a mystery to me. I watched her with unwilling interest, hypnotized by the clear white energy. And I was apparently a mystery to her, a more understandable matter, as the battle I was waging was not often acted out in the open. And during the days following her engagement—what with her busy hours with fitters, friends and rejectees—the enigma of Daphne only deepened.

"Why, oh why, is she seeing all the men she used to date?" I asked Toni.

"Why do you think?" Toni threw back at me.

"I don't know. She doesn't need to hold on to most of these characters—they're not in her groove any more. But she's going to such trouble about them. Last night, for instance, she spent an hour dressing—and wearing one of her new outfits, too."

"Which one?" Toni snapped.

"The green satin suit from Bergdorf's. She looked magnificent—and who do you think she was seeing?"

"All right, Mr. Bones—who was it—I mean, which creep?"

"Red!"

"And weren't you furious?"

"Not exactly. I was mildly annoyed—but I've known she was seeing Red for some time, she told me. Besides, I wasn't seeing him any more when she started up with him. You remember, he was on that getting-even-with-women kick at the time."

"Yeah, all right, so I remember. What happened? So she saw Red and then what!"

"I don't know, honey. Tonight she's getting all dressed up like Mrs. Astor's horse to see Peter—he's that radio director she used to date."

"What do you mean—used to date? She's been seeing him straight through the Sir Harry regime. I tell you, Joyce, you don't know the facts of life. That Daphne, she's a man-eater. These glaciers, they like to crack open men's heads. Think they're pumpkins or something. Well, I've got to go. Tell you more later—"

I didn't get it. I did notice Daphne looked happier when she was seeing the men to whom she was apparently saying good-by than when she was in the company of Tom, her betrothed. I saw her eyes sparkling as she went out to her dates, and knew that somehow, somewhere, Daphne was getting something she needed, but I didn't understand what it was or why she needed it.

CHAPTER TWENTY-FOUR

. . . . . .

ONE BRIGHT SPRING MORNING I AWAKENED EARLY, FRESH FROM THE memory of a dream. I sat on the edge of the bed and stretched, blinking in the sunlight, as the recent sights and sounds and smells of the dream came back to mind, taking time out to remember so I could repeat it to Dr. Vespers when I saw him that day. This one was something new, I sensed that much, but just how new and remarkable I didn't find out until some hours later when I finally sat opposite him during my lunch hour, listening to the familiar crunch-crunch of the tuna fish on toast.

"It was like a movie—in Technicolor—complete with sound effects and *smells*. When I woke up I felt happy and refreshed, it didn't seem too different from the real day there in the yard."

"What happened in the dream?" he asked, between crunches.

"First I was walking down a patch of country lane I guess—anyway there was grass everywhere. The grass felt nice and velvety and there was a brightness and warmth around—not exactly fulfilled—it had the feeling of trees overhead keeping the sun out—but I felt maybe it was going to be very warm *soon*. That was all there was in the first part of the dream, except, oh, yes—I had a slight feeling of apprehension about not knowing where the path would end."

"But that isn't all there was to the dream, is it?"

"No. First act. In the second part of the dream I was in the country somewhere, only this time it was warm and bright, with lots of green grass and trees, blue sky and golden sunlight. I saw a tall man in a blue shirt with his sleeves rolled up standing on top of a hill. Looked like he was threshing wheat. I could hear the threshing sound and the idea was I was to get up there and join him because he was waiting for me to complete the task. I walked on up through the mounds of grass or wheat, and next thing I was there on top of the hill with the man, he must have been sunburned because he felt warm and full of the sun. I don't know just how we got together on the threshing machine, that part isn't clear, but next thing we were riding it across the wheat fields in order to thresh the wheat I guess. We went faster and faster through the wheat or whatever it was, and the smell kept getting stronger—it was almost intoxicating. I could hear other sounds—like horses stamping in their stalls and neighing and people calling to each other across distances, halloa, something like that, a cheerful sound. And we kept going faster and faster, I wondered if it was safe, the machine was going up in the air and the wheat was falling behind us making a kind of a slushy sound and smelling stronger and stronger. This isn't safe at all, I thought, I should never have gotten on this damned machine, but the man had a tight hold on me, and we were climbing—I don't know whether it was up to the top of some mountain or off into space—I could still hear the wheat falling as we went—"

I noticed he had stopped eating his tuna-fish sandwich.

"Go on, child, go on." He was leaning forward. "I think it's the dream I've been waiting for."

"The next part, I felt myself beginning to fall, and feeling, I should never have done this, now God knows what will happen. I was falling down some kind of a runway, sort of bouncing as I went, it was like bouncing down a high ski jump and I kept feeling something warm accumulating underneath me. I was coming down faster and faster, I was going to land somewhere, but somehow it didn't hurt and I wasn't afraid, and then just as I started hitting bottom, I could feel a great deal of this warm stuff under me. At the same time I heard voices calling—it seemed like people were watching, maybe from a nearby hill top, and I heard the horses neighing very loud. And then, as I collapsed into all this warm stuff, I could hear the voices calling, and it sounded like applause. What's the matter?"

Dr. Vespers was chuckling. He had completely forgotten his tuna.

"What's so funny?"

"Bravo! Can't you see something special about that dream?"

"Well, yes—in a way. But I can't see why you're so delighted about it. It was a nice enough dream, but it's only a dream."

He chuckled. "Only a dream? Did you ever read Schniztler? Remember his novella where the husband and wife dream of their lovers? And when the husband tells the wife about his dream of the beautiful nymph bathing naked—she resembles the girl in the villa next to theirs—the wife realizes she has lost him, because she knows nothing is *only a dream*. Read it sometime." Then, "Don't you know you have had a decisive dream?" I said no, I didn't. "Don't you see what your unconscious is saying in that dream? Come on now."

"I can see it's a very sexual dream. The threshing of the wheat and the feel of the warm stuff and the horses neighing and the smells."

"And don't you remember when you woke up you said the world outside the window didn't look too different from the dream?"

"Yes, I remember. But it was a bright day after all. I can't see anything so special about that."

"It means the unconscious has caught up with the conscious— even the colors are alike. The dreamer feels the same about the two worlds—why, because a union has been made."

To my amazement he was stretching his hand across the desk.

"Let me congratulate you, child. You're cured."

"What!" I pressed his hand out of politeness. He leaned back, smiling. "You mean my analysis is finished?"

"It would be dishonest for me to hold you—after this dream."

I couldn't quite believe this.

"Patients are always afraid of happiness," he explained. "The bright light always hurts the eyes—after the dark."

I said yes, I could see that. "But I still haven't resolved my problems. I'm still not living. I'm still apprehensive. I still haven't had—"

"An orgasm? Don't tell me—you don't know—you had a marvelous orgasm—in your dream? It represents the dictum straight from the unconscious—permission for full sexual fulfillment. The horses neighing—the ride up and then the soft fall down—the warm man with the threshing machine. I wish I were young like you, with life ahead of me."

"But, Dr. Vespers, I was alone in bed."

"But you weren't alone in your dream. You know a woman can be in bed with her lover and both can still be alone. You weren't alone. What about the waiting man? Can't you see what happened—the hill you rode together—the thrill of getting to the top—the victorious ride down—the applause coming from the other side? Were you alone there?"

"No, not there, but that was in a dream—something that happened in my sleep—or as you say, in my unconscious mind—"

"There's no other place where psychic health can come from. You were together with a man on the deepest level of your being—where your destiny is decided. I wish half my women patients were where you are in life."

"You mean I'm well?" He nodded, smiling. "Actually *cured?*"

"Yes, child." The toasted tuna-fish sandwich was cold on the plate—the poor man hadn't eaten his lunch—but he was smiling. It was time to go. "Don't be afraid of happiness. I know it's new to you. Not being afraid of love and men is a whole new cycle—and no wonder—after your experiences. I'll tell you the truth, you got well much faster than I expected . . ."

We were walking to the door together. It was all slightly unbelievable, like something happening in a movie.

". . . whole new cycle. You're meeting new people all the time. The right man will come along and when he does—don't be afraid. Think back to the dream. You'll land on safe, warm ground. You can always come back here if you want to—just call me any time. But meantime don't stay in the sick room. Go out and live."

Now I was walking out in the street. Walking slowly at first—thinking, or trying to think.

Cured, I thought. Was it possible? Yes, of course it was possible—but true—was it true? You heard what the man said. "People are always afraid when they get well. They want to go back to the sick room. They don't like the brightness after the dark."

It sounded reasonable. "You won't feel anything for a while," Dr. Vespers said. "You won't feel the rush of new health immediately. It takes time—months, sometimes longer. The patient resists, draws back, tries to wait and hide."

Hearing myself pronounced *cured* was an anticlimax, no doubt of that. But Dr. Vespers had treated hundreds of people. He ought to know. And my cure was one of the best, he'd said, meaning, I suppose, the most complete. But why didn't I feel joyous about it? Why wasn't I eager for the new life?

I turned the corner at Madison Avenue and walked on, still trying to reason. I tried to imagine living without anxieties and handicaps but I couldn't. As I came near the office I remembered I hadn't eaten my lunch, I still wasn't hungry but seeing a familiar luncheonette I went in and ordered corned beef and coffee.

As I drank the coffee slowly I remembered the dream. The warm, blue-shirted man with the threshing machine—where are you now, and what good are you to me? A black thought darted through my head like a poisonous snake. Suppose the dream turned out to be a phony. Oh no, that couldn't be. Patients are always afraid of happiness, he said. *You're cured.* But just suppose I wasn't cured . . . then that would mean . . . another year and four thousand dollars for—come on, say it—for an orgasm in a dream!

But I *was* cured. He'd said so. And now it had to be true. This was just me, slow to react, I decided, as I hurried back to the office, wondering why it still felt the same down here: slightly cold and damp, as if I were still in the frog pond.

CHAPTER TWENTY-FIVE

. . . . . .

IT IS UNCOMFORTABLE IN THE FROG POND, BUT SELDOM IS IT UNENDurable. The frogs squirm, they croak and groan, but only a few die of their doom. I was not one of these. Six months after my Technicolor "cure," there I was croaking away with the best of them.

New weather, international news, new people, new plans. I found time to work in the Presidential campaign—writing speeches and releases, organizing groups, planning rallies. The hotel headquarters was a lively place, filled with alert friendly people who had a mission to accomplish. The atmosphere was charged, I was part of something alive—a change after the phony glamour back at the office. Everything we did at campaign headquarters had to come off quickly, so we saw the events actually taking place before our eyes shortly after they came into our minds, which is a satisfaction in itself similar to baking a cake and seeing it being eaten. Quickened now with the urgency in the air, I found myself enjoying the daylight hours and wishing they would last longer.

I met a good many new people, the way anyone working in a political campaign is bound to, and among these was a lawyer named George, who for some reason everyone called Hitch. George wasn't particularly attractive: indeed his sleepy dark eyes with those heavy lashes, combined with a certain high cackling laugh he had, made him seem almost feminine. He was quiet, too quiet in fact—except for his nickname he might easily have melted into the atmosphere like the dozens of other hangers-on. Hitch had no special duties to perform but he knew the bosses and would drop in for meetings, sometimes making suggestions but often saying nothing at all, and he was always present at the parties. No one seemed overly fond of him. "You always meet that kind around a campaign," one of the girls said. "Something to move the window shades up and down," somebody else replied. Some hinted he had a darker side, was unpredictable, and said they'd heard stories, but no one seemed quite sure and the subject was quickly dropped.

For some obscure reason I noticed that Hitch had an exhilarating effect on me. He was not especially witty, he didn't talk well, yet in the few dates I had had with him, spaced across the weeks, I noticed that while in his company I felt gay and excited. I thought about this and was utterly unable to explain Hitch's appeal, yet appeal he had. Before I knew it I was waiting for his calls and wondering how he felt about me. I began to splurge on clothes—bought new hats and dresses, and saved them to wear with him. Hitch was attracted to me, I could see that, but certainly not devoted. I would often wait a week or more for his call, and then find myself dressing in a state of frantic expectation, rushing to meet him and wondering if I was overdressed, thus revealing the tremendous interest I was trying to conceal.

After a number of these evenings with Hitch—sometimes we were in groups, sometimes alone—I realized I was in love with this odd man. So far he had made no effort to touch me, and while at first I had found this soothing and delightful, now I was becoming eager with desire, almost to the point of torture. Here was one man who was a gentleman, I told Toni and Daphne—who took his time, understood women and was at the same time interesting.

"He's probably impotent," Toni offered.

"Or a fairy," Daphne suggested.

"You know there are plenty of fairies who don't know they're fairies and keep pretending—just like there are impotent men who think they are potent and it's all the woman's fault," Toni explained.

"New York men who take you out all that time and don't lurch —there's sure as hell something the matter, ducky," said Daphne. "He might be a pervert."

"Or a murderer." Toni smiled at the idea. "When are we going to meet this Dreamboat?"

I could hardly wait until I could arrange to bring Hitch home and show him off, but what with his sudden calls at the last minute, and Toni and Daphne having a busy time of it in the evenings, it was some time before this was finally arranged. One night, Toni was having some "names," and when Hitch heard who they were he said he would be glad to come. All dates with Hitch were frustrating, and this was no exception. During the party, he paid little attention to me. I noticed him making his way around among the important guests, but I didn't mind. Not being an important lawyer himself, I assumed he thought knowing important people would gave him additional importance. Whatever his reasons, he was there, I had some need of him, and I knew I would be alone with him afterwards.

It was quite late before we left the party to go out for dinner, and during the confusion of getting away I hadn't had a chance to find out what impression Hitch had made on the girls. As soon as we had settled in a restaurant and ordered dinner, I was just about to call home and ask, but Hitch got the idea of telephoning first, he often telephoned, and I waited patiently for his return. A short time later I called and Daphne answered.

"What's the matter—have you two got telephonitis?" What did she mean, I asked, sensing already what she was about to say. "Your Dreamboat just called me for a date Saturday."

"Are you going?"

"Hell, no. What would anybody in her right mind want with that one? He asked me not to tell you, but I didn't promise."

Toni came in on the upstairs extension. "I'd taper off on that guy, honey. There's something queer about him. I wouldn't like to run into him on a dark night."

"You mean you didn't even like his looks?"

"Some people might, I guess—the kind that like those dead green orchids."

Somehow I knew they were right but it didn't matter in the least. My Hitch was odd in more ways than one. He lived alone, had been married and was now separated or divorced, and up until his phoning Daphne he had seemed rather to avoid women. I felt miserable about this Daphne business—chided him about it too, feeling more than ever there was something queer and sneaky about him.

"What do you care?" he asked, smiling. "That couldn't affect us. Anyway I'm a lawyer and she knows some pretty important people."

The people he had met were friends of Toni's, I explained— Daphne had met them for the first time.

2 1 6

"Why didn't you tell me?" He chuckled. "I wouldn't have wasted the call."

There was more to it than that, I knew. He was attracted to Daphne. In fact, as he spoke, some piece of his true self swam toward me from those dark waters. He wants a woman who can't feel, because he can't feel—anything but hate. But the bright piece of truth faded quickly in the fog of longing.

Three weeks went by without a call from Hitch. As the spell of rejection caused by his interest in Daphne slowly disappeared, I began enumerating the various important people I knew to whom I might introduce him, thinking that if he didn't call soon I would have an excuse for calling him. Then, in his absence, the excitement abated. I began to forget him, but so did the edge go off living. I felt dull, cold, sad. Hitch, that queer, sneaky, sleepy-looking man whom no one else seemed to want, he opened a secret door in me, and now that he was gone it had banged to in my face.

Meantime I had met another man. Roger. A thoroughly nice human being, also a corporation lawyer, but successful, intelligent and well liked. I enjoyed the time I spent in his company. He was much more attractive than Hitch—besides being alert, considerate and good-natured—and I could see that he was genuinely fond of me. Why couldn't I like him, I wondered, as I now saw clearly Hitch was a cheap climber, with no particular character or intelligence. What was there about him that thrilled me? Why this longing? What was inside that locked room that only he could enter?

I reasoned with myself. It was certainly foolish, this feeling for Hitch, but not exactly desperate. I had already begun to forget him. And now if Roger, the good, continued to pursue, I would yield and all might yet be well. And thinking over these matters, I felt encouraged and even eager.

And then one night Hitch called. And there I was, dressing to meet him in a frenzy of expectation, wondering how I looked, feeling insecure and full of queer hot and cold sensations. Feeling happy and sad, and slightly afraid. I had bought a new dress and now I was afraid to wear it, thinking it might reveal too much of what I felt.

This was the night it happened. I was alone with him in his apartment. He was standing behind the bar pouring drinks, and I was sitting on a stool watching him.

"Don't look so eager!" he suddenly shouted. The words jarred me, but I said nothing. He was leaning forward across the bar, staring me in the eye. Things were going wrong: this wasn't at all the conversational tone I had anticipated. "You'll get it," he went on, still in the rough jarring voice, as he went back to his mixing, "but in *my* time—in my damned good time."

"Get what?" I waited, wondering miserably what he had meant by the words. Could he possibly mean making love? Could any man alive refer to the act of love with such absolute hate?

"You know what." He pushed a drink toward me. "Don't give me that innocence stuff."

He was frowning angrily as he came around to the front of the bar and stood staring down at me.

"I spotted you the first time I saw you." He was speaking very coldly. "I saw it in your eyes—and in every move you've made ever since. I know what you want. You're my kind and I'm your kind."

He took a rough, painful grip on my shoulder—just as I caught the fury in his eyes and lost all desire in the sudden sense of fear and foreboding. I moved back on my chair and then jumped forward, a nervous reaction to the sound I heard. The telephone was ringing.

"I'd better go answer," I said quickly, trying to shake loose from his grip.

"Why—did you tell somebody you were coming here?"

"Yes," I lied instinctively.

"Yeah? Pretty smart, huh? Well, baby, it's too late now."

Before I could make another move he started slapping me in the face. He slapped so hard and so fast his face was quickly blurred into one great red surface in which a big star came and went. I felt myself wavering on the stool. I reached out frantically to hold on to the bar but I must have missed it for the next thing I knew I had fallen dizzily off the stool and landed in a heap on the floor. In one swift movement of a charging animal he was beside me, beating me with his fists. I saw his face now through dazed eyes, the face of a man who vaguely resembled the Hitch I had known but was more like the head of some crazed animal, particularly the open

2 1 8

mouth showing teeth and gums in a wild gruesome snarl, and I screamed in terror.

"Hitch, for God's sake, stop! What's the matter with you?"

But he kept on hitting me until I burst into tears.

Something must have happened then. The blows stopped. I looked up and saw him staring at his hands, wet from my crying, and then getting slowly to his feet. The telephone kept ringing as he stood there looking from his hands to me and back again.

"What are you crying for—damn you!" he muttered crazily. There was a difference in his voice now: he wasn't quite as sure of himself, he was bellowing, trying to get back the old wild feeling that had been interrupted. "What's the matter with you? You've been waiting around for it long enough. You knew what it would be. You wanted it. *What did you have to go and cry for?"*

This was my chance. I got to my feet and started for the door. He recovered enough to block my way. I had to think quickly, it was now or never. Tears bothered him, that was all I had to go on —that and some fear he felt of the unknown person on the other end of the phone.

"Toni and Daphne both know where I am," I blurted out between sobs. "They didn't want me to come here. They both suspect you—"

"Yeah? Of what?"

"Of being what you are." His mouth fell open. I knew I had registered with that one. "They are both coming up here—if they haven't heard from me—that was the way we planned. That was them calling on the phone. They must be in the neighborhood. They won't be coming alone. If you don't let me go right now, you'll be disbarred—when you get out of jail, that is—"

He was confused now. He kept drying his hands.

"Jesus, this is all going crazy. You mean—it was something else you wanted? The regular thing? Why, you—" The snarl was back on his face, that awful crazy open-mouthed snarl. But he stopped. "Get out of here—if you know what's good for you. You'd better do it quick, kid!"

I grabbed wildly for my bag and coat which I'd left on the bar, cowering as I passed him, and ran through the door and down the hall.

I got through that one alive somehow. I knew it was all over as I

219

looked at the nice empty protective elevator. But the next time—
the next—and there would be a next—*what about that?*

Something in my eyes. He had seen *it* in my eyes, he said, and
in every move I made. I would like to have asked him, what had
he seen in my eyes? It wasn't *I*. Was it Devman—and the thing that
Devman wanted? To do me in—why, yes—maybe even to see me
murdered—*was that it?*

But this was no time for asking questions.

During the coming weeks the truth folded over me like a shroud
as I saw my "cure" with Dr. Vespers for what it was: about as
phony as a three-dollar bill. Why, that whole damned business was
nothing but words! And as for his prophecy of love and health, after
this latest crisis it looked like a box of chocolates in a storm at sea.

And all this time I had been waiting for the cure to show up.
Waiting, waiting—everybody was waiting. Irene, she'd been "cured"
by Vespers, a married couple we knew, and a friend of theirs—they
were all waiting.

The words blacked out for me. The neon-lights wouldn't work
any more, short-circuited by the Hitch incident. I couldn't blame
Vespers, all he knew was those words, but, oh, how I hated them
those days. Three long years I'd been at it now, and three of these
witchmen. All this biting, gnawing, chewing, swallowing, masticating
and then spitting out my insides—for nothing. A Barmecide's Feast,
with nothing to eat but the names of the dishes. I remember quoting
Dobson's Ballad to old Vespers one gloomy afternoon on the phone.

> *Life,—'tis of thee they fable so.*
> *Thou bidd'st us eat, and still denied,*
> *Still fasting, from thy board we go:—*
> *"Where is thy feast, O Barmecide?"*

What happens now, I wondered. Now that all the pretty signs
are gone and I am alone with the devil. I tried to contact my unconscious, reaching for it as a mother calling a wayward child.
Devman, where are you—my son, my soul, my pigmy self? And
what will you do next?

Now I knew what he'd been doing in that dream about the wheat field and the man in the blue denim shirt. Making a fool out of me. I could almost see this other part of myself sitting on my shoulder listening while the kindly tuna-fish-eating doctor told me I was cured —laughing his head off. I felt bitter now, and genuinely alarmed. This last time Devman had moved more slowly, employing subtlety in his operation. A man of many faces, this, and among his masks, dear God, was the face of love. Ergo: the one with whom I had felt so safe, Hitch, the gentleman who didn't reach, the same was he of the snarling mouth and brutal hands.

I relived that night. It happened again and again in my mind, from the beginning up to the miracle of my escape, and each time I was convinced at the end that the game was lost. There was something sinister beyond compare behind this episode. I knew, and I didn't know—or rather I didn't dare know. Devman wanted me dead.

CHAPTER TWENTY-SIX

. . . .

IF YOU HAD CANCER, AND YOU KNEW YOU HAD CANCER, AND YOU HAD
paid three doctors to remove the cancer without having had it removed—what would you do? The chances are you would go to a
fourth doctor. You would not exactly rush to go under the knife
again, but you would go on seeking—shopping, listening, inquiring,
looking everywhere for the man of reputation and experience, the
great surgeon who had made a lifetime study of the problem.

Months passed before I heard of Dr. Portzweig through a paper
he had published in a psychiatric journal, explaining a new technique
he had developed founded on an entirely new concept. The theory
sounded complicated; I couldn't understand most of it, but a few
of the learned man's phrases, leaping from the mouths of excited
converts, instantly caught my attention, and one in particular stopped
me cold. *The wish to be denied.* I listened, and it was exactly as if
I had heard my name being called.

The next day I got hold of the journal and read Dr. Portzweig's
paper which he had delivered in an address to a group of psychiatrists. Before I was halfway through the paper I knew I had had
the right hunch for once. At last I had stumbled into the hall of
Science. Here was a man who had indeed come upon a discovery,
a whole new concept. For some reason the great man seemed fascinated by writers and had applied his new technique to many of
the great European authors who had come to him ready for suicide,
he said, and gone away cured. Although this was the least important part of my life at this time—so many other horrors needed first
attention—I felt glad I was a writer if that was the ticket of entry
to the great scientist. I devoured his words to the end of the paper.

Yes, this was it, all right. I could see clearly and sense intuitively that here was the doorway to hope. This man could cure me if he would—that is, if I could somehow manage to get to him and inveigle him to take me as his patient. He would be busy, of course —perhaps inaccessible. Maybe he didn't see people for treatment any more, was too busy with his research. Or again, if he did see people, his fee might be prohibitive.

And yet there was his name, address and telephone number— strategically placed just beneath the last printed line of his paper, and now staring invitingly up at me. What was there to stop my calling him up and asking his secretary whether or not it was possible to make an appointment? I went straight to the phone.

A heavily accented male voice said, "Halloa." I wanted to speak to Dr. Portzweig, I explained.

"Ya ya, this is Dr. Portzweig. Who is this?"

I gave him my name, explained briefly that I'd read his article and wanted to make an appointment.

"Ya, so when do you want to come?"

"Could I come this afternoon?"

"Let me see. Ya, can you be here at three o'clock?"

I said I could.

The tide had turned at last. Great minds were at work on the invisible demons that plague men's souls; some of this had slowly seeped over into my corner and I had been quick to respond. I congratulated myself that the minute I had heard Dr. Portzweig's one-line description of the plague, *the wish to be denied,* all apathy and discouragement had instantly disappeared; further, that on reading his immortal statement in the scientific journal, I knew at once I was coming closer; and that now, standing in his doorway, awaiting the presence of the great man himself, I could actually feel the light coming my way at last, much as the cancer patient feels when he sees the X-ray machine being wheeled in, and my heart was gladdened.

A portly little man opened the door, nodded briefly, a bare jerk of the head, and showed me into his office. He got quickly into the problem. After ten minutes talking back and forth, I knew this was the most intellectually alert and mentally aggressive human being

I had met among the doctors. I was amazed at the accuracy of his questions, the way he pointed them expertly at the sore spots, nodded briefly, said Um-hum or Ya-ya, and went on to the next. Whenever he talked about writing the questions would come faster, his voice went up a peg, and a strange excitement seemed to quicken his entire being.

Whenever he talked about the "mechanism of creation" with all its attendant moods, spells of idleness, fears, elations, depressions, and especially the awful emptiness that comes after the glorious liquid has gone dry, his eyes would shine so brightly I wondered if, possibly, he might be having a fever. The vitality and enthusiasm of his inquiries were so contagious I found myself opening up nooks and crannies in my own life whose existence I myself had hardly suspected. The experience was so altogther exhilarating for me I wondered why he occasionally looked impatient, as if he couldn't bear to wait for me to give him the answers to his questions.

The day was dark and muggy, and as we sat opposite one another in the misty yellow fog of the drizzling afternoon, the shadows half-concealed his face, making his skin look soft and watery. His small mouth wriggling as he spouted out these remarkably wise clear words, his eyes shining bright as beads—the over-all effect of the face above his collar was that of an angry oyster. The gods had not been generous in their endowment of his person, nor indeed, for all the other great gifts, had the cursed fates been able to abate the fury in his breast. Sometimes, as he explained this or that point in his theory of the "mechanism of orality" in terms of what his patients had done or were doing, he spoke with a peculiar anger and impatience, as if these very acts were performed in a spirit of personal vengeance against him.

In spite of these obvious "personality defects" the great man had, it was impossible to listen to Dr. Portzweig expounding his theories without reacting with wonder and respect. Whenever creative people get "blocked," he said, they are all reacting to an injury suffered early in life, at the particular moment when as babies they first discovered that their mother's breast, the source of their food supply, was not attached to them but instead belonged to somebody else. If, after this first rude shock, the baby finds this person possessing the milk comes at his call, lets him have all he wants, and treats him

2 2 4

tenderly, then all may be forgiven in time, and the original wound will heal over. But if the mother-person does not come at call, keeps the infant waiting, lacks tenderness at feeding, removes the breast before the infant has had his fill, or commits any number of other acts, the baby gets the idea he is being denied, which may shape the rest of his life, leading to untold tragedy.

This, the bare premise, sounded reasonable and yet profound. I thought of my own longings, the sense of some early ecstasy long lost and never recovered, but never had I traced it to my mother's breast. Unfortunately, this was just the beginning or first layer of the trouble, the doctor explained. What happens to people who have suffered this early refusal is, they conceive of their mothers as "refusing monsters," and go through life projecting this image on all other people. Why do they behave in this perfectly crazy fashion? Because, and here's the switch, they want to be refused again and again ad infinitum.

"Always to remember up here we are talking about the hunconscious," Dr. Portzweig would explain. "Consciously a person may want success more than anything in the world. Men think they want to be millionaires—to have yachts and drive Cadillacs—but this is only make-believe. Psuedo-aggression. All the time in the hunconscious they want failure, they want to be back there with the refusing monster, the mother who turned them down cold in the first place."

The reason writers took to words was because the words came with a flow like milk, and this was their way of *owning,* so to speak, *the original breast.* When they became blocked, he said, that was because they were refusing to "give milk." He had saved many of the great writers of Europe by making them give instead of refuse— this milk which took the form of words, coming this time from themselves.

He lost no time in getting down to cases. "Ya ya, I should say you do need chychoanalysis." In spite of his accent, he was quite clear in his meanings. After I had told him some of my problems and gone over my three other efforts, "Objection to you is not that you tried. Objection to you is you haf let all these months go by without doing something." I said, "I'm doing it now," but, glancing up, I could see he was already doing it for me. He had his engagement book in his hands and was busily flapping the pages. "Hit chust so happens I have a free hour coming up in the afternoon. Hit came up chust last week—so you are fortunate." He named the hour and the price, and I agreed to start.

This man had purpose, he was serious, he had culture, and he worked hard, with an almost obsessive eagerness. Besides, I recognized what he was saying the way one inevitably recognizes a great truth: for the truth is never new, it is something one has always known, usually deep down beneath the surface of the thinking or reasoning mind, and that one must greet with joy as a reunion with some long-forgotten friend. I was thinking of this as he explained, "You hunderstand you haf to come on time," and I reminded him of my other analyses. "You haf never been touched," he allowed. "A virgin psyche?" I asked, surprised. "Ya ya, a virgin psyche," he was getting impatient. "Masochists always make chokes."

This is it all right, I felt in my bones as I went home, my bag bulging with papers he had written on various phases of the human problem. This man knows what he is doing. Here I will be cured.

He found in me an eager student bursting with curiosity to unravel the conundrums, one who had suffered enough to need to change—but mainly a writer he could himself study and use to prove his theory. It troubled me to see how much emphasis he put on the written word, especially the fame and position success in that field would bring, as I felt I had other more pressing problems that needed his more immediate attention. The fact that here was a human being in great distress meant little to this particular scientist: distress had already been investigated, the "mechanism of creation" had not. But if that was the price he extracted in return for the ride to peace, I decided, let him investigate to his heart's content.

He talked continuously, explaining the complicated scientific points, so there were times when I felt fenced in with these theories of his and even exhausted by the complications. As I began to unfold the story of my early life, I noticed the learned man had a decided tendency to brush away certain outstanding incidents if they conflicted in any way with his theories—or to change them to fit his theories. Since my mother had died very early in my life—and my father was obviously deranged—I laid much of my trouble at his door and said so.

2 2 6

"Why did you not leave your father?" he demanded, frowning impatiently.

"But where would I go—a little child? Besides, the trouble started before I knew anything—at the walking stage—"

"Ya, a little child even could get away—" adding, with a sharp look, *"unless the child wanted the punishment.* You wanted the punishment."

I thought this over. It just wasn't so.

"Your trouble was your mother. Your mother didn't want you."

This was true, in a sense—and certainly easier to accept.

"You projected your mother's opinion of your father onto him. That was your hunconscious trying to cover up your masochism. Look at you now. You squirm every time your masochism is mentioned."

He was right there. I did indeed often squirm uncomfortably— as who wouldn't? If it was true I practically came into the world wanting to be badly treated, then the situation was gloomier than even I had suspected—but this the professor just couldn't understand, and had no interest in understanding. It became obvious to me after a time that, while to me the analysis was an emotional experience, full of pain and peril, to him it was an intellectual process.

He was the happiest when I sat there like a dunce agreeing to everything he said, and when I interrupted to put forward some fact— "But, Doctor, my father was not all there—he talked to ghosts— had quarrels with unseen spirits—" Dr. Portzweig would impatiently bring me back to his theory of my case. "Then why didn't you inform on him?" "But I did—to the few people I could trust. Try to remember we're not talking about an adult, not even an adolescent. We're talking about a *scared little kid*—practically a baby." All these facts he brushed grandly aside, as being beside the point. "You wanted to be denied. You probably provoked your father."

I gave up trying to correct him: obviously he knew much more about my childhood than I did. He went on, after any interruption, reeling off the horrors of my case as he saw it, as casually as if he were calling a weather report. I wanted to die, I wanted to be destroyed. I wanted to be denied.

The treatment had by now fallen into a pattern. The doctor would ask the question, I would give the answer, describing this incident or that experience, he would reel off the black unconscious meaning.

(I didn't quite swallow all this. I was at war with my own unconscious mind, I agreed on that: some part of it, a very powerful part indeed, was out to do me in. But *why?* That was what I wanted to know. What was the reason for this terrible business? Whenever he would explain the reason in his scientific abracadabra it sounded at first possible but questionable, then doubtful, and finally much too glib. There was another reason, a deeper reason, that his theory seemed never to have contemplated—and that was the reason I wanted to find more than anything in the world.)

By this time, however, there was a great deal on my mind. For one thing, I had begun at first to suspect, then to see, that he was getting my case all wrong. This wasn't entirely his fault. He seemed so bent upon my learning his theories verbatim and reciting them back to him that I don't believe he had actually heard more than half of what I had been trying desperately to tell him.

It was obvious after a while how things were going. As he would ask the question, and I would give the answer, I would always draw a huge 0 while he drew 100 on the theory. If I mentioned that, in spite of my troubles, I had so far managed to work, that was because I was a masochist. "This silly journalistic nonsense you do satisfies your need to be denied." As for "my projecting the refusing monster" on people in general, if I said I liked people, managed to get along pretty well with them, that was because they were all hopeless neurotics and, again, satisfied my need to be denied.

If I talked about my compulsion which I felt was at the very root, and possibly was even the core, of my illness, and which seemed to come directly from my father, not my mother, he went wild and shouted. "Ya, there you are trying to break the rule. That compulsion is nothing but a smoke screen put up by the hunconscious to cover up the real love of denial."

It seemed to me—in fact I could almost say I *knew*—there was quite a different element in my particular problem than a desire to be denied or any projection of the refusing monster. I saw clearly that I reacted *automatically,* totally against my will, out of some deep-seated terror I didn't understand, and that had nothing to do with a desire for punishment or denial—in fact, quite the reverse. And this I wanted to track down and cure, if it were humanly possible, for the simple reason that to continue to live with it was not possible.

This terrifying symptom was most certainly *not* a "smoke screen thrown up by the unconscious" to cover up the truth. It came, I was sure, out of some wholly unique and utterly panic-making personal appearance—something that either I had seen happening to someone near and dear, or something that had happened to me—that was too terrifying for the memory to endure, but that, with raw head and bloody bones, kept rising up beyond the surface of my mind and taking possession of me. I was sure because I knew I lived with panic, with a feeling of danger, with murder in the air. And this I had to get up and out of my system, and now—here with Portzweig, the scientist and God's angry man—as I saw the Frog Pond looming once again in the distance, I would say, sometimes in a very soft voice, "I feel there is this unique terrible thing—behind this compulsion of mine—and if you would just let *me* talk—we could maybe get it up."

"Who's stopping you from talking?" he would scream. "Who wants to talk to you, anyway?"

"Please don't get angry, Doctor. This is something special—"

"Ya, all neurotics think they have something special. They're all alike. They always think their case is unique."

"But you are wrong, Dr. Portzweig. I don't think my case is unique. I have the very definite feeling . . . that this terrible reaction I have to men . . . comes from a unique experience. And if you could just forget your orality theory for five minutes I'd tell you—and maybe we'd get somewhere. I don't want to talk about the autarchy any more—I want help—and all this learning your theories doesn't help me feel any better."

"These arguments of yours are stopping the analysis. Look, if you cannot see what your hunconscious is doing—the prognosis of your case is very bad."

"What am I doing?"

"You are projecting on me the refusing monster. You are deliberately trying to provoke me by trying to use your case to disprove the rule. I've told you time and again there is absolutely nothing hunusual about your case. Neurotics like you are a dime a dozen. The only hunusual thing about you is your talent—"

"The hell with my talent. I want to be able to sleep—and feel peace and some joy in life—"

"Chust listen to the masochist. The hell with the talent. That is the only thing there is to you that is in the least worth studying. Besides that, you are a masochist, a narcissist, an exhibitionist—just like thousands of others. And if you continue to interrupt the analysis and start a scene—we'll have to end your analysis. I couldn't have more than one patient like you during the day or I'd be too tired at nights to do my work!"

I found myself thinking of Dr. Portzweig during most of my waking hours. No matter what I was doing, the short, stout, angry-faced little man would come walking into my mind, usually shouting at the top of his lungs, and I would stop dead still to look and listen—frightened, yes, but equally fascinated and bewitched. Now I had another problem: my emotions were excited in the exact proportion as his impatience and ill-temper increased. The "transference" had set in with a bang. And on top of this problem was a further, possibly a worse, problem: I could not possibly discuss this with Portzweig, though I wanted very much to do so. "Ya, but these transferences only hold up people's analyses," he said, when I first broached the subject to him.

I thought it over by myself, remembering with a sexual tremor the little man's soft homely face, always puckered with anger or impatience. There was absolutely nothing attractive about him, I thought, as I remembered him in my fantasies—not even his eyes, which, while extraordinarily alert, were about as friendly as two gun muzzles. What, then—what did I find to like in this man I didn't like at all? Why, he lacked even that odd attractiveness that many homely men have, some magnetic warmth coming no doubt from their need to be loved, that makes them seem warm and even charming. Old Portzweig warmed to nothing but himself, his fame and his theory. He would accept any amount of flattery and preen himself at its sound.

All these facts I would review in pictures, but just as the facts about Hitch had not affected my feeling of attraction toward him, so now the facts about the real Portzweig only increased my desire. No one else could possibly want him, I thought, and that means simply that alone on a desert island—the kind of special desert island that comes and goes at will in fantasies, and may include magnificent hotels thrown in at random—I would have him all to myself. So the ink

2 3 0

sketch from reality would blur in the hot waters of longing, and there in place of this screaming, slightly wild little man stood a great and godly being, the living essence of all that was desirable in men.

Meantime, Dr. Portzweig went ahead full blast, expounding his theories and relating all of my problems to them, always proving how right they were. The reason for all my trouble was that I was still reacting to having found out how my mother's breast really belonged to her instead of me, as a result of which I wanted to devour the poor woman and thus appropriate the whole works. There it was again, I thought. Oh, to be eating Mother, now that April's here. And here I was, all dressed up to resemble an adult, sitting at my typewriter chewing up words and spitting them out on paper, just to spite this poor woman for removing her tit from my mouth before I was done.

When it came to an estimate of my character, I listened to the doctor in pure amazement. "Ya, but you are Spiteful," he kept saying. "I call you Malice, Incorporated. Always starting a quarrel. Always trying to provoke me. Always trying to start an argument—and make a scene."

I would let him finish, then sometimes I would quietly remind him. "But, Doctor, you are talking to one of the world's worst cowards. I never quarrel with people. I am afraid of attack, don't you remember?" Soon, however, I gave this up as I saw it conflicted with his theory of what "oral people" were like.

So we would shortly get back to the babies, those cannibalistic little bastards who are sitting around planning to murder their mothers. I saw quickly this constantly chewing over the orality thing pleased and and soothed Dr. Portzweig. So, I relapsed into a negative and frightened state, letting the doctor handle the analysis according to his whim.

He was at his merriest chortling and chuckling over patients past and present, always denouncing them in the end, "Neurotics are never grateful," and often complaining about their injustices to him. I heard stories of frigid women, homosexual men, Lesbian women, and people longing to commit matricide, patricide and homicide, and of how he had fixed them all, one way or another, all confided to me much as a mother confides kitchen secrets to a daughter-in-law new at the game.

I heard about the European housewife who had never had an

231

orgasm. Among other reasons, she hated her husband because he made her account for every pfennig she spent, producing receipts for even an ounce of salt. "Ya, so you want to know how spiteful women are. In a state of transference toward me, this woman made a cake one day. She took some of the batter and made a fat little man with a round stomach like me, then she put eyes in it so it looked even more like me, and she put it in the oven. *She put me in the hot oven and baked me.* But that wasn't enough. Then she took the little man out of the oven when he was cooked—and ate him up. So she ate me." He chuckled.

"What happened in the end of the analysis?" I asked. "Ya, she had a decisive dream. She was in a restaurant having dinner with her husband—and I am sitting at a table with my wife. And what am I doing—the same damned thing that her husband was doing. Going over the bills with my wife, and making her account for every pfennig she spent during the week. So you see what the hunconscious was saying. They're all alike. He's no different from your husband or any other man. So you might as well have your orgasm with your own husband." I enjoyed hearing the story, except for the expression, "Decisive dream," which reminded me of that Technicolor dream about the wheatfield. Was she, the heroine of Dr. Portzweig's fable, having one of these, by any chance?

Apparently the doctor held these patients in great contempt, including me, but in addition I seemed to arouse some kind of special wrath in the good man. At times I wondered about this. Was it possible that I—lowly, degraded and hopeless as he said I was, and as I was willing to believe I was—still had something he didn't have, and that for some ungodly reason, he wanted? No, I promptly decided, that was some figment of my own imagination, some crazy notion that flitted in out of nowhere. Besides, it wasn't just me he hated. It was all writers. It was the entire literary mecca. And other meccas, too. He hated his elevator man who called him *Doc.* He hated taxi drivers, "In this country, they call you Buddy or Mack." He hated other analysts. "They do not hunderstand orality, therefore they cannot cure."

Occasionally another emotion toward those odd people, the writers, would come out. After he had said what a contemptible lot they were: "Megalomaniacs! Hunconscious repetition machines! Bursting with oral spite!" he would sometimes remark, "Ya, but the writers often get the insights from the hunconscious before the psychoanalyst gets them. The writers cure themselves—and are paid for it yet!" This, for some reason, always brought a wild gleam to his eyes.

On one occasion, after an unusually bad prognosis of my case, I found him in a somber mood. "So you are not the only one who cannot solve the conflicts. Today I thought we would discuss the murderer who must die in the electric chair." After the first chill of repugnance, I listened to my brother's fate. "He too has tried to solve his conflict—and failed. He makes his peace with the world before he goes to meet his death. And what does he feel? Great relief. He actually feels peaceful. All his life he has bargained to get the noose around his neck—because that was what he wanted. Nothing would satisfy him but the ultimate in punishment and disgrace. And when he knows at last he is going to get it—pay the supreme penalty—he asks forgiveness. What is your reaction to that?" I found it ghoulish, besides I doubted it, but quickly he informed me, "The dignity of man. It's all over—the record he couldn't change. He pays the price with dignity!"

But it wasn't over with me. I was into another analysis that was failing rapidly before my eyes. I was facing problems too great to be handled alone, and that by now I didn't dare bring to this extremely impatient man for solution because some of them concerned him. I had tried, and whenever I did, the conversation took the form of a battle between him and me, bringing with it the inevitable pronouncement of a bad prognosis: i.e., I was incurable, and if I did not stop projecting the refusing monster on him, he would have to give me up.

But the problem was there, growing larger and larger, and once I blurted it out. "I don't exactly think of you as a monster—but well, you'll do until one comes around." I started to say more, I had it all ready to say. "I think of you as a terribly angry man who hollers at his patients and who hates everybody. But I am at the same time in awe of you, afraid of you, and sexually infatuated with you. You are now the boss-man in my fantasies—and this is quite a problem. Because I see that I am attracted to monsters—something I never knew before. All along while I have been trying to live and love, a monster must have been lodged at the door of my soul, and he is not too different from you."

I didn't say all this. I said only a small part of it. What I did say brought down the house. This *projection* of mine was very serious, he said, and unless I could see it, my case was completely hopeless and he didn't want to be bothered with it any further. He shut up after his pronouncement, I could see he was furious. I left shortly afterwards.

CHAPTER TWENTY-SEVEN

· · · · · ·

ONE NIGHT COMES BACK TO ME AS A TURNING POINT IN THE THERAPY. A friend with whom I was dining spoke to me suddenly.

"You look very *funny*. What's the matter? For God's sake, talk about it. Tell somebody. Tell me."

I told him the whole story.

"I think you need some expert advice," he said as soon as I had finished. "If it's all right with you. I'd like to call up my doctor—and ask him what he thinks."

He was ending an analysis with a well-known analyst who had helped him greatly, he informed me.

I said it was all right, in fact I would welcome it, and he left the table to telephone. He was gone some time.

"Well, I think I've got the answer," he said, when he returned. "I told Dr. X the whole story. 'Why doesn't she just leave the analysis,' was his first question. 'If the doctor himself has told her to go and she's a nuisance and all that, why doesn't she just leave?' I explained to him. I said, 'Well, doctor, I know you or I could leave—but I don't know if this girl could leave. I don't think she could do anything right just now.' We talked it over a long time."

"Yes, I know. And what did he finally say?"

"You have a sadistic transference and should leave the analysis at once."

I knew, of course, what I should do, but it was helpful to have another opinion. I didn't know what the phrase meant, but something was creating havoc in my insides, and if that was it—well, anyway, it had a name.

"Does your doctor know Portzweig?"

"Yeah, he knows him. Says he's autocratic. Very bossy and conceited. Says he's got these orality rules or theories—say, you didn't raise any question about those rules, did you?"

"Well, yes—at first I did. I thought maybe my problem had something different. Why?"

"My doctor says he's up to the neck with those theories. Gets sore as a pup if people don't bow down before them. He says he's a good analyst—or he used to be—if anybody can stand him."

"What do you mean—he used to be?"

"He hasn't seen him for years. I guess he doesn't get along too well with the other doctors. Exhibitionistic . . . narcissistic . . . thinks he's the center of the universe."

The center of the universe. . . . But these were all the epithets the great man had applied to me. Was it possible—was it humanly possible—he had never even seen me as I really was? A terrified cowardly little creature with an automatic reaction to attack. Was it possible the same Dr. Portzweig—he who had written such a brilliant paper that had won me over—was all the time talking about himself?

I was still down for the count the following morning, but some part of me—the lowly, hopelessly inadequate, conscious mind—was working. It was standing up—fighting. Portzweig says your case is hopeless—yes, but is it? Get on the phone, you coward. At least you can clear up one point in all this maze.

Remember your friend L, a charming woman, and one who wishes you well? She comes from his very city—and she knows every analyst. Ask her, and she will find out for you, and tell you the truth. And then there is S—he will know. An analyst himself, and a friend. And what about H? These people will all bring you the impersonal truth.

The answers did not come in the same day they were asked. I inquired about Dr. Portzweig from three people, and only one spoke to me immediately. This was the doctor, an eminent and very famous analyst. He had had "bad experiences with him," he said. "Orality, orality, orality—well, everybody knows about orality. There's much more to analysis than sitting around listening to this. The patient must get the hostilities out of his system—and if you have to contend with the doctor's hostilities, what can you expect?" So I wasn't crazy! And

I was thrilled to hear the news! "So I was right in my opinion?" "You have only to see him at one of the meetings, my dear. So you've still got your trouble? Of course you have! So you had resistances to his personality? Who wouldn't?" The second one, also a doctor, said Portzweig should be working with "hardened criminals." Called him "crude, conceited, overbearing." As to the prognosis: "He likes to wrap people up in their coffins. Maybe he figures that will give them a jolt." But it was the third one, my woman friend who came from his own city, who gave me an insight into his character, explaining the extraordinary ambition for fame and prestige, the incredible, "abnormal" interest in publication.

Now I knew the facts. There remained for me only to see the doctor in one last visit—or else to write him a note—and end the analysis. Don't be a coward again. Go on.

This was the last "treatment" and I knew it. I was still afraid of him, but not quite as afraid as before. I was talking softly, a trick I had learned when I wanted to bring in some pertinent reference to my problems. "I hope you won't mind my saying so, but I have an awful aversion to people who holler at me. If we could just talk quietly—just this once—" I went on to discuss my recent desire to do away with myself. In all justice to Portzweig, I don't think he realized the damage he was causing me. His orality rule was such a consuming passion with him, requiring such constant vigilance to prove it—and use those proofs in his papers and other writings—it must have been difficult for him to relax and listen. I have a tremendous problem with the world, I wanted to say, but it is still a lovers' quarrel, I want to make up, but you are out for the kill. What I said was probably not that, but somehow I did say, "Well, doctor, I have good news for you."

"And what is the good news?"

I said, "I'm leaving the analysis. Today."

Now, I thought, now he will relax, we'll say good-by pleasantly as two ships passing in the night, wishing one another well, being sorry that we met in such dark waters. But I saw quickly, and to my absolute amazement, I had been wrong again. An awful look of fury, disappointment, resentment, and bitterness came over his face.

"So when did you arrive at this decision?"

2 3 7

I said, "Oh, I guess I arrived at it some time ago—it took me weeks to do it."

I waited. Maybe I had been wrong. He must be pleased, he ought to be pleased, after all those cracks about what a nuisance I was, always trying to break his rule, always making scenes. Not to mention his many weary "Oh, but it's hopeless with you—we had better stop this analysis!"

He said nothing for a while. He was white with rage.

"I thought you would be pleased, doctor," I said.

"Aehhhh," he let out. "That's the trouble with analysis. The patients have the choice in their own hands. So they leave before they can see what their hunconscious is doing." He thrashed around in his chair. "Well, I'm sorry it hasn't worked out," I heard a voice say. He yelled, "So what did you expect?" I saw myself trying to calm him down, listened to my own voice. "I expected we would have more of a give-and-take relationship. I am sensitive to people hollering, and now would you mind giving me back my papers?" He was astounded at this. "I haven't finished with them. You can get them some other time." I said, "No, I want them now. Please give them to me now." He glared at me, but calmly got up and got them.

Then he asked suddenly, "What brought you to this decision?" I told him the facts, as I saw them. And then, without realizing what I was saying, I had told him the rest. "And so I investigated you—I wanted to find out if I was really crazy in thinking you somewhat peculiar—or maybe was I right." He became intensely alert. "So who did you ask about me?" I said, "I'd rather not mention any names," adding that it didn't matter, I had not said anything bad about him. "But I insist upon knowing—who did you ask about me and what did they say?"

I repeated, in a modified form, what had been told me. Again, to my amazement, he spent the rest of the time trying to find out who the informants were, especially the woman. It was no use: I wouldn't have revealed my sources under any circumstances, but seeing his absolute fury, I was sworn to protect them now. Was it possible he was, as the woman had said, "very spiteful and vindictive"?

He was becoming almost inarticulate in his fury.

"You! Who needs you?" he kept repeating. I said nothing. But I was thinking. Why was I ever sexually attracted to you—making you the hero of my fantasies—you disagreeable, unpredictable, conceited, crazy little man?

And now I was getting up. "Well, doctor, I hope you'll be fine." He looked as if he was about to burst. "You—*you* hope *I'll* be fine."

He stopped as we reached the door and stood there, choking on the sludge of his rage.

"Hif you stop this analysis you'll never be able to do anything again!" Now he was getting it up and letting go. "You'll find you won't even haf your memory. Hmm . . . I could tell you plenty. Hif you weren't my patient, I could tell you what I really think about you." I was just wondering what more there could possibly be when he shrieked again, "Ya, you leave here and you will lose your mind!"

I moved off just as the door slammed to in my face, the outraged little man still muttering his imprecations behind it as I went to the elevator.

Now what? I wondered as I looked dimly around in the old familiar *cul-de-sac*. There must be another aperture somewhere, though not exactly yawning in my face. And once again I heard myself croaking the inevitable *vincit qui patitur* as I slipped back into the smooth oily surface I knew so well, where other slippery, web-footed amphibians were busy wiggling and groaning, back in the dark old pond.

CHAPTER TWENTY-EIGHT

. . . . . .

PEACE GERMANY SURRENDERS UNCONDITIONALLY

The big black words were jumping around the living room, leaping from newspapers brought in at various times by Daphne, Toni and some unexpected drunken visitors who remained just long enough to complicate our day. It was going to be a busy day, too, with everybody dressing to go out.

"Save me the Times," Daphne chanted as she emerged from her room, resplendent as a butterfly in a navy blue and yellow cape costume, and flung another batch of papers on the sofa in which the words QUIT and SURRENDERS were featured largely. As Daphne stood looking at herself in the mirror over the mantel, I found myself wishing she would go on out for fear she would read my mind and find out where I was going. "Tom says the streets are so crowded you can hardly walk," she muttered. Then, "I haven't had time to tell you, but I think this new doctor's going to be the end of our Toni. And if you ever go to another one of those so-called doctors, Joyce. . . ." A group of soldiers passed by chanting *"Der Fuehrer's Face"* so loudly I lost the rest, but they were soon gone and I heard her asking, "Who's your date?" Before I knew it I had said, "Dr. Osborn," but by that time it was so late she had to run and in the end I shared a taxi uptown with Toni.

The traffic was fierce. "We should have stood in bed," Toni said as our cab inched its way up the avenue. "Thank God my audition isn't until five. I told Jim I'd meet him at six-thirty. I'm kind of engaged now, you know, so I like to be on time. Oh Joyce, a doctor yet —it's true he's from Brooklyn—but that makes it kind of homey. If I hadn't gotten to this Horney analyst I'd never have been able to like a normal man." I asked what she meant by this and she went on to explain. "Now like before—well if I'd heard a man wanted an actress that would have made me angry. I wanted to be loved for myself at first glance—or very shortly thereafter."

This struck a familiar note. "Please fill me in on that," I asked. "Well, people have needs," she began. "Now take men like David— he's one of those men who needs a rich girl to compensate him for what he thinks he's losing in marriage altogether. I mean he thinks he ought to be paid for marrying a woman. That means his homosexual component, such as all men have, is kind of *large*. Now Jim is more masculine."

I asked, "Does he fit your fantasy?"

"Oh that. I'm practically over that. Those sexual fantasies are infantile. The minute you get real genuine sexual pleasure you don't want that stuff any more." I asked if she had enjoyed the genuine sexual pleasure with the doctor from Brooklyn. "No, not yet," she replied, "but I know I will. I won't get that involved until I know when we're going to be married."

I looked at Toni with envy. Imagine all that burning inside sex life she had lived by—nullified in a single experience! Lucky girl. Then I remembered she hadn't had the experience and wasn't quite so envious. Could these fiery abysses we'd both known be by-passed by one experience with the Brooklyn Pangloss? Perhaps they could, and if so she had run into a handy little chap . . .

Everybody else was getting well. Everybody was moving away from the island of the sick. Soon I would be left alone, I thought, as I watched Toni get out and run down Madison Avenue. I thought of the more-sick-than-I people I knew, those nameless lepers who appear with their tinkling bells to partake of the leavings of the healthy, and told the driver, *Hurry*.

The handsome, sunburned, gray-haired Dr. Richard Osborn was waiting for me, watching with that slightly sensuous smile I remembered as I meandered my way through the crowd toward his table in the restaurant on Fifty-ninth Street. Despite my knowledge acquired the hard way, not to mention the growing shadowy hunch that psychiatry was a swindle, all the old hope rushed up in me as I saw him. (This time it will be different.) I had seen him a few times since the far-off night at Irene's, after which he had given me the heavy news of Silent Simon, the novice at the game who didn't even know how to novitiate, so now his drollish talking-down-to-the-little-patients conversational gambit was not new.

"Well, so we want to go again? . . ."

"We still have our trouble," I informed.

"Of course you still have your trouble. And you want to go again because so far you haven't been at all. . . ." A look of shock must have revealed itself. "Now, now, don't worry—I know—you're counting the time. But you mustn't think in those terms—the unconscious takes its own time. Now then, first we will eat and then we will plot. . . ."

It was going pretty well. I enjoyed watching his round, benign face and listening to him talk in that way he had of cutting himself in on the problem. Making it seem almost as if it were he, not I, who was facing another operation.

"It always takes time—and money—but now we know this is not as we read in the little happiness-for-all magazines, do we not? Now we know—"

I decided to cut in. "Yes, we know all that. As soon as possible, please find me someone—the best for my case, as you know it—money no object. You owe it to me. You didn't help me in the past—you knew about Portzweig, yet you said nothing. Oh, I know—the ethics of your noble profession and all that. You'd let a doctor murder your best friend rather than say a word—you call it *ethics* but the dumbest people know it's plain cowardice."

"Ah, so we're getting cynical about doctors at last. That's a good sign. A step forward. The four phonies you went to taught you that. Sometimes this very loss of faith is the beginning of the cure. But it's not too easy to find the right one. Ah, I see you don't believe that either. That's good. Listen to me, my dear. Do you know how many there are who can do this thing? Maybe ten—you can count them on the fingers of your two hands. And if you find one, you are lucky."

"Only ten. But that's terrible—"

"What's *terrible?* You thought what happened with Rudie Simon was terrible—"

"It was, too. Going to a doctor to have a cancer removed—and he stands right in the middle of the operation calling up another doctor to find out where to cut. That's just about it when it comes to the psychic thing—only worse."

"That's good. The ghost who stands behind the analyst. Perhaps you don't know about ghost surgeons—"

I said I had heard about these. "Well, you see what happened with Portzweig was even worse. If you get with one of those who has too many aggressions of his own—he will use you to get out his aggressions instead of yours. I know because I sent patients to him—but never again, of course. Now, now, let's not worry about a situation that can't be helped. Wait until you are analyzed—then you won't identify so with human distress."

I said, No, I would never be indifferent to other people's troubles.

"Now we know what we want to do and I'll have to find the man —just the right man. Wait a minute—I have someone in mind—yes, yes—but I don't know if he has any free time. You'll be patient— you see, these men are all so busy . . ."

Three weeks later. Dr. Silvers was his name. Of a bright sunny day I made my way up to another office in another street. This time it was Eighty-fifth Street. A lucky number, according to Daphne, who thought I was going to see a dressmaker, because it added up to thirteen.

"Are you absolutely sure about these numbers?" I asked.

"Of course I'm sure," Daphne replied. "The thirteenth card of the Tarot—Death or the Skeleton Mower. Oh, it doesn't mean what you think. It means *creation*."

"How about all the other people living on that street?" She asked me the woman's name, I told her "Silvers," and she worked it out. It came to another thirteen. Things were looking up. "Whatever this woman does will come out all right," she promised.

I rang the elevator bell and a short time later was talking to a tall man with glasses—rather pleasant, I thought, but extremely ordinary. I neither liked him nor disliked him. It was a month or more before he said much of anything, but there was that about him which evoked easy talking in me. I had just begun to think maybe here was another Simon who couldn't speak because it was summer and his control was on vacation when he spoke at last, quietly, in answer to a casual remark of mine: "There's something I want . . . some relief I find in these awful experiences—"

"You want to be murdered," he said.

"*No*. No one could want—"

"That's what you've been saying. You're also afraid to live—for fear of your life being stopped. You're afraid to die too. A word keeps coming to me as you've been talking. Reprieve. Think about that. A whole life full of promise—stopped aborning—given over to *reprieve from murder*. You'll give up anything—love, happiness, success, creativity—just to stop this one thing from happening . . . and give yourself a reprieve from murder."

Reprieve—from murder. I went away cringing at the impact of the words. This was crazy, insane, yet instantly I knew these flaming words for what they were: the simple brutal truth. The word stayed with me. I looked it up in the dictionary. Reprieve: "To grant a delay of the execution of (a condemned person: as, 'You shall not die: She has reprieved you,' Swinburne's *Chastelard,* Verse 2); hence, to relieve temporarily from any evil; also to postpone (punishment, etc.). In general, a respite from impending punishment, especially from execution of a sentence of death."

So . . . this was it! This was what took the wind out of my sail! This was what caused me to stop my own opportunities! If I was waiting for the killer to arrive, and listening for his footsteps, anything I did might bring him nearer. Now at last I was stepping up to where the real doctors were. Daphne was right, thirteen was my lucky number. With the past four still in the periphery of my mind, to come upon Silvers was like walking off wet cement into a warm lighted interior.

An inquiry had started up. We went from near to far. If I knew I was going to be murdered, I would certainly want a reprieve. I would do anything to get one, anything humanly possible.

"Consider what you have done—and are doing," said Five.

I did, and once again was shocked as actual experiences came and went before me, all betrayals of what I wanted, some sad, others dangerous. All dedicated to bringing about a reprieve—was that possible?

"But I don't consciously think that I am in danger of murder."

"No, not consciously—but I think sometimes even consciously you feel in danger. Think of that."

I thought and began to see more and more, and talked of it all. Why had I such a feeling of identification with the Emperor Jones, the man running from the oncoming mob in O'Neill's play? If I let my imagination loose just a little I could easily glimpse myself running through a forest with the shadow of an ax-man close behind. "But I don't know who he is—I think he might even be part of me. I am the killer—is that possible? Or is it insane? Could I be put away for having such a thought?"

"It isn't insane. Besides, you can't *go* insane—and insanity is almost never inherited."

This was such a relief it was almost worth the price of the ticket. I talked more freely, knowing this, of the greater dark unknown where Devman dwelled—because knowing of Devman's existence had convinced me of the dual nature of my self which seemed to be the greatest threat to sanity. Everybody was dual, said old Five. I shouldn't worry too much about that. Thing for me to do was to straightaway figure out *why* I was waiting for the killer. A helluva business.

Wasn't there something in the very nature of my case, especially the sexual compulsion to yield, that wouldn't be believed? Wasn't there perhaps a great primordial tendency for men to ignore the idea of any horror connected with the seduction of women?

"Let's think about this now," Five kept at it. "Seduction. What does the word mean anyway? Surrender of chastity. It's generally used in the sense of wrongfully inducing a woman to consent to sexual intercourse, but even in the courts of law, which of course are run by men, this point is difficult to prove." Obviously he had something on his mind. He went on and on about this, so much so I wondered at first just what he was driving at.

"In England, for instance," he claimed, "the woman seduced doesn't even have the right to bring an action. It goes back to the old master and servant relationship. In the old days, suit was brought by the father, and before he could win he had to prove he'd lost his daughter's *services* because of illness and confinement. Take even today, in some states it has only recently become a felony to seduce a girl under the age of thirteen and a misdemeanor to seduce a girl between thirteen and sixteen."

I had never contemplated the lawful aspect of these matters and couldn't see what it had to do with me. "I want you to see how unusual your trouble is. The average man would have a tendency not to believe your story about losing your voice and becoming an automaton. Yes, I know you're going to tell me doctors should be different, but let's just forget about them and think about people—just plain men."

"If that's the case—why did *you* believe it?"

He said a strange thing. "The cat. The first time you saw a cat—as a very young baby—that was the first terror you remember. That was when I knew you had already had this trouble for a long time." And then it hit me again: that was true, he knew, he knew things, perhaps even more than I knew.

"For the misdemeanor of seducing a girl under sixteen by guardian or parent—provided it could be proved—would be punished by a short term in jail," he said. "Plain intercourse just isn't recognized as wrongful by anybody—including the courts of law."

I said, All right, so what did that prove? I certainly had no intention of bringing any of my seducers into court. "And yet you say you loathe them one and all. If there was any way of getting even with them you'd like to do it, wouldn't you?" I said, Of course, wouldn't any woman who had yielded against her will. He gave me an argument even on that.

"Not if the men fell for her she wouldn't. Most women, even say they did yield against their will—they would get angry only if the men lost interest afterwards. Didn't keep calling them up, that kind of thing. But that's not the case with you. It's you who do the running away. The men come after you for re-orders—and you keep the door closed. What you do has nothing in common with ordinary female behavior." My, it was refreshing to hear these current facts after all that hogwash about my mother and her thorax.

Five went on. "It's usually the man who runs away—you know that, don't you? And hell hath no fury like a woman scorned," he quoted, with the abysmal lack of originality now casually identified with psychoanalysts. I saw that. Whereas in my case it was I who ran away. "Creeping out in the middle of the night like a criminal," he quoted.

More. I was reversing the man's role. Men were the ones who

wanted to do the leaving, turning a deaf ear to the poor little woman's pleas. It was usually the man who left "the scene of the crime, as you call it—and by the way, why do you call it that?" More. Why was it a crime in my case? What was there about the act of love that was criminal? Well, because it was virtually having sexual intercourse with a person who wasn't there mentally.

"But you were there mentally. All the time your mind was active—you told me that more than once. You never stopped thinking. And your thinking even led you to acquiesce, didn't it?" Yes, yes, I remembered, my thinking did indeed lead me to acquiesce. "But why? What did you think would happen to you—if you didn't acquiesce?" But that was where I came in. I didn't know that and we were at it for weeks, with me getting alternately baffled, panic-stricken, or angry, with me feeling I was just on the track or something and then, bang, away it went, lost in the dungeon.

Came the time when Five accused me of being the seducer "in a sense." Said I was looking, watching, waiting for these men. Now I was up in arms. "What the hell do you mean by that—in a sense? In what sense?" Wasn't I aware all men represented a threat? Further, there was only one way for me to appease that threat. I struggled and shuddered around with that one, a staggering *cheval de bataille*. My trouble had intrigue, plot and counterplot and underplot, with more hocus-pocus and mumbo-jumbo than the cabala. Five went on calmly taking it in his stride. "You know you haven't finished with this compulsion. You're young and beautiful, you're right in the heat of it. You know it's going to go on and on." I asked why he had to remind me of that, why rid me of the happy notion that one day I would wake up and the whole thing would be gone like a bad dream?

"Neurotic hope," he explained. "The longing for the magic cure. Let's get back to work. There are going to be more men to be appeased. They'll all be doing exactly the same thing—and with you doing exactly the same thing. Because each one is only one down and how many more to come? Let's think about this. Suppose every time you are alone with a man you will feel the same. Let's figure that out. You're alone with a man now. How do you feel?" I picked that one up quickly. "In danger—but only slightly. I can reason the chances are you won't attack. It's only a thousand to one you would."

"But you do feel a certain danger? . . ." Yes, of course, it was always there—fear of sudden attack. "What kind of attack?" I thought, but I didn't know—possibly a sudden springing, pouncing motion. "With my hands?" No, the danger wasn't there. "Where is it, do you know?" No, I didn't know. There was the possibility of being smothered. Besides, every man was carrying a secret weapon, unless of course I knew him and knew he was not. All right then, consider the absurdity of my situation. Why did I *have* to yield? Why couldn't I leave before yielding? *Was it because I would then feel the armed man was still seeking me?*

I didn't know the answer, but I knew this Five was digging in pay dirt. Terrifying, but exciting, we were working together like a couple of detectives about to break a case. Time to go, but something jumped inside me when he said, "Next time the killer strikes maybe we'll be more ready. We're setting a trap for that sonofabitch."

Meantime, I had started clinging to Dr. Silvers in my mind, feeling a sneaky sense of comfort and warmth, something that apparently "normal" people feel in the cradle. So many others had clung and were clinging to me I sometimes thought I was living in a room fresh out of chairs, but Five was the only one who had brought out this creepy, embarrassing emotion in me. This was absolutely necessary, said Five. There was just no getting well without it. "Underneath your trouble you are a very feminine female," he commented.

The more clearly I saw the pattern the more enormous it became. I was not just compulsive in my sexual yielding to dangerous people, the whole business represented danger to me; I therefore yielded everywhere. I was afraid of shopkeepers and landlords, friends and enemies, bosses and servants—and more largely of success and failure. Living in this world, nothing was real or in its genuine dimensions, it was all out of scale. "But there was a time when you were in real danger," said Five, always bringing me back.

"We never know how a case will end," said honest Dr. Silvers at another time. "We don't know what cures people. But you won't break your compulsion by staying away from men."

There was more, which I, of course, promptly translated into my own words. Go out with men but keep on the alert. You're the only one who can ever find out why you become paralyzed and yield against your will. But there's a reason. This Devman as you call him has something on his mind, he always has. Keep alert and find out what his reason is. This compulsion is dangerous *right now*. It causes you untold shame and misery *now*. It is against your best interests right now, today. But once, at some past time, it must have made very good sense and served some useful purpose. You have to find out what that purpose is.

"Do you know?" I asked.

"I wouldn't tell you if I did," Dr. Silvers replied. "The point is, the past is the same as now to your other self. Keep alert, just go along with Devman and find out what he's doing. Try not to be horrified by the experiment next time it happens, you're there in the dual role of actor and detective. You are watching from behind the curtains. Do you think you can do that?"

I thought I could—but it seemed more dangerous now than before. "I might run into something bad—or somebody really violent."

"You have already."

"But not a real killer. It would be ironic to run into one of those— just when I'm being treated to find out what attracts me to the type."

"I don't think you will. You haven't so far. Anyway I'm not suggesting that you pick up somebody at a bar—or anything of that kind. But you're meeting men every day in your work, they're not exactly the violent type. I'm merely saying the next time it happens, if it should happen, try to see the whole thing through. Put everything you've got into it."

CHAPTER TWENTY-NINE

· · · · · ·

THAT *give it everything you've got* KEPT COMING BACK TO ME.
Crazy, all right. A therapist advising a thing like that. Still the thing I
had was crazy, maybe the hair-of-the-dog business might work. There
was little chance of seeing any "whole thing" through those days, as I
had little interest in the people I saw, even had to be prodded by Five.

There was Manny. About five foot one, he wore expensively tailored
suits that remarkably disguised his body—or whatever there was
underneath, but his fat dimply white hands and big wrists, hanging
out of the mysterious vault-like ensembles, gave him away. He was
forever grinning, eating, and simultaneously talking, a running gabble
of slightly sinister asides about clients—he was a public relations
counselor—friends, intimates and casuals. "Yes, Murine is pretty all
right—I wonder how that hysterectomy came out." Or, mentioning a
famous movie producer, "Yes, Marvin's a fine boy. I brought him a
toy last week—" Mentioning a well-known actress, "She's been rest-
ing so I thought I'd do them both a good turn, but she turned out to be
too old for his jaded appetite. Twenty-six—ten years too long on the
vine."

It was Manny's habit to indulge in these running commentaries
on people's private lives, and to be with him was to see the door constantly opening into firesides, bedrooms, hospitals, bathrooms, parked
cars and divorce courts, and swinging back on hinges oiled with this
heh-heh-heh giggle which, combined with the sound of food going
through his choppers, gave a total impression starting with a laugh and
freezing slowly into quiet horror. Whenever I went to visit Manny's
magnificent old brownstone in East Sixtieth I had the feeling of entering a new world in which emotions such as love, honor, admiration,

indignation, fear and all human warmth were as outmoded as open sewerage. If any of this stuff got loose and slipped into your conversation, any one of those sharp rich handsome emancipated guests he always had around looked at the speaker with raised eyebrows.

I was at a loss to explain my interest in Manny—was it anything besides a general interest in the sinister? Or his in me, for that matter, the shenanigans of his ilk being a species of nightshade to which I was not particularly addicted. I had known him for quite a while. Old Manny's substitution of attractive female personalities in the literary, art and theater world in place of call girls, to excite jaded clients, was a twice-told tale. Besides, working with Five and seeing this arena more clearly, I was no longer compelled by it.

Nevertheless, I couldn't completely walk out on this bum show. And, I reasoned, as I went along to a party at Manny's, I might "do myself some good." Indeed, walking up old Manny's black steps into his bright cold hell, I was inclined to laugh at the whole thing. What had he to offer in his Stygian creek that could come anywhere near the hot licks of my flaming fantasies? I would have to go into those, said Five, but meantime, maybe there was another way. What could there be that could hold a candle to Devman's special private theater? . . . Besides, the food and drink were always magnificent. Manny was a lavish host. I might meet an old friend or, better still, make a new one.

Manny always had an angle to any invitation he issued; he had no time for simple friendly acts. The use I had been or could be to him on the magazine wasn't enough to wangle an invitation to the brownstone—a three-dollar luncheon would have taken care of that. I couldn't figure the angle but, oh well, I was merely performing one more irrational service to my unconscious, taking one more ritualistic step to satisfy some demand. And in a world that was now as gray and empty as the inside of a mausoleum on a rainy day, I actually looked forward to the party at Manny's as being at least slightly more similar to the powerful Technicolor stuff going on inside my head.

I was glad to see the butler serving champagne, the carpet felt good underfoot and old Manny looked more like Fu Manchu than ever, smiling the nastiest, wettest smile in his repertoire as he took me about the room introducing me to the fifteen-odd celebrities who were already well into the wine and appetizers. I was glad I had bought the red velvet Christian Dior number right out of the window on Madison Avenue as, going from world-famous novelist (that smiling cobweb of a man who was always nibbling and chewing), to radio commentator (cool and busy), to movie actress (hot and busy), in rapid succession, I sensed Manny Manchu must have had something in mind, otherwise I had gotten in just under the wire.

Mein host took me in a circle around the room, ending up at a kidney-shaped sofa where sat a squat, round-faced man who might easily have been Manny's younger brother. Feeling fresh out of conversation, and being suddenly stuck with the squat man—Fu Manchu had now disappeared—I tactlessly asked him if he was related to Manny, which brought on a roar of not very amused resentment. "Hell, no," he bawled, and I saw I had offended him. "What makes you think anything like that? Do I look that bad? I'll have to change my barber." A desultory silence threatened; I saw I had been stuck with the least amiable of the guests and muttered something about their both having the same color eyes. "Didn't you get my name? Didn't Manny tell you who I am?" I had to answer no to both questions, so he informed me.

He was Hal Burman, *the* Hal Burman, I gathered. I remembered the name from my Hollywood days and quickly classified him as a producer of B-pictures who had wielded some might in one of the studios by marrying the president's daughter, from whom he was subsequently divorced and was now producing something or other on his own. I'd heard he owned or operated bogus diamond mines and/or other capital-gain tax-deductible enterprises, the general impression being that while Hal was not quite on the up-and-up he was a good kid just the same and worshiped his ageing mother.

Having quickly decided that Hal and I were not soul-mates, I was ready to abandon ship in favor of a more promising group standing nearby when the novelist appeared beside me and I saw my stock rise instantly with Hal. We three must have talked quite a while, starting with the usual self-conscious dialogue that nobody really believes before falling into more useful subjects like how much it cost the novelist —Willie by name—to run his house in London as opposed to the cost of his joint in New York. Not to be outdone Hal came up with some imposing figures about his hacienda at Pacific Palisades and ran these against the place he was buying in Rio. They waded through the figures, took a few strokes on the surface with names and were swimming down into gossip—who was behind the gang operating in the state of New Jersey—when the butler rolled back the doors to the dining room and people started floating toward the food.

Nothing happened, time passed away, smiling like Manny as it stretched through the house. I disliked Mr. Burman so heartily it was pleasant to keep leaving him flat. That must have happened three or four times, I lost count—old Hal kept turning up at my side in any small group I happened into—but there at the door as I was leaving with Willie the novelist for a "nightcap across the street," knowing that I would never again see him in this life and probably not in any other, I managed a neat good-by. It was Manny and Hal, talking to Willie and me—Manny whispering, "But you're not going with him— Hal wants to take you home," and me whispering back, and then in the out-loud good-by, there I was calling Manny Hal and Hal Manny. Hal gave me a mean pale look as Willie and I swept off into the night.

Again I had misjudged old Manny, I thought, as I awakened the next morning. Nothing but his generous good nature had prompted him to invite me to his dark corner. He was the first one to call as I arrived at the office, and once again he had nothing on his mind but pleasant complimentary chatter. The mogul named Hal had taken a fancy to me, was in fact giving a party that afternoon and was most insistent . . .

The séance at Hal Burman's suite at the St. Regis Hotel had about as little in common with Manny's exultant suggestions (He knows everybody . . . Never know who you'll see at Hal's *soirées*) as I had in common with Hal. My first impression—the place was bursting with ostentatious flowers; two people, a man and a woman, were sitting very stiffly on a settee; and orchestral music was issuing from somewhere—well, it looked more like a cheap funeral than anything else. A tired man named Al from Manny's office was seated on the sofa beside a well-dressed, over-rouged girl named Ruth something. And there was Hal, of course with Manny. Hal seemed to have undergone some change since last night, I couldn't quite tell what it was, but it rendered him somehow easier to dislike. (Oh yes, it was his smile that had changed, or was it just that he was wearing one for the first

2 5 3

time?) He started to kiss me on the cheek, missed and I felt a slight cool sense of him around the ear, as he handed me a present.

"Hal's running for Mayor," said Al. Manny and Hal went into the other room where they stood talking together, then Manny returned. The telephone rang, Hal called, "It's for you," and Manny and Hal disappeared, this time for quite a while, or at least long enough for Al, Ruth and me to give out on conversation so completely we began repeating ourselves like a record going over the same track. "I wonder where that waiter is with the drinks—does he think we came here for fun? I wonder where that waiter is with the drinks—does he think we came here for fun?" Manny reappeared just as a waiter did actually come in with whiskey, soda, ice and a trayful of appetizers, and after a slight wait the desultory conversation started up again very much as before—with Manny and Hal running between the two rooms answering telephone calls and conversing in a heavy droning sound.

I had just finished talking to Toni on a hallway extension and had stopped before a mirror to comb my hair when I heard Manny and Hal in another of those dronings. This one sounded like some kind of deal, Hal wasn't so sure it would come off and Manny was reassuring him. Hal rumbled skeptically, he was barely audible, I couldn't make out what he was saying, but Manny roared confidently. "Yeah, sure, I know you can, kid . . ." Then Hal's low *berloque,* monotonous as a bee in a bottle. Then Manny's roar. "Sure she's funny . . . What the hell do you care? Things to worry about—she's funny! What am I— a psychiatrist? Yeah . . . sure . . . so maybe you both could . . . so what's bad with that?"

They must be talking about Ruth out there. Poor Ruth, she could use a psychiatrist or two. Those awful glasses she had to wear, that high, sad laugh coming out of all that rouge. I would talk more to her, I decided, as if that could help, and was moving away from the mirror to do my good deed when Manny started up again. It was a short roar this time, a few words, I could barely make them out—he must have moved further away from the door.

It wasn't Ruth they were talking about. I was eavesdropping on a conversation in which someone was being procured for the capital gains boy from Hollywood. I stood there, listening now in horrible fascination for more. I knew who they were procuring—then No, it couldn't be: why, this was a casual visit, well-meant . . .

They were coming toward the door, the voices sounded louder. I moved quickly off into the bathroom. It was me they were talking about. No, it couldn't me. *But it was. It was.*

The whiteness of the bathroom brought the situation up sharp. I could see my face in the mirror, pink as lipstick. So people knew about it. It wasn't a secret any more—something I held locked in my breast, confided only to doctors. It was getting out now; it was hopeless. Manny knew. So that was how it was, after all the trying. Manny knew, and if Manny knew . . . what next?

The thin string of hope, the chance I thought I had of coming through—living it down—snapped in the middle. I was going down— and those nice hard black heels of Manny's shoes were raised to speed the parting guest. Going down. The sharp bright room gave me no quarter. Hell, I was already down. How much further down can you go—being procured by Manny—not as a sweetheart, not even as an "interesting experience"—not the full meal, oh no, just an appetizer, a little snack to serve the fat man between airplane flights!

Shell-shocked was the word Manny used. *She's shell-shocked . . . What am I—a psychiatrist?* He knew what it was, this being shocked; he could see with those shrewd hard eyes in his fat face. He knew how it worked, being shell-shocked, and how to work it.

What would I do now? I couldn't say what I would do in the far future now, but meantime there was the immediate now to face. I couldn't spend the rest of my life in this bathroom, I could use a drink, but I hated to face the party going on out there. Al and Ruth, for instance, were now people removed forever from my orbit as people who knew, or just possibly might know—about this little deal. Now I would have to face them, even say something to them. The conversation about the liquor had been killed with the plethora of it out there but there was still the rain. I would have to see Manny—and Hal, the cactus plant.

They would all look at me, knowing about this deal. Just suppose that now when they saw me they would know something more: they would know that I knew. *You know . . . that I know . . . and I know . . . that you know.* I thought about murdering Manny. I could see myself, pistol in hand, shooting straight at the heart of that expensive custom-made suit. It was fun too, before it faded in the blue-white light of that cold bright bathroom, leaving me with the nasty grim truth staring out of a whole world of hotel bathrooms.

I opened the door. The first object I saw was the empty sofa. Ruth and Al had discreetly disappeared. There was no one in the room. Where had everyone gone? There wasn't a sound except the patter of rain against the windows facing on the gray hotel court, and in the silence I suddenly remembered the rest of what Manny had said. *"Oh, no no no money, kid. Don't try to figure her out. Just move in . . . just move in . . . just move in."* I wasn't sure whether he had said this three times or twice or twelve times.

I was standing near the desk where the drinks were when the door opened and a waiter entered, moving quickly across the room. I was near the sofa so I sat down while the waiter busied himself placing a bucket of ice on the table. "Oh, Mr. Burman said to tell you he's making a call, he'll be right back. Shall I fix you a drink?"

I nodded, watched him mix the drink and hand it to me, then started drinking. After one more I began to notice things. My, but hadn't old Manny emptied the place quickly! I couldn't have been gone from the room more than five minutes! And then Hal having the waiter come back to watch over things. My, weren't these clever men! I could almost see them talking together, only now it wasn't Manny but Fu Manchu saying, *Oh, no no no money, kid,* but somehow I couldn't seem to remember Cactus at all, his entire face had eluded me as if I had never seen it in all my life.

The waiter must have gone. I poured myself a drink this time, a stiff one, and felt the better for it. I must make a note of this, I thought, a few words on white paper, a big white square is better than a human face to reveal a confidence of this kind, saying I have reached the bottom of the barrel. And then somehow I was walking to the door, leaving a dead monkey in the room behind me, when I ran smack into Cactus himself, smelling strongly of talcum powder and Listerine. Oh yes, that was how he looked, of course, but could I ever have forgotten a face as commonplace as that? Why it's like forgetting how a white saucer looks!

A conversation seemed to follow—my, what a dialogue was that!— with him saying, "Excuse me, dear, I must have come on velvet feet," and me replying, "Why, certainly—that is if you'll excuse me," and him following with, "What for! I bumped into you—I'm an awkward sonofabitch." We stood there looking foolishly at each other. I had a vague feeling the room behind us was completely empty now—yes, the room must be empty, but someone else had recently been here—oh yes, that waiter—what happened to him? Then this smelly Cactus plant fellow was saying something, and frowning. What was he saying? A question of some kind. "Don't you feel well?" Oh yes, I feel well. How do you feel, Cactus? How does it feel to be a Cactus?

I looked at the clock on the table not far from Hal's plump hand, then at the hand with those neatly manicured nails and the inevitable solid gold ring containing three genuine diamonds, then back to the clock, one of those ornate pink and gold copies of sixteenth-century French timepieces: 7:31. The fat hand moves over next to the pink alabaster ashtray. The whole business would make a good cover for a cheap horror story. (Or is that just your idea, you with all that time on your hands to think up things against innocent ex-movie producers or cactus plants?) 7:32. Now Hal's hand is moving in a lordly gesture or his idea of same as he says something about "Fresh appetizers," grandly disdaining the mounds of caviar and smoked salmon left on the plate. 7:35. Calling on the phone to order something or other, then grabbing up the others one by one, my how he can eat and drink, too. And talk. ". . . nothing I like better than conversation, Manny's the one to tell you . . . I mean conversation with real people, kind you know you tell something to woan get repeated in circles can do you some harm. . . . And people used to say to me how come a young man like you—after all, that was ten years ago, I was just coming up—with your athletic build, clean-cut, marry a girl like Nadine? . . . How much stock did you get? That kind of thing. Well, all right—so I got control of the studio for a while—and so I went home nights to Nadine. What people don't seem to understand is, man's married to a woman looks like a horse, for two hundred dollars gets himself a face once a week looks like a rose, don't you see? Now which is he goina think about, you understand—the horse or the rose I ask you? . . . Only trouble is sometimes after a while, especially if you and your wife don't see eye-to-eye on the basic things, horse keeps coming at you even when you're with the rose and vice versa and that's one hell of a thing

2 5 7

is for sure. Another thing why that type of thing can cause trouble no matter how good the business is going and when that kind of thing starts going on why it don't matter about beauty no more, it's all the same that physical stuff is, I tell you it's all the same, and then you've gotta have a kinnered spirit, somebody that under-sta-a-a-nds. . . . Why sure this little dame Manny innoduced me to was fine—I mean she was a good little kid all right and I had the will, well, what I mean is I was ready and I had the enthusiasm and that kind of thing—and so did she, this actress he maybe mentioned to you—but what the hell can you do about a thing like that? Why I mean with two people of a like kind and seeing eye-to-eye on things . . . and nothing happens just nothing and what can you do about a thing like that? And then I met you and you were backward, why you were reluctant and disinclined and argumentative. You didn't think my jokes were funny why you preferred that fairy and Oh Yes the crownin' insult you thought I looked like Manny. I told Manny you didn't go for me—I told him, her I gotta have, I said—and he said sure you would come to a party here—and here you are and now we're going to have a real little talk."

7:55. The trance state is on. No, no, that couldn't be, not with you—dear God, not with Cactus. But everything is up front, big and bright. I am in danger, and I know it. I am up with it too, face to face with the most excruciating humiliating feature of the Stygian ferry when I see all of this in great shafts of extra light and when I know I can get away. But how? The thing to do now is to move quickly without anyone seeing me. I must keep alert because now, face to face with the murderer, with the imminent possibility of gar-roting, suffocation, strangulation or that other unmentionable that is something like smothering—it is clear, all clear, and I am in the midst of it. This is that silly talcum-smelling Hal Cactus who is touching me, oh it's only soft stuff now but he is dangerous, I know he can change in a flash. Closer, I know now he carries a weapon, I can feel his *sabreur*. It's all right for that foolish doctor to say why don't you run away, just leave quickly but now any move can mean trouble. This is what people don't understand. "You're so attractive—where did you get that sunburn?" Why from the rain, of course, you smart little fellow you. Where did you get those pretty capped teeth that shine so brightly in your funny little mouth?

8:05. He is just pretending with all these phony compliments. There's only one way, I see it now, just one escape. I must be crafty to come out of this alive, and craft is simple and inevitable as breathing. Yield, the voice commands. Yield to the little fat man with the dry breath and all those crazy capped teeth. He is Cain, the assassin, hiding behind the cheap toilet water. An Apache, a hatchet man, a bandit,—the very bandit for whom you have been waiting in fact—and this is your chance to outwit him. Where did I read it, *The push of death has swung her into life. . . .*

Suddenly, as I was being caressed by Hal, I became aware of two Hals there in the room moving back and forth before my eyes. One was Hal Killer, a murderer with a great bludgeoning weapon secreted on his person, who was about to spring on me, the counterpart of all the murderers bent upon my destruction. And just at his side was this foolish little California fat man with the unctuous voice making pompous Sunday supplement comments: "I'm going to do things for you." Listening to this oily voice, watching the dimpled hands and the black shiny sweet-smelling hair, I could see quite clearly the man who was making all this fuss and breathing so heavily had no intent to kill. But the other, the man inside, that was a murderer all right. That *thing* was the other man.

I moved quickly. Cactus looked genuinely perplexed. I had my voice now, "Sorry to break up Manny's little deal—" Cactus looked funny, gasping with disappointment. "What do you mean, Baby? I'll see you don't lose anything. Don't leave me, please—just stay and talk a while." Now he was talking again, all about his wife and his long visits to the beautiful girls in the whorehouses and how he found a girl who looked like Marlene Dietrich when she was very young, only better, and how he was now past that stage and he had to have something different. Then my voice was gone but I still knew, in that horrible knowing I had, what was going on. Cactus was taking hold of me, and the thing was happening. No no, dear God, not with this—let a storm come, an earthquake . . . but the room was very still with only Cactus moving. I remembered that plan, that terrible plan I had with the doctor, right now while the thing was happening. "Keep alert the next time it happens. . . .We've got to find out why. . . . It's the only hope now."

But I wasn't finding out anything. Merely enduring another ordeal, building to another blackened memory. Being thrown once again into the devil's mouth. He, the thing that operates me, is taking one more bite from my bleeding hide. The feeling of murder is in the room. I must be very quiet, do everything the man says, because maybe— somehow—in that way I can placate the enemy. Now it's Cactus, tomorrow who knows? This one and then that one, the jungle is filled with these creatures carrying weapons. And the smell that always comes with the experience, a funny close smell like the inside of some old house long closed.

I am acting strangely—I know it too—I never knew it quite as clearly before as I know now. What is this crazy thing I am doing? Why am I staying here with this man *when I know I can get up and leave?*

I look past his shiny hair to the door. About seven yards, twenty-one steps, and I could be out. Gone. Why don't I go? Why do I stay here?

Because a tremendous force is holding me here. Because a powerful inner voice is saying, Don't move. It is dangerous now to move. I never quite knew why before, but now I know.

I can smell the talcum powder. A memory awakens, glides like a snake in the shadows of the quiet room. I go after it. The talcum powder smells like death. The murderer had talcum powder on him.

Who is this plump, ageing stranger with the shiny hair coming closer by the second—hairy, and powdered with talcum powder? But I know, it's the man from California, and for some reason he brings with him a sense of impending murder. And that is why I am here with him at this terrible minute in time.

I could see the clock over his shoulder. 8:55. Afterwards, if I let the killer do whatever he wants, I may be able even though killed to get up and go away. It has always been like this, it will always be like this, so what is there to find out? Well if I could find the weapon somehow and hide it—but where can I hide it? Meantime I stared in stupid fascination at the damp overgrown pink mushroom leaping out of his hairy thighs and as I did I recognized in one blinding flash that this was the murder weapon! It had to be. There was nothing in the picture before me but the man and his penis. *No other weapon.*

And there was only one place to hide that particular weapon.

And if that is the case then Cactus, this foolish fleshy revolting little man, is not an actual murderer . . . because . . . as soon as the weapon is out of the way then I will be safe from the killer.

I continued staring stupidly at his ugly naked body into which the streams of past and present came pouring in one burning fountain of memory, a fountain so bright and alive the body which contained it was hardly a body any more but rather the generic substance of the male jungle in which I had walked. I looked in the mirror and saw us both in the love act. A fat man leaning over a woman. Even there in the mirror I found myself looking for the weapon, knowing he had hidden it and that in the yielding it would be destroyed. *Yes, I am doing the right thing, following the one clear line in a dangerous situation,* and as the weapon is being melted, so is safety coming on apace! Now Hal's two faces are moving faster in and out, and I can see Hal Sillyman and Hal Killer, and then, slowly, it is Hal Killer's face that begins to look *absurd,* and now there is just one Hal and he of course is silly. Now Hal with the shiny stinky hair and all those diamond mines and those sharp friends and all those capital gains is the only Hal, and the other killing Hal is shadowy and as I look at him he fades into nothing. The weapon is gone leaving Hal the ex-movie man, ha-ha.

What to do now? Don't say anything. Old Hal Cactus looks done in, but he is murmuring chivalrously those gay phrases. "You're a great little kid. Just right for me. And I thought I was through—can you tie that?" And then he was snoring.

I got up, smiling. I had a queer feeling of walking out of a whole dead world. So are you great, Hal Movieman, I thought as I began a hurried leave-taking. A great little experience because on that white hulk you call yourself I found out something I needed like hell to know. But enough is enough. I've got it, brother. And maybe, it's barely possible, why it's probable, I won't ever have to do anything like this again. Sleep Hal Diamond Mines, lying there like a dead animal, sleep, little movieman, the hero of my nightmare. *Good-by.*

CHAPTER THIRTY

· · · · · ·

THE NEXT DAY I WAS AT IT TOOTH AND NAIL WITH DR. SILVERS. THE early murder experience had moved up with the smell of the talcum powder—and now there it was, just over to the side in the shadows. There was the murderer full of talcum powder saying, "Don't move, don't cry out—" The main clue that stayed with me was terror of the feel of hair on a cat. But I could see now it was human hair, I could almost feel whose hair it was. "But I can't really remember what happened," I told Five, disconsolate and confused. I could by now put the whole thing together: an attempted assault, committed on a baby—leaving an impression of murder. I could almost remember, but not quite. "Did you know?"

Dr. Silvers said, "Yes. I didn't know immediately, but after a few weeks you had given me all the clues. It had to be, just like that. But you had to discover it for yourself—unfortunately by reliving it." The original traumatic experience kept rising and falling, but never coming completely alive. I couldn't remember those very early years. "You may be surprised what you'll remember, now that this area is freed. There's a man higher up, and he's the one we've got to bear down on. Remember the one we've caught is only his cohort. But if we bear down on him he may sing, and then we'll know everything." But even if we didn't, he said, it would be the same.

The relief I now felt was the most remarkable for its sense of joy. I knew I would never again be held in the grip of this terrible and dangerous involuntary duress, never again be the victim of this Hobson's choice, the most humiliating and blood-curdling aspect of my trouble. And now at last I took a look at this Gorgon's head, a pigeon-hearted glance at first. There it was, the great dead hulk, caught in the trap of this, my fifth inquisition. Better late than never, I thought, and *sauve qui peut!*

Now to the task of burying the corpse. A huge dead monster lying around the corner of the soul is not sanitary. I crept over and stared at it, wondering at its size—How often I could have been killed, and all the other "hydras and chimeras dire." A regular dinosaur of a creature, still bloated with the huge meals it had eaten off me, its fangs encrusted with my blood. Would it rise up again, perhaps not forever, but maybe for one more meal or two? I shuddered, and drew back. Or was it gone for good, dead as the old doornail? I moved forward now and looked again, fascinated by its enormity, wondering how I had ever managed to live with that thing inside me, and turned away at length, satisfied that it at least looked dead.

I will always remember those first few days after my great insight in the arms of old Cactus. The fresh feeling of release and joy would rise up in me just walking in the streets. I noticed the men looked entirely different than they had before, and as I felt the difference I saw clearly the compulsion I had suffered had included all men. Now it was different. Now it was gone. In crowded buses, or walking along the streets, looking at men, it was as if I were seeing them for the first time. There they were going along—some kind, some unkind, some interesting, some dull, some tall and others not so tall, some good-looking and others more plain. They were not murderers any longer, and I was not their victim. I'm free, I thought, as I went along. It has gone. Look at all these people taking freedom for granted, they can never know the way it really tastes. Sometimes I would laugh, not caring who saw me, as the feeling of relief and joy would burst over me suddenly, and sometimes people would glance in passing, bewildered or even amused, for joy like fear is contagious, but I didn't care. The whole world wore a new face.

"You're in love, of course," said Toni. "What's he look like?"

"Terrific," I lied. "Practically a god."

"When will I get a chance at him?"

"Soon. Any minute now."

It was true, in a sense. I had fallen in love with him of all people who had been the villain in the story but how could I tell her or anyone what I saw now in the face of the living life? I noticed a curious brightness and closeness in ordinary objects—an ash-tray, a table, a window, the furniture in the room seemed ingratiating and conciliatory rather than threatening, the trees in the outside yard were no longer silent masses in a mysterious background but beautiful living things of hope and grace, and there was a carnival spirit around me everywhere.

"There's much more work to be done," said Five. "We've only relieved one area of your problem—oh, I think it will make a great difference—but you see how long that took." I saw all right: the first and only genuine help I had ever received in these years with the witchmen! "I don't like to have to tell you—but a trouble like yours has seven heads. Strike one head off and the other six come up higher. We haven't cracked the case yet. We have to keep right at it." I went up there drunk with the champagne of victory, came out sober as a judge. You can't win!

At least I knew more about my unconscious, old Devman, as I called him. So he was not the crazy wild man I had imagined. He had kept me hidebound in the compulsion to yield because, as he saw it, to yield was the only safety. Knowing this made quite a difference. I knew now for a fact I had been correct in the one persistent feeling I'd had: I was stuck with an outraged baby, a baby who continued facing a murderer, even though there were no more murderers. In this sense the original experience was not actually dead; instead it was still going on somewhere, and occasionally something happened (with Cactus it was the talcum powder) which caused Devman to travel with the speed of light from the present back to the so-called past, creating a collision in time. And something was blown up.

All this had taken over a year, I was well into the second before the yielding compulsion blew up, and this was the sole accomplishment in these years of doctoring. Now, I naïvely imagined, now I can begin to live. But I wasn't living. The only change was in the fantasies going on in my head. Whereas before my secret daydreams were of being a slave girl purchased by a ruling prince and living as his creature, now an entirely new drama was being enacted in that theater inside, resembling a series of Technicolor movies, less sexually stimulating than the slave girl and the prince series, and more depressing.

In this series I was marrying a man who had no face—there was something up there above his neck of course, everybody has something above the neck, but his was vague and grew vaguer as the film rolled on. I was myself a kind of department-store dummy dressed up as a bride, and we were beginning together a plastic love-life. I can remember it now. As we take off on the plane, I begin to see we have something vital in common: we have both lost our heads and what greater bond could any two people have in common than simple headlessness? This seems to be Dr. Silvers' fault for having removed my head, turning my entire future into this paper stuff, whereas all he needed to do was to breathe on me and this would have changed me from a bisque dummy into a woman—but he was stingy to the end, even with his breath! Meantime my paper man and I go on rustling our bisque bodies together, making the cheerful sound of paper crinkling in a waste-basket.

"So the fantasies have changed," said Silvers. This meant I was "growing a new Oedipus" or "getting a new frame of reference." This was progress, he said, but to me it felt like standing still. I was still in the frog pond. I was finding out slowly that many others whom I had thought traversing the high road were actually leapers like me, swimming out their cursed time and having little light to cast on the human situation. The two women who I thought were so much better off than I, and so much wiser, living it up in the sunshine of the real world, were somewhat less than that. Sometimes, seeing Daphne those days, I would remember the sense of wonder she had first stirred in me at the mystery surrounding her, the remarkable secret something from which she drew that faith and sustenance I didn't have, and that made her seem by comparison as cool and swift as someone flying by on skis.

"No, I don't think she's flying by me on skis any more," I confessed to Toni. She was still a mystery though. I didn't understand her long engagement to Tom Richards, the amount of time they spent flying to Texas and back, the endless hours consulting with architects and decorators about the home they were building in Connecticut, the theater repertory company they started and dropped—all seemed rather a grand waste of something or other.

"There's something funny going on there," Toni commented. "I don't know what it's all about, Joyce, but I can tell you one thing." Eagerly I asked, "Yes, like what?" to see if she had reached the same conclusion I had. "Well, it's this place," she finally told me.

"She's always talking against it—ever since she came to live here, she's been saying it's terrible down here—bad vibrations, ghosts, all that Southern spook talk. Still and all, I don't know . . ."

"She doesn't want to leave here—is that what you're trying to say?"

"Ye-ah. Something about this old joint draws her like a magnet. Of course she's having herself one hell of a ball right now—I mean with Sir Harry and Tom taking her around. And with all the other men she's been able to attract now that she has this rich man. After all, she stands to lose something with marriage."

I knew what Toni meant. The place and the sharing of it, begun so informally during the war shortage, had developed into a convenient way of life—"for the time being," as we always said. There was comfort in having the other people around to talk to in off-minutes, we often included one another in engagements and activities, there being an extra edge in having a friend present with whom to discuss people and events the next day, as we each learned from watching the other handle problems and fight monsters in the long walk we were taking more or less together.

I remember one night that somehow seems like a peak in my non-living state when I expected "real life" would start up any minute. It was toward the end of the week—Friday, I think. I was dressed and waiting to go out to a party at Deirdre Mann's, putting on last-minute lipstick in my bedroom. Toni was sitting on the sofa in the living room, smoking and angling for a talk fest, the way she always did when about to end an anlysis or a love affair.

"My doctor says my problem is prenatal," she was saying. I said, "That's a new one, at least it's a new word to me. How does she fix that?"

She finished drinking a cup of tea she was taking with rum and lemon "to keep from getting a cold" and lit another cigarette. "They haven't found out how to reach these prenatal states yet. I told Jim and he says he thinks it's highly unethical—I mean her telling me such a thing as that. So I asked her why in hell she took me in the first place but she said she didn't realize the prenatal angle at the time."

A peal of laughter rushed across the room from Daphne's corner where she was pinning a veil on a dinner hat, preparatory to an evening on the town with Tom.

"Everybody's prenatal," she screamed, between giggles.

"What's so funny about it?" Toni asked.

"Well, look now, Toni—can't you see how ridiculous that is? Prenatal. Why don't you just get married and forget those damned doctors?"

"You forget everything by getting married, huh?"

"Well if you've got to be prenatal why don't you be prenatal in Beekman Place? There's a house coming up right across the street from that one we're getting—as a matter of fact, you might be able to get in before we can. I tell you, it's a great street for prenatalers. Tom says this is the time to buy property."

Toni listened with some interest. "With whom would I move in?"

I said, "What's the matter with Dr. Aranson?" but I knew from the way she drew in her mouth there was plenty the matter.

"Eh, I was out there Sunday and I met his mother again. She wants to marry him herself, of course. Jim says she has a heart condition and she can't live long and then of course he'll get married right away. A bunch of *meshugahs* those Aransons. It's like his mother's his wife, you see—"

"That Mr. Meyers brought you home night before last, for instance," said Daphne. "He looks like he'd love to be prenatal with you in Beekman Place."

"He's very nice," Toni admitted.

"Look, if you haven't anything to do, why don't you come out to dinner with Tom and me?" Daphne asked her. Toni said she couldn't do that, she was waiting for Jim to call, they were going to dinner at his brother's house.

"Everything's in Brooklyn with them," she wailed. "I told him he had to come for me, I'm not taking any more taxis to Brooklyn six dollars or more."

"Where are you off to, Joyce?" Daphne asked me. From the interest she was showing in Toni and me I sensed she wasn't too pleased about her evening with Tom. I told her Mrs. Mann had asked for her, I knew she'd be welcome if she and Tom were at loose ends, apparently it was going to be one of those brawls Deirdre and her tired husband gave to entertain their guests, and she said she might come later. Then the bell rang, and Daphne went on out.

"I wonder what's going on with her," Toni started, as soon as the door had closed. "Oh well, whatever it is, it won't last long. Life is so damned easy for those wax women, Joyce. I tell you, I wish I'd never started to get myself melted down."

I asked her once again before I went out if she wanted to change her mind and come along, but she said no, she was already starting to sniffle and she mightn't even go out with Jim.

I wondered fleetingly about the three of us as I bade her good-by. They were on the brink, too—even Daphne, she was hemming and hawing a bit these days. Who would win, I wondered? Who would get out first—if there is any getting out—out of the frog pond to the sunny side of the hedge? Or was that an optical illusion, the *couleur de rose* of my small spot in the old fishery?

CHAPTER THIRTY-ONE

· · · · · · ·

AN HOUR OR SO LATER AT THE MANN PARTY A GOOD-LOOKING MAN
named Sykes Kenyon,—I thought I'd seen him or someone like him
before—crossed the room to stand beside me. I had caught his face
the minute I saw it as he entered my orbit, a weather-beaten kind of
face unusual to this habitat and standing out in the hazy crowd like
a darkened sun in the twilight. Deirdre threw his name out at me,
"Sykes Kenyon, dear," using it like a whiplash. We said hello. I had
the impression he wanted to talk. But he was so surrounded by other
people, I quickly withdrew.

Some time later this same man crossed the crowded room to stand
beside me. "I've been waiting to talk to a doe in a green dress," he
said. "I've seen you before—I believe you know that isn't a gag." I
had the definite impression I had seen him before, or was it someone
who looked like him? No, that wasn't very likely, yet there was something familiar, a familiar vague feeling somewhere, I couldn't go
further than that. Yet we were talking to each other—warmly,
pleasantly, almost intimately—as if we had known each other, or
like people trying to remember where it was we'd met before, groping
for names and otherwise getting along when a group, a man and three
women, led by Deirdre Mann, came over to claim him. And in a few
minutes he was surrounded again and so was I, albeit by different
groups.

It must have been hours later—Daphne and Tom had come by
after all, the food had been served and forgotten, it was nearly time
to go—when I saw this Sykes Kenyon again, this time talking to Red.
I slowed down to look at him, and again the sense of something
familiar hit me, but this time I was thinking about him. He was

good-looking but that self-possession was almost arrogant, at least this total composure somehow rubbed me the wrong way. Why, from the way he moved and looked he might have been one of those tall, comfortable people Daphne kept bringing around, those remote, tentative people who one knew were men because of their male clothes but who had no more live problems or personality than so many steel vaults. One of those, no doubt.

He caught my eye just then and turned around. This time Red formally introduced us, and now I had a better chance to see what he was like. The steel-vault business was deceptive, I decided, talking to this dark-complexioned man, with black eyes and brown bushy hair, and that tan weathered skin and a scar like a shadow just over his left eye which never quite disappeared. We talked about San Francisco, he had lived there for three years. There was more hebetudinous patter. Deirdre had turned on her radio, people were dancing. Red danced off with Daphne and Sykes danced with me. And for some strange reason the original attraction I'd felt flashed out like a light the minute I touched him.

He called the next day and asked me to have dinner with him, adding quickly that other people might come along—Red, for instance—and was that all right with me? I said it was and he came with Red and another couple, an actor and his actress-wife, Jan and Mira Harley. Later, listening to these four people loudly discussing the relative merits of a play Sykes wanted to produce in which Red thought he might invest some capital and the Harleys act, I saw clearly this wasn't a date with me Sykes had made but more a convenient place to come and promote himself. It didn't matter; I was in fact amused at the rapidity with which he had maneuvered me into being a pawn in the obvious game, deciding I didn't mind serving them liquor and listening to the discussion, when Toni called.

She had been at her mother's since the night before and the two women had apparently had another quarrel. "Look, Joyce, I have to get out of here right away. Because you see I turned down one of those Christian Science meals of hers, raw eggs with raw egg sauce, and we're not speaking. And I don't have anything to do tonight and I'm kind of hungry and I thought if you or Daphne were going anywhere . . ." I told her to come right along, I didn't know where

Daphne was—in her room, I thought, but there was company here and dinner in the offing. When I came back Daphne had drifted in, coming out of her room when she heard a play being discussed.

It seemed like hours before the seven of us finally took off for dinner. Later, Toni and Sykes managed to leave the table immediately after dinner—we had just ordered coffee in the crowded, smoky eating emporium—and repaired to the bar together. While I had long since given Sykes up in my mind, some part of me was still groaning and wailing at the decision. I knew that, as I saw Toni and Sykes talking together excitedly like two long-lost lovers, torn apart by cruel circumstance, who have suddenly and miraculously been reunited. There was coffee and brandy, Red began tearing into the play now that its main defender had left, the Harleys began looking worried and talking about going home, Daphne moved beside me and began pounding my ear.

"Don't look so depressed. Sykes Kenyon and Toni—they deserve each other." I didn't find the matter quite as funny as she did. "Did you know, for instance, they call him *the monster* around radio row? Listen, baby, he's been married three times—always to rich women from whom he gets alimony. The last one was out West somewhere and he sued her and collected. It was in the papers. Oh, he's talented all right. He can play the piano and write shows and act and direct. But he's rough on women and unpredictable. I tell you, he and Toni were made for each other. Will they have a ball!" She was howling.

I didn't completely believe Daphne, but later, when Toni and Sykes had finally returned to our table, I began to think at least part of it might be true. That was when a tall, attractive red-haired girl came by and stopped to speak to Sykes. He stood up to greet her, talked courteously for a few seconds, then suddenly his voice changed. "Yeah . . . all right, Terry, but not now—this is not the time. . . . Can't you see I'm busy? So long. Scram—I've said all I'm going to say—"

"Did you have to be so rude?" Toni wailed plaintively. Sykes looked down at her, more pleased than the situation seemed to warrant, said, "She'll be back," and continued talking as if nothing had happened. But the jarring note had affected the group. I was relieved when the party finally broke up. As we went for our coats, Toni pulled me aside.

"Is he anything to you?" she asked in her most intense voice.

"No," I said. "Nothing at all. Why?"

"Well because—Look, darling, something very *funny* has been happening. You saw me talking to him, didn't you?" I nodded assent; she went on, growing more intense. "Well, it's something very interesting—very peculiar. I can't tell you now—but maybe I'll see you tomorrow. I'm very excited about him."

I tried to tell her what Daphne had said, especially the bit about the alimony, but she brushed me aside. "Oh, people have their own personal reasons for what they think—especially Daphne. She was crazy about him at one time—did she tell you *that?*"

Toni's "maybe I'll see you tomorrow" must have burned out somewhere in Sykes' torch. It was two weeks before I heard from her again, this time on the telephone. "Look, I can't talk to you now, darling—they're waiting to take us out to lunch—but do you mind if I come down sometime this afternoon?" she gasped. "It's all right if you'll be out—I want to get my things . . ." I didn't know who the *us* or the *they* were, but her voice had a new exuberance, and she was spontaneous and decisive. "I'll be there around four. I'd love to see you, Joyce, but if you're busy, we'll get together very soon. Good-by now, doll—and listen—don't worry about a thing, you hear?"

Something had happened—I was eager to hear about it—but when I returned home it was nearly six and I assumed she would have come and gone. I was surprised to find her still there, standing in the midst of the debris in her old bedroom with one suitcase packed and a dozen or more outfits laid end to end across the bed. "Hello, sweetheart. Look, I think I won't pack these things—I'll just put them over my arm and take them as is in a taxi, what do you think? Because, you see, we're going out tonight and I don't know which one of them will be appropriate and so I don't want any of them to get messed up, don't you think I'm right? What time is it?"

"Six o'clock. Tell me what's been happening. Is it a job—or a man?"

She laughed. "Both, darling—I mean this man is a job—in fact, he's the job. Gee, I forgot, honey—You don't know anything about it. I've been so busy I haven't had a chance to think—and maybe that's good."

She talked as she went over her clothes and I heard the news. "He's the perfect man for me, darling. Here's what's so spectacular. I never thought it would happen, and now here it is. The knight with the horse and the sword. In fact, this is the works. Oh, it's so *healing,* having a good relationship . . ."

"Stop long enough to tell me what it's like."

"Well you see I never thought I would ever find anybody to really fit my pattern—and here's what's so funny. You see he didn't think he would ever find anybody to fit his."

She seemed more solid than ever before, thriving with vitality and excitement, and—yes, she gave me the impression of having somehow been rebuilt or put together. So, Toni was out of the hospital. Toni was leaving the island. As I watched her scooping up her things, the room becoming emptier by the minute, there seemed to be something symbolical in the way she was discarding all the old reading matter, those piles of the *Daily Worker,* the society columns and the books, *The Function of the Orgasm* and *Neurosis in Our Times,* junked together in the corner with worn brassieres and girdles from times past.

"Don't you want to take your books?" I asked.

"I don't think so. The place is lined with books. And anyway I don't have time to read any more. I'm living, baby. Look, I've got to run now, darling—but I'm longing to talk to you. I'll call you over the weekend maybe. Could you just help me get these things into a taxi?"

Yes, she was like a new city, she was definitely in business, her eyes were clear and bright, and whatever she had found, or whomever, seemed to have removed all her old troubles in one fell swoop. As I followed her out, both our arms laden down with her clothes, we went on talking.

"You haven't told me his name. What is it—so when I call you and talk to the maid, I'll know who I'm asking for?"

She giggled. "Sykes, dopey. Sykes Kenyon. He's the man I met with you that night—don't you remember?"

I remembered all right. I remembered so well I didn't say anything. So, this was the man who had brought Toni happiness. I had been attracted to him, I remembered, but had quickly turned away, and now he had done all this for Toni in such a short time!

We were standing in the cold street, waving for a taxi. "What's the matter, honey?" What was the matter? It was simple this time. I was green with envy. "You look funny, Joyce. Did you have a crush on him?"

"No," I lied. "I hardly knew him."

"Oh, that. Daphne hardly knew him, too—but wait till I tell you what happened between *them*. Listen, next time, darling—you'll come see us in Sykes' duplex. It's the most beautiful place I've ever seen —with a garden and a fountain. Well, maybe before that we'll have a chance to talk. I want to hear all about you."

Then the taxi we had been signaling stopped, Toni piled in with all her clothes, the door closed, and she was gone. I went back into the empty apartment, alone with my visions of the happy couple.

Weeks later she finally found time to call me. "Joyce darling, you can give away that box of clothes I left with you. The other stuff— well I might come down there tonight and dress—if you're going to be in—and maybe we could go over it and see if you want some of it —and the rest I'll take with me." I said all right, I thought I would be home. During the afternoon, I opened up the box and seeing the cheap flannel suits, overalls and heavy shoes she had worn while trying to be a worker, I felt as if I'd stepped back into the era of Toni and the Marxian doctor. These days, living in Sykes' duplex, the overalls would have seemed like costume stuff for some old Leftish play.

She arrived promptly at six—complete with high heels, mink coat and one of the familiar cock-eyed but very becoming fur hats she liked to wear. After the usual Hello darlings, followed fifteen minutes of passionate telephone dialogue with Sykes—"Yes, darling . . . Oh, did you? . . . Oh no, sweetheart—I don't think we'd better have all those people at the same time, Lover—because as you say I am not quite that developed socially, sweetheart—Okay, baby, I will . . . And if you want anything you can call me here at Joyce's . . ." Then she went over her clothes, settling before the mirror to make up her face, and as she did she talked intermittently. "Oh, Joyce, it's so wonderful being well. It's pure excitement—this life Sykes and I have together—and of course it's growth-making. You see here's what's so curious about this thing. He and I are made for each other—

psychically I mean. I mean Sykes has the drive—the absolute need to do the exact thing I need to have done to me. Like I told you that night—you remember when I first met him—and we were sitting at the bar—"

"But you didn't tell me," I reminded her. "You haven't told me yet —and for God's sake, what is it?"

"Oh, you mean I forgot to tell you? Well, I guess that's because I've told everybody else and so of course I thought—I assumed I told you. You see that's why I'm so grateful to you—because you introduced me to him. And because it's such a terrific coincidence. I mean, darling, it's a problem finding a man who meets your fantasy —and who happens to find in you the exact girl who meets his fantasy."

"What fantasy?" I screamed the question. "You mean the one you told me about—that's like mine?"

"I guess so, Joyce—but I've forgotten about yours. In my fantasy I'm a slave girl and I belong to a king. I've been so damned busy with this fantasy I've lost out on lots of jobs. The king is cruel and wonderful and brings me to the palace—and whips me and does all kinds of marvelous things. It's terribly exciting—meeting somebody in real life who has a fantasy in which he's the king. Now tell me about yours."

"In my fantasy the man is a prince. He buys slave girls in the market place, I'm one of them, and has them brought to his palace."

"Oh yes, I remember. Well, isn't that something? Well now like I said Sykes's fantasy fits both of ours because he does the slave-buying. Can you imagine what it's like—I mean the slave-dreaming girl meets the king-dreaming man in real life. And they're both in the theater. What's the matter? I guess it's never happened to you, huh, honey?"

"No," I admitted, full of longing, fascination and resentment, as I remembered my own secret fantasies which had returned and which I seemed doomed to live out in my head while here was Toni having hers right out in the real world.

"It does seem funny—two of us having the same fantasy life, doesn't it? Tell me more about yours, Joyce."

And thus encouraged I blurted it all out. "Sometimes he sees me in the market place—sometimes it's the forest.

"Sometimes he's on horseback—sometimes in a carriage?"

I nodded.

"Jesus—you, too!" Toni howled with laughter. "I'd forgotten about you having the same fantasy. I have trouble enough with the king, honey. I can't be tangling with your prince. And now listen—your prince, is he tall?" I nodded. "Very rich? Of course he's handsome— and he's generous—and he's cruel—" I nodded to every quality she named. "With different kinds of instruments? And whips?"

I nodded. "The instruments alone can take hours," I allowed. Now she nodded, her eyes wide with wonder. "Sometimes the fantasy starts out tenderly—but he always turns somewhere in the middle. Of course when it starts I know he's going to turn. In the end I am completely conquered by him—pinned down—overwhelmed—I mean over-powered—helpless. And it hurts . . ."

"That's him all right." She was looking very serious. "I mean that's the exact same guy in my daydreams, with some exceptions, of course. I'm practically always a slave. Jesus, I see I've been smart, I mean in keeping you away from Sykes. You dream of being treated cruelly and whipped at the post and that kind of thing—and Sykes dreams of doing exactly that kind of thing. And you know something he told me?" I waited with increasing interest. "You know originally he liked you very much. That was before I cut in, of course."

"Yes, I remember—"

"He said there was something he could see in your eyes."

The telephone rang. I answered. It was Sykes, calling to speak to Toni. I listened as they talked, my face burning as the words of love I heard first dampened the minutes and then dried them brittle. There was no use now. Toni had him, this remarkable thrilling man, Sykes Kenyon, and as it looked to me at that time he was the last fantasy prince left in the entire world. A prize.

Toni was walking quickly away from the telephone. "Listen, darling, I'm in a terrible rush now. I've got to fix my face now and listen, you help me, won't you?" She settled in the corner of the sofa and started making up her face right out of her bag. "The people are up there already," she went on. "Sykes is furious—I'll get it tonight all right. But I don't dare go up there without my face just right. Sykes says everything must be perfect, it's his theatrical sense, and I can see what he means. Now look at this white make-up, he likes it the best, and tell me for God's sake have I got it on right?"

I thought the make-up was on straight anyway, though the effect was slightly ghastly. But I was envious as I watched her fixing it up, even though I listened as she generously went on handing out advice to me. "Darling, you'll never get well until you indulge your fantasy. Maybe no doctor would tell you that. Maybe you just have to stumble into it in life."

"But that's such an accident."

"I know it is, but it's the only way. Bring it out into the open and live it up—and then you'll be well suddenly."

"You mean you're well now?"

"But of course. Completely. It's the healing."

"I see. I'll look around . . ."

"But you see you have to be so careful, Joyce. I mean—well like I say, you may have to wait and just fall into it one day. Or maybe never."

"What do you mean—never?" I think I detested her at that minute. "My fantasy life plagues me to death. I find it exhausting. Oh, I'd do anything to stop it!"

"It's no good to feel that way about it, honey. And it's no good to feel ashamed of it, either."

"But you can't feel any other way. It's nothing to feel proud of."

"Well most people have a secret daydreaming life. All imaginative people do. And for all I know all the unimaginative people do too. I guess most people feel ashamed about it. My doctor says she has an awful time getting people to come out and talk about what they do in this sexual dreaming. They just won't tell what they do or what gets done to them."

I understood all about that: it is not easy to reveal to another that your fondest desire is to be done in. "And all the time it's draining off their energies and keeping them from living."

"There's only one answer and that's to live it out."

She had the make-up on full now and was beginning to take it off.

"Most people can't do that," but I had to notice how hopeless my own voice sounded. "You can't make a fantasy happen."

"Oh I know, and that's why I'm so fortunate. I've found my dream-boat—and he just happened to be going my way. You've got to

2 7 7

remember it's very complicated, dear. One chance in a thousand, finding a man who likes to do these things to women, and knows how to do them. And in addition has intellect, and talents. Does that look like a smudge up there near my eye?"

I said no, it looked like a shadow, and she decided to leave it alone. I watched her close up her bag and slip into her coat. She screamed good-by as she ran down the stairs. And then she was gone. I heard her walking in the street, and then I heard a taxi start up, and I thought some more about her. She was going up there to the duplex Sykes had, a shining place, no doubt. I envisioned an enormous group of rooms—the New York version of the palace where the king of Toni's fantasy was waiting. The place seemed terribly empty with her gone, leaving me alone with the pictures of all that I had lost.

CHAPTER THIRTY-TWO

. . . . . .

SUDDENLY IT WAS CHRISTMAS AGAIN. AND THERE WAS I, OBSERVING the familiar lighted trees, people hurrying along loaded down with packages for their loved ones, and feeling the sense of excitement and expectancy in the air again. I was in the midst of wrapping packages the night before Christmas Eve, with Daphne standing by waiting for Sir Harry and Tom—they were a regular threesome those days— when the telephone rang and Daf ran to get it. "It's Toni," she called. "Wants to know if you'd like to go to a party with her. Look, you'd better talk to her. She sounds funny."

I lifted the receiver and heard the old Toni voice. "Eh, it's this goddamned *goisha* festival here again, gets anybody down. Listen now, like I told you Sykes is putting on *Outward Bound* tonight—and Sol Meyers—he's that rich man, Daphne met him—well he's giving a big party afterwards and can you come? Because listen, if you can, why then maybe I'll come on down to your place and get dressed. I'm just leaving the dressmaker's and I've got this new dress Sykes designed and it looks kind of crazy and maybe after I put it on, why you and Daphne can tell me maybe I'd better not wear it." I said yes, I'd like to go with her to the party, and she could come down.

I was just about to say good-by when she spoke again. "Don't tell Daphne—but I'm breaking with Sykes." I said No, unbelieving. "He's destroying me," she went on in a low voice. "My doctor thinks loving a man like this—brutal and unattainable—is deliberately staying on an infantile level. Anyway, oh God, I think he's got another girl. Don't tell Daphne, hear? He didn't come home last night and—I'm too depressed to talk any more. I'll be right down."

Later, I was dressing in Toni's old room, and she was making up before the mirror—using Daphne and me for her audience—before I realized she had not really broken with Sykes, no matter what she thought.

"This new stuff I'm putting on my face cost eighteen bucks a bottle. You two tell me now—is it the same color as the dress?" We both looked, and decided the color of her skin with the skin lotion was the same as the cocoa-colored velvet wonder she was wearing, and that the effect was stunning. "Because you see, Sykes says it has to be the same shade as the dress, and it is if it's put on right. He usually does it for me. And if it's on right why then it should make me look like a continuous stream of cream!"

"You look like a stream all right," said Daphne.

"I have to be careful how I look tonight because this girl who's interested in him is going to be there. This Sharon Dougherty. Do you know her, Daphne?"

"Yes, I know Sharon."

"Well, what do you think?"

"I wouldn't worry too much about her taking him away—if that's what you mean. She's got a million bucks of her own—she owns buildings—and all the men she wants. What on earth would she do with him?"

Toni actually turned away from the mirror. "But what do you think of her? What's she like as a person?"

"As a person? She's more of an operator. She's one of those beautiful jobs from Texas who keeps marrying millionaires."

"Have you ever talked to her?"

"No, I don't think she talks much to women . . . unless maybe it's somebody very important. Let's see, the last time I saw her—we were at the same party but she didn't say a word to me until afterwards— just as we were leaving, we happened to be powdering our noses at the same time in the john."

"Well, what did she say?"

"I remember just one thing she said. I was brushing my hair and she commented, 'You have very dry hair, dear.' That was the only conversation we had."

There was some last-minute talk about our plans for the evening. Tom was having some people in at his suite at the Waldorf, Toni and I were invited but we didn't see how we could make it and still see *Outward Bound*. The general idea was that if we didn't make it to Tom's party, Daphne was to bring Tom and Sir Harry down to Sol Meyers' so we would all meet there later. Then the bell rang and Daphne went out, saying, "That must be Sir Harry. Well, Merry Christmas, kids. Don't worry about Sharon, Toni. I just can't see them together."

"I think Sharon's in just the same—and I'm out," Toni announced, the minute Daphne had gone. "Of course I'm not sure yet—but I know she's the one he's seeing. Joyce, I've got her on my mind all the time. He told me about her—I guess I think about her more than he does. Even when I'm with him, I'm thinking about her."

"She hasn't got the right pattern for him. She can't possibly fit his fantasy."

"But he's fascinated. Wait till you see her. She's been married to three millionaires, and I hear they're all still crazy about her. Daphne doesn't dig her."

"Maybe they're too much alike."

"Maybe. Say, that's an angle. She's never had to give anything. She just takes—and this is what fascinates Sykes. He told me she doesn't ever see very much of her husbands. They're all too busy fox-hunting or something that rich people do outside of the house."

I tried again. "But her needs can't possibly fit Sykes' needs. It's some temporary aberration he's got—maybe it's just another promotion scheme. You two really had something."

"Things like that don't matter to him now. He's fascinated by money. He thinks maybe she'll put on his play—you remember that terrible thing he wrote." I nodded. "But it's more even than that. It's the feeling of money around—big money, and people just having it without doing anything—that fascinates him. He told me about it, he says he's always been queer for girls with money. You know he's gotten alimony, don't you?"

I made a suggestion. "If you feel so upset about the situation—and you think this Sharon will be there tonight—why don't you just not go to the party?" But the minute I'd finished saying it I realized how stupid it was.

"I can't *not* go, Joyce. I have to go." She took out a cigarette but put it down unlit. "It's my only chance to keep them apart."

"But if you have to get over loving men like Sykes—well then every time you think about him, all you have to think is, Right at this minute he's probably giving Sharon the same treatment!"

I must have said the wrong thing. Toni looked at me with absolute hatred in her eyes.

"You're a square!" she screamed. "You just don't get it. I'm jealous as hell of what he's doing or going to do to her."

She got up off the stool and began walking in the small space between her bed and the door. Her eyes looked shiny and scared.

"I've never had anything like Sykes before. He takes over and tells me what to do . . . He makes me feel like a woman. Inferior—leaning on him—female. You never know just what he's going to do, you have to keep jumping to keep up with him, but you feel so feminine, Joyce. And you feel so alive." She put her hand on her stomach. "Have you got any Scotch?"

When I came back with the bottle and the glasses she was slumped down before the mirror, busily wiping the make-up from her face and putting on new. She seemed uncertain in her movements, she kept starting and stopping, and seeing that glazed look in her eyes and red spots in her cheeks and the dry burned-up lips, involuntarily I turned away as if I had seen some sick core sending out germs. She was sick, I knew, as I busied myself with the drinks, but when they were ready she was still sitting there, doing nothing at all, and as I glanced at her I suddenly remembered Cheetah, Daphne's cast-off cat, sitting in the butcher store window looking out at nothing. I put the whiskey down noisily and hollered, "Wake up, Toni! You're going out, remember? It's getting late."

She looked around and reached for the whiskey, and slowly the vagueness went out of her eyes.

"Oh, thanks, Joyce." She finished the drink and reached for another, poking me with the glass. "I was feeling funny. I kept seeing that girl—and she seemed to be growing bigger and more beautiful—and then I couldn't seem to think about anything else." I got into my dress and began putting my things into the evening bag that was new and too small. By the time Toni finished the second drink she was looking much more normal, standing up and straightening out her dress.

"I feel like doing something to him . . . but what can I do? I can't kill him, you can't kill people, you just get put in jail. For some reason

2 8 2

I don't feel like doing anything to her—this new girl, I mean. I can't feel it's her fault—it's just him, I keep thinking, that's how he is." She pulled up her stockings and began wiping the tips of her slippers. "I don't know what I'm going to do—but I'm going to do something. I'll be playing it blind—but there'll be something—there has to be something I can take away from him. There always is something like that—something a person wants . . ."

"Tell me about this Meyers boy. Daphne thinks he's great."

"One more drink, and then we'll have to go. He's no boy, darling. He's a widower with a son my age, but you know I like older men. Makes sports clothes. He's thinking of going on regular television. This is his first show tonight. Sykes has been promoting him like mad. One of those lonesome manufacturers . . . I haven't met his son yet. Acts kind of desperate—the way he asks total strangers to his place—everybody he meets with Sykes or me."

"But maybe these people won't come—after all, if they're strangers?"

"They'll come, the bastards. They're all lonesome, too. This Sol can't stand to be alone. He says the silence scares him."

"Then you have things in common. How many times have you told me when the phone doesn't ring it scares you?"

"All right, so the silence scares me too—listen, you don't go around telling people stuff like that. Because if you do they take advantage—think you're on a bargain counter."

"I'm not going to tell anybody."

I looked at the clock in the dining room. We had talked so long we had to rush now to make it. As our taxi drove through the rainy streets, filled with crowds of last-minute Christmas shoppers, Toni remembered the eye shadow Sykes had given her which she had forgotten at the last minute. "It's too late to put it on now," she said, "so that'll be just one more thing I haven't got any more."

At the broadcasting station we shuttled between the viewers' room and the studio, standing in the dark a good part of the time watching the actors speak their lines. It was warm and tense as it always is in these places, the air becoming more stifling from the rising anxieties of all these beautiful people. During the first act a tall sunburned girl in a tight-fitting pink brocade dinner dress walked on the set, a pale fur coat slung over her shoulder like a scarf, and stood watching the play. "That's her," Toni whispered.

The most remarkable feature of her personality for me was the way she had of balancing the expensive-looking coat on her shoulder without the use of arm or hand. It reminded me of the comedienne I'd seen in a Yiddish play downtown who made her entrance dropping a mink coat before her and walking calmly over it. "Look how she watches him." Sykes, in shirt sleeves and perspiring under the lights, was busy overseeing the show. The girl was indeed watching him, but so was everyone else who had come on the set, including me. I remembered this was the man with whom I believed Toni had found such happiness and it caused me a turn of envy.

Other people meandered on to the set, and in time we were surrounded. I met a big good-natured hard-breathing fat man named Sol Meyers who handed me a plump soft hand, looked at me with big soulful brown eyes, oddly out of place in his plump white porcine face, and said in a heavy gruff voice, "Hullo, I've been waiting to meet Toni's best friend. I know you must be a sweet gull if what Toni says about you is true." Next in line, apparently Sol Meyers' partner in the firm of Van Cleve and Meyers, manufacturers of Meyers Magic Sportswear, appeared Mr. Van Cleve and his wife. The introductions were going on apace when Sykes appeared suddenly in our midst. He was poised and charming, with just the right change of tone as he spoke alternately to Toni and me, and then to his sponsors.

Then the tall girl came toward me, still giving her coat that ridiculous casual treatment. Now she was beside Sol, a young giantess standing a good head above him, smiling a big toothy smile showing the dimples in her pink cheeks as her thick blond hair fell back from her head like a horse's mane, and out of her big healthy brown eyes came a wide cold empty stare. For some reason the voice that emanated from her pretty mouth in answer to the masculine chorus, "Hello, Mrs. Dougherty," or "Merry Christmas, Sharon," came as a shock: it was crisp and almost bossy, a busy young matron answering the inquiries of the servants. I remember saying something or other to her—it must have been about the show because I remember her saying, "Oh it's all right—kind of depressing though. I guess I like musicals best—if they ever get on teevee." Sykes winced as this epic bit of tactlessness flew through her perfect teeth, but Mr. Van Cleve guffawed sympathetically. And her hair gleamed, her diamond earrings flashed and the curve of her bare suntanned shoulder was so attractive that no one seemed to mind except Toni, who had lost her voice while Sharon was being introduced to her.

In the sparse ten minutes before the last act started I saw what it was Sykes had that made him so interesting to women—besides the complicated bag of psychic tricks and physical exercises, that is. A certain almost sly ingratiating way of turning his full attention on the woman to whom he was speaking, his big brown head moved first over Sharon, and this *mise-en-scène* completed, he came and stood over me, inclining his shoulders and body forward until he enclosed me like an open umbrella and leaning closer than was necessary he spoke in a soft slightly tense voice, as if what he was saying was of the utmost importance and for my ears alone. Whatever he asked, "What do you think of the show? Tell me the truth, please," or "Try to come to the party at Sol's, won't you?" the questions fell down from him in a tender whisper, sounding as if he were speaking into a hush-a-phone and offering a trip to some low-pressure paradise all his own.

"Say, Sykes, don't you think that moved pretty slow—there at the end?" The man named Van Cleve cut in. "I thought you said last night you were going to plant some more business—didn't you think so, Sol?" Sykes straightened up, a look of polite boredom on his handsome face, as Sol left Sharon flat and joined his partner.

"I told him if he don't watch out it's going die on its feet," Sol announced. "This kind of religious stuff shouldn't be so slow, should be some wise cracks thrown in, people moving or something. I told you that last night, boy—"

"It can't go fast and have any effect," Sykes sighed the words. Sol glanced angrily toward him; he was about to say more when the bell for the third act started ringing. Sykes left the group immediately, followed by Sharon, who smiled tentatively at Mr. Van Cleve, who smiled broadly back.

"What do you think now?" Toni whispered as we made our way back to the viewers' booth. "She's terrific-looking, isn't she?" I said, "Yes, but awfully cold. It won't work, honey—" Sol was just behind us, I shh-shhed her to pipe down but apparently she couldn't. "No-body's that cold, he's only just started on her . . . Absolutely devotes himself to you . . . nothing he won't do . . . Even the wife of the super in his building—she must be sixty—she's got a crush on him a mile high." Sol kept mincing behind us, he was listening attentively. "There's probably another man like him somewhere but who's got the time to go looking for that. Even if I found it it wouldn't be the same. But I'm not giving up. I can't. You saw me talking to Clyde Van Ness—he played the boy—he knows Sharon. Well he told me something—she thinks Sykes is rich—he's been taking her around and throwing parties. That's why he asked me to take my clothes out—"

Sol was almost abreast of us; I stage-whispered, "We have an audience!" We were just entering the viewers' booth when fortunately Sol's partner buttonholed him, and Toni continued uninterrupted as we made our way to our seats. "It hasn't started yet—the sex between them hasn't started yet. There's something he does . . . an absolute trade mark of Sykes Kenyon. That's not his real name, by the way. The sonofabitch stole it out of a book."

The door to the booth was opening, a question of seconds now before Meyers and Van Cleve would be taking their seats near us. Already Sol's sad excited eyes, the whites bright in the light from the hall, were searching the darkened room for Toni.

"Always has the new girl answer the phone when the old girl calls up—I know because that's what he made me do with Thelma. She'd call and I'd have to say, Mr. Kenyon isn't here now. I felt like an awful heel. . . . Well he told me he was giving this dinner party to promote the play—I wasn't invited—but when I called I knew nothing had happened because Sharon didn't answer the phone." The whispering stopped suddenly as Sol settled in the empty seat beside her. "Oh hello, Sol—"

Van Cleve and his wife sat beside me, Van Cleve making remarks about radio and television that were obviously supposed to be funny. He had a hard crusty laugh, an oppressively energetic delivery, indicating in the home circle he was the life of the party, and Mrs. Van Cleve, a small woman with a large duck-shaped torso all wrapped up in tight black satin, and a head of pale blue curls, roared so heartily with laughter I wondered how she performed the trick. "Charlie is always like this," she confided. "Nothing bothers him, he's always like this." Thus encouraged, her husband began aiming his words like stones thrown out into the room, followed with those guffaws of self-appreciation. "Well when's the skywriting gonna start?" "How do you people like the postwar cruise?" and "Anybody wanna take down the story of my life?" having caused Mrs. Van Cleve to roll toward me with another confidence, "He's just getting started," I gave her a benign look of general agreement just as the lights in the booth went out, causing everyone to be furtively grateful.

The last act of *Outward Bound* finished, stroking the audience with the comforting thought of life going on after death, our group was now standing outside under the canopy in the rainy street, waiting for Sol, who had gone off to find his car. Toni, still tense but lovely in her beige velvet coat, was telling Mrs. Van Cleve the remarkable prospects awaiting us all in the brave new world of television, I found myself facing Van Cleve. I was just being told about salvation through squandering—or what a naughty business this donating money to Europe was—and feeling colder by the minute when Sol's car drew up to the curb and his big comfortable voice hollered, "Come on in—don't get wet." By contrast to his partner old Sol, with his plump hands and thick smiling lips and conciliatory voice, was warm as a dish of hot meat. "I'll take the gulls in my car, Charlie—you take the missus and some of the others—"

"But you invited the whole cast, Sol," Toni reminded him. "We'd better wait for Sykes so he can tell them where to go."

"They know where to go." Sol laughed as he helped us in. "That Sykes—you never know what he'll do, anyway. He might take hours."

Sol had to deliver a Christmas package on the other side of town so we were late in arriving. Obviously it hadn't taken hours for Sykes to arrive. In fact, as Sol's butler opened the door into the Meyers' apartment—which the lonesome widower Sol shared with his taller, more remote and less interesting bachelor brother Paul, a lawyer—one of the first faces we saw in the large rooms, filled already with some fifty people, and carloads more arriving, was Sykes. He left the fireplace beside which he had been standing in a group, talking to the Van Cleeves, Sharon, and some members of the cast, and made straight for us, but Toni by-passed him so quickly I lost track of her and found myself standing in a corner of the room alone with him. He began where he'd left off at the station, with that hush-a-phone business. "Hello, Doe dear. I'm so glad you got here. I know you're going to help, I just know it. When I first saw this brawl I thought, won't go, just won't go, but now things seem to be brightening up— I mean getting worse."

I thought I saw Stream making straight for Sharon, Sykes must have seen them too, he blinked his eyes and gasped, "Eh, women!" as he grabbed two glasses of whiskey from a passing tray. "Here, have this with me, let's see what it'll do," he muttered as he simultaneously refused another tray of mouth-watering appetizers. I remember trying to make out a Latin inscription over Sol's gray marble mantel; Sykes translated it "A small loan makes the debtor a troublesome enemy." It seemed funny beneath a gargantuan painting of a hostile-looking woman with a cold sneering smile. I was listening to Sykes, one drink finished, another half-finished while he looked for the butler to bring him more, talking to me against a circle of people who drifted in and out. "We're short on time here. A high wave is about to roll the schooner on her beam end, as you no doubt know. I know you're Toni's confidante, she tells everything, a man hasn't got a chance with you women, I mean his privacy isn't worth a nickel." I muttered appropriate words of denial, I didn't know a thing about anything. "I'll bet you know every move I've made for the last forty nights and days, including the Christmas list I slipped into my robe this morning." The butler appeared with fresh whiskey, a maid with champagne, followed by Toni and Sharon with Sol and his brother Paul, "Here, you gulls have some wine," and pretty soon we were drinking and talking and moving in one of those mob scenes where dozens of people met dozens of other people, conversations sprang up to be interrupted aborning by new conversations springing up.

Time stretched. Faces grew larger. Sol's excessive politeness waned, his boundless enthusiasm faded, his mild little stories died away. The lady to whom he had confided secrets of pushing dead stock at Christmastime patted him on the sleeve and moved off, on the arm of a heavy "associate" of Sol's who wanted to show her the art works, "Pictures like that, you won't get tired of looking at so fast." We were sitting on a sofa facing the piano, just beneath a group talking important high-sounding music criticism at each other: I can't imagine E-minor startling anything but birds. . . . After all, dear, the era of atonality is not exactly new . . . I was referring to the Czerny variation of the Ricordanza. I think Sol has the new album, haven't you, Sol?

Sol said yes he had but he was not jubilant about it. In fact, the childishly eager fat boy was not jubilant about anything, was indeed sitting so heavily on his great golden sofa I wondered vaguely what awful problem was troubling him now, as I watched him dawdling with a plateful of caviar pancakes as disinterestedly as if it were a plateful of beans, when he whispered something in my ear. "Look at her! Just look at her watching them!" Slightly in his cups now he leaned against me, his black silk eyes moving furtively from Toni to Sykes and Sharon and back again. He knew—oh, how he knew!

Suddenly he lunged toward Toni who was sitting at the end of the sofa. "Your friend don't look so good tonight, huh, Toni?"

Toni swallowed. "Well, no—now that you mention it. But you ought to be busy with your guests, Sol. Your party's a big success—"

"I told him go home early last night—that's what I told him," Sol cut in, mercilessly. "He looked already tired from the night before, but I don't think he went home. Where do you think he was?"

A sharp cruel look flashed like a knife into his soft eyes. Toni shrugged and continued watching Sykes who was now sitting at the piano, his hands running lightly over the keys lazily plucking a Chopin étude, with the blond giantess leaning over talking down to him. Desperately Sol turned back to me.

"Joyce, you're a smart gull. You tell me, what does a fine little lady like Toni see in a man like that? If you could just explain me that, I tell you you'd be doing me a favor. That would be the best Christmas present I could get if I could just know the answer to that one. Fine little lady like Toni, I tell you . . ."

"Oh, they're both interested in the theater. But I don't think she likes him any more. Why, Sol, do you think he's so bad?"

"Bad? He's a bum—a drifter." Sol placed the plate of caviar pancakes disgustedly down on the table beside him. "Listen, Joyce, you know I could take an interest in that little Toni. A gull like that she needs somebody looking after her. She needs protection. She's a little beauty, and she's smart—I tell you is that little Toni smart? She could go far, she's got class—but look what she's doing throwing herself at bums like that." He sighed, shaking his head heavily and blowing a fishy odor toward me. "Look at her—all eyes for that— that faker, just look at her."

"This might be the last time she's seeing him. After all now, what's in a look? She likes you too, I know that for a fact."

"Aw now, Joyce, she don't know I'm alive," he said, adding almost prophetically, "She'll never know I'm alive. She don't even want to see me—except in a crowd maybe like this. I know when a woman likes me. Listen when a woman likes a man she don't do that way. Just look at her face—she's in a daze, I tell you."

I didn't agree about that. Toni was not in a daze. I recognized a certain *après moi le déluge* look. It always appeared in a crisis, flashing like a steel flint behind the fierce hard little smile. There it was now . . . when had I seen that look? Oh yes, I remembered, it was the look she had cast upon poor Alphonse, he who had left the mating incompleted in the cool arbors of Santralls Park. . . . I made a mental note, we were all sitting on the edge of a volcano, Toni was going to do something, as I felt old Sol coming up close again with that sad fishy smell, keeping me glued to his side as he ladled out gobs of oily sorrow. "Lissen, Joyce, I'm not feeling so good. I worry about that gull, ever since I knew her—party and all. I tell you, Joyce, she's got something on her mind. Lissen, a man letting women come together—they should look each other in the eye—one's coming in, the other one's going out—I tell you he should live from trouble. Why I even told that Sykes, 'Don't bring the other one here,' I said. He couldn't get out of the engagement, he said. A date with a woman can't be broken don't exist, I told him, but he says no. Well you see what he did. Now's his hard luck what can happen."

A pretty gay-looking little French woman, all shoulders and legs, accompanied by a tall gray-haired man with a long face enshrouded in a terrifying black beard, approached the sofa. "Sol," she pronounced it Saul, "my dear, I want you to meet Count Ferrere," and poor Sol rose heavily to his feet. Then Toni came beside me, she had moved into Sol's place while it was still warm. I didn't know what to say any more, the thing that had happened between the two lovers seemed hopeless, the water had been polluted by the classic slush. "She really is marvelous-looking, isn't she?" I took another look at the raw-boned blonde with the pretty face; she was standing still as a statue with those empty staring eyes, and said, "Why don't we get up off this sofa? Look, honey, there's a big party going on here—" She went on exactly as if she hadn't heard me. "He'll change her just like he did me . . . can't imagine what he can think up. Changes your clothes, your style, your make-up. He even changes some people's conversation, or their accent, like a director on stage with a new play. I'm the only one he ever broke down and confessed to, you see . . ."

She might have gone on cataloguing the thrilling horrors of *l'affaire Kenyon,* but just at that minute a new group arrived. There was more champagne and everybody was talking at once. The actor, Van Ness, had pulled Toni up off the sofa. "Just doing what a whole lotta other people are doing," he was saying. "Just wantsta make love to a whole lotta money. It's an aphrodisiac for a whole lotta people ina theater."

And then we were all standing in Sol's bar, it looked rather like a night club, the way people came and went, their faces reflected in the antique mirror behind the life-size wooden bar with brass rail, together with the small candle-lit tables, the busy white-coated bartenders, the dozen of uplifted white arms. I was paired off with an Englishman named John Wormsby and found him entertaining. In fact, listening to some fairly literate British drollery on the habits of Sol's amazing Maecenas abroad, I forgot all about Stream and her troubles. Things were going faster now, the way it always happens when the party moves into second swing. Once I ran into Sykes talking earnestly to a tall stately woman, when Sharon came by and said something to him.

"Leave me alone, Godmother," he called back to her. "I'll be Cinderella again soon but it's not midnight yet."

Sharon apparently didn't understand the symbolic language. "Your watch must have stopped," she said, in a flat voice.

"I mean the generic midnight, dear," Sykes went on. "The pumpkin time of the soul. Here, Joyce, you tell her about those things. You'll have to catch on to this kind of talk—but all that's for later."

I remember being pleasantly aware of the Englishman, as the great bulging roomfuls of eating, drinking, talking humanity rose acoustically into an aching pandemonium of human dissonance. Sol came by, smiling broadly—he believed the louder the caterwauling the greater the success of the party—and saying, "Merry Christmas, Joyce," and "Merry Christmas, John" and "You know, this John Wormsby's a great fella, I tellya, I never thought I'd see him here tonight, never know what can happen this world." The rooms seemed as if they might burst their wood-paneled seams before people started leaving, murmuring full-mouthed bellows of thanks to the Meyers brothers. "You must come to see us, Mr. Siegal," a regal lady told Sol, while her husband, eager to be gone, kept saying to Sol's brother, "Good night, Amiel." But Sol was so pleased the celebrities were present in his home, their cat's concert was dulcet harmony to him.

Besides, as it was now becoming evident, Toni herself, the source of his *locus standi,* the magnet whose attraction had after all drawn these master spirits to his groaning board, his Toni, had completely recovered, was indeed sitting happily chatting with Sharon Dougherty at the far end of the bar. "She's calmed down now—see?" Sol whispered, clutching my arm in his frantic happiness. "She's made friends with that Dougherty girl. Smart. She's got a head. That little gull don't have to play second fiddle to nobody."

It must have been just about then that Daphne grabbed me by the hand. "Come on, doll. She wants us to join her." I said, "How do you know? It looks like they're having a confidential chat." But Daphne kept pulling me. "Come on. She sent the bartender over with a message. Looks like we're going to see a happy ending—Toni's giving the bride away and all that . . ."

Now it was just the four of us sitting at the end of the long wooden bar, Daphne and I on the two stools at the corner, Toni and Sharon at right angles, facing the mirror. "Sharon, you know Daphne Johnstone, and this is Joyce." The two girls had been drinking a great deal of champagne. Sharon's face was a bright pink, the big vapid eyes looked watery, but Toni seemed the personification of unruffled calm.

"I wouldn't let any man do a thing like that to me!" Sharon was talking now in a flat voice. "Why didn't you just call the police?"

"Well, after all, in the theater—you wouldn't want it to get in the papers."

Daphne looked at me out of the corner of her eye. We both kept deadly quiet; sipping champagne was a kind of relief. I remember looking in the mirror once and seeing the tall girl and the small girl repeated ad infinitum; the scene had an eerie quality. Apparently neither of them realized Sykes was sitting at a table just beneath them. He had turned around toward the bar to listen. His face was strained and white. I remember seeing it, too, showing in that crazy antique mirror, a white block repeated over and over again.

"But these qualities have absolutely nothing to do with his abilities," Toni went on, exactly as if she were discussing the time of day.

"Well after all, that's your affair," Sharon muttered. "I mean I don't know why you're telling me—after all, a man doing a thing like that—"

"I started talking about the play. I'm going to help you and Sykes, Sharon. I'm ready to do everything I can. Daphne and Joyce have both read it, haven't you?" She was turning now to us. "Daphne, you tell Sharon what you think of *Dark Incident*."

"No good. Hasn't got a chance." Daphne was obviously unsure of what she was supposed to say and flying blind. Things were getting crazier by the minute. Sykes was just getting up from his table, and being pulled back by a drunken actress.

"Well Joyce read it, didn't you, dear?"

I said, "Yes, and I think it stinks."

Now Toni started behaving very strangely. She glared at Daphne and me.

"I thought you two were my friends. Listen, Sykes has a future and you know it. I've been trying to give Sharon a good picture of this thing. Who knows better than you two how I'd like to see him get back on his feet? I wouldn't like to collect the two thousand dollars I loaned him, no? And it's coming off the top—he promised me soon as he gets a bankroll. So you go and tell Sharon stuff like that."

The faint smile around Sharon's mouth disappeared abruptly. Her face was changing, had changed. She seemed to have received a piece of information that was moving her like news of love or death. Her mouth fell open. She was frowning.

"I expected you two—to back me up—and what did you do?" Toni was getting loud. For some odd reason the bar had quieted down. The only sound, besides Toni's irate voice, was a great boisterous laugh going on behind us somewhere, it sounded like that actor, that Clyde Van Ness. Sykes had gotten up from his table and was approaching the bar. "Come on, let's go," he said to Sharon. "I'm not going anywheres," she called back, without turning from the bar. The bartender cut in with, "More champagne, girls?" and everybody said yes. The drunken girl at the table got up and started pulling Sykes back.

"Nothing like that," Sharon was muttering, still in that flat tone, the crisp British bit was entirely forgotten. We all lifted our glasses and drank with relief.

2 9 3

"I think a girl like you could have a fine effect on him," Toni went on, in that calm sweet voice. "You could put him back on his feet. That's just what he needs—a practical person with a solid background. After all, it couldn't mean anything much to you—a little bankroll of fifty thousand dollars would get it going. And I know eventually he'll make good, it may take years but say ten, fifteen years it's bound to happen. Why one day you'll wake up and . . ."

"Not with that man I won't!" said Sharon. She drank off the champagne and nudged the bartender for more. "It's not the first time—I mean men picking up big tabs—pretending they're okay—" She leaned slightly on the bar. "I guess I just don't like men who don't have any money. I mean a man hasn't made his pile it's like they're not men to me. They just leave me cold."

Toni smiled broadly, then started giggling. "You're going to give him the watch, aren't you?" She was shouting again. "After all he gave you those earrings—even if it was on my savings."

"Hell I am!" Sharon weaved unsteadily on her stool. "I'll give that watch to my good friend Arty Mannheim. We're going out tomorrow and he surprised me with this bracelet. Just imagine, you know, I was going to give him a picture tie."

We all thought that was very funny. Sharon was laughing, Toni started, too, and then Daphne and I started laughing uncontrollably. The rest of the bar business is kind of vague. I remember seeing Sykes reflected in that bar mirror, the drunken girl was pulling on his arm desperately and he was slowly tearing her fingers off, one by one. And Sol beaming like a great Santa Claus, saying Merry Christmas to everybody, and whispering to me just as we were all leaving. "They're both fine people—she's a sweet gull and he's got ability—you don't see people like that every day." He was forgiving, placing the imprimatur of royal academy upon Toni and Sykes, believing them to be old masterpieces and wanting me to share the discovery. I don't remember leaving, or how we got into the limousine—Sol, Toni, Daphne, Tom, John Wormsby and I—only the singing on the way home and everybody kissing everybody else good night.

I do remember the telephone ringing. Toni and I were eating ham and eggs in the kitchen, I must have answered because I remember Sykes' tense voice demanding to speak to Toni and her hollering, dangerously near the open phone, "Tell him I'm not home . . . because you see it's the truth, I'm not home to him any more!" And the one sensible moment that occurred when Daphne came bursting back into the place—she at least was sober and smiling. She sat down with us, grabbed a plateful of food and a cup of coffee. She obviously wasn't finished with the night.

"For God's sake, how did you ever figure it out?" she managed to ask Toni, between eating and chuckling.

"I had to do something to keep them apart—so I kept playing her like you play a safe—fishing around for the combination. Only nothing worked. And then I remembered something this Clyde Van Ness told me—about how she stopped speaking to him because he tried to borrow some money. That was when I started—and I kept on until I hit home straight down the middle."

I asked her, "You didn't really lend him two thousand dollars, did you?"

"Not exactly. But he asked me for it—and that's practically the same."

"And the funniest thing, I mean the scream of the whole party—that was when Sol asked Sharon if she wasn't going home with Sykes. And he said, 'I thought you two were going to keep house.' And Sharon said, 'That's what I've been doing at that bar for three hours.' I didn't think she had it in her."

We went to bed laughing, everybody was in a good humor for once, and all together at the same time.

CHAPTER THIRTY-THREE

• • • • • •

THE LONG WINTER DRAGGED ON. "WHERE AM I NOW?" I ASKED SILVERS. I had a "positive transference," he said, was beginning a "new frame of reference." This was about where, under happier circumstances, I should have been at the age of five or so. The lucky people climb down off their parents and go on to the fuller enjoyment of life, but if there has been an interruption, a sudden break, the others may spend the rest of their lives in a papier-mâché world, loving the unattainable and never going on to anything more.

The sense of rejection, the platform on which the unattainable emotion took its stance in the soul, would hit me as I looked through glass doors leading off the doctor's office into the Silvers' family dining room where a Negro maid could be seen setting the dinner table, as I imagined the happy group filling up the empty room, myself and all the other rejects left outside. Lucky bastards, I would think, hoping they choked on their roast lamb and boiled happiness. After a spell of rejection, I would be stuck again with the "spanking fantasies."

These had been with me a long time and for very "good" reasons. (I was always at a loss to figure out where the other thousands got theirs from.) I was in grammar school when these moving pictures started their long run inside my head. Mr. Lark, at the boardinghouse where my father dumped us kids between housekeepers after my mother's death, definitely attracted me sexually. The wit of the table. A salesman, he traveled in dry goods and was often gone for two to three weeks. He had balding red hair, wore eyeglasses, and had no teeth in the front of his mouth which caused him to laugh in a queer way; he would pull his upper lip way down over his gums to hide the empty spaces. My sister and I had quite a time imitating him; I had him down perfect. It seemed to be always summer then and Mr. Lark always wore a thin shiny reddish-brown suit nearly the color of his thinning hair. The material of that suit looked slightly unnatural to me, stiffened with age and about to crack like tree bark—fascinating to behold. He had light-green eyes with pink lids and big soft dimpled hands and he was an Elk. And, oh yes, he smelled faintly of kerosene and cheap cologne. While Ernest Lark was certainly not physically appetizing, I see now that he had something, as the saying is, for one already attuned to the thrill of human oddity. Besides, he had some querulous distinctions. He had the only voice around the groaning board with no Southern accent and no hint of people talking in their sleep. He barked what he said with a kind of command, or so it seemed in this soapy vocal wetwash.

"Everybody talks about the weather, but nobody does anything about it!" he would say, making no mention of Mark Twain, and the folks around the table would laugh as if they were hearing it for the first time—a common custom this: the well-worn *bon mot* became funnier as it grew soothing with familiarity. Or, referring to the hostess, "Miss Mary's looking fit for slaughter." Or to Miss Mary's very ancient aunt who wore all-black which never seemed to be washed and smelled accordingly, "I see you're flirting with me again, Auntie," or "I saw Auntie jumping over the fence." There were other bits of Larkiana that always brought down the house, for some incredible reason I can remember them all. In an atmosphere where very little at all was said—after the greetings came only the sound of plates passing before the other sounds of eating would set in and the requests for more food—Mr. Lark's seedy wisecracks came like a whiplash in the sleepy circle. I see now it was his voice that attracted me—his sharp spoken commands, his vanity, his physically familiarly odd appearance—so I fastened on him in my search for the object to place my love and so speed up the fascinating daydreams.

Late in the afternoons in the quiet before dinner, I would go alone to my room where I would enter the recently discovered theater that was mine alone. The curtain would rise in the twilight in there and there would be Mr. Lark waiting for me. In a big chair with his big hands waiting to hold me—but first we would talk and flirt like grown-ups. He would say remarkable things and I would answer . . . and then he would get mad and scold me. Now the scene was changing, getting nearer to the thing I knew and wanted. He would scold me, undress me and whip me, and this was altogether wonderful and thrilling. To be called to come down to dinner just as Mr. Lark, the powerful and furious, had gotten me into a marvelous position for whipping, was very disconcerting. After the intense burning life being enacted in there, capable of such swift change and surging drama, it was sad to have to face the intrusion of the foolish "real" world where love and life were watered and cooked down into cold oatmeal. Wet and hot from the dream, I would reluctantly tear myself away from my conqueror who was still sitting in the chair, and go heavily to the bathroom to wash and sigh as Mr. Lark would recede into the distance within, becoming finally small as a doll as I came downstairs, leaving him way back there in the darkening shadows, his white hands now empty and lonely for me. I was the victor in the drama in a sense for I could leave my conqueror at will and he would have to wait for me until time, opportunity and the hunger called me back to raise the curtain again, Dr. Silvers pointed out; but all of this I knew and had known a long time.

As time went by, the fantasies grew stronger and lasted longer, and disappeared only at those periods when "reality" became so intensely troubled it absorbed the need for the other secret pleasurable pain. At those times when the fantasies disappeared I would sometimes remember them, but the theater in there was in darkness, the doors were locked and sealed up and I could not go inside. Sometimes I would stand outside the theater where the drama of love and cruelty was closed down and at those times I had nowhere to go for that was the only play running on my street.

These days, Toni and Sol were to be found constantly in each other's company, and they often wanted me along. I found Sol good company and wondered at Toni's indifference to him. He was the nearest thing to a man she had encountered so far, though his troubled expression and the nervous irritation he took out on his chauffeur revealed some profound lack. He was a genial and generous host, he had incredible talent for dollar-making, and he expressed a humble joy at being in our company.

One hot Saturday afternoon, after Sol had taken us to lunch at "21" and recounted some fascinating details of his early struggles in the streets of New York, I found Toni moody and irritable the minute we were alone, flaring up at the very mention of his name. "Oh, Joyce, he fascinates you because you're a reporter or a writer or something. Anyhow you like to hear anybody's *story*. But I'm more interested in intellecutal people—or spiritual people." I said I found Sol highly intelligent, and his story showed vast energy and enterprise. "That Forsythe Street saga, it's news yet for a hot Saturday." There was no persuading her. But back home as she threw down her bag and dropped her shoes, I could see she was sad and assumed she was thinking about Sykes.

"Aren't you getting kind of tired of your fantasies?" I asked.

"Sure. I'm still pretty busy with them, though. You're on a different kick from me."

"How so?"

"You've got that all-out *goisha* streak in you. Me, I live in this world, this dirty stinking crazy world, it's mine, it's me. Eh, you think you'll get over your troubles—the fantasies will just disappear—fly out the window."

"And you *don't?*"

"I don't think anybody gets completely free of them until they die. And if you must know, Miss Inquisitive, that's why I can't get so excited about Sol."

"Well then, listen—you told me the trick—I guess I knew it already, but I heard it spoken out loud first from you. Why don't you pin your fantasies on Sol?"

"You think I'm not trying?"

"Look, Toni, I know you like a kind of unattainable and slightly cruel man. Well, I don't think old Sol is exactly the complete humanitarian, dear." Seeing her eyes widen with interest I went on. "I have reason to believe—in fact I can even see Sol stepping all over people to get something he wants—and not caring a damn."

She sat up on the sofa. "I think you've got something there, honey. You know, just last night I found out something about Sol. He persecutes his servants and screams at taxi drivers. Well, last night he hollered so at that poor chauffeur, that Marvin—he's been with him a year, that's the longest he's ever been able to keep a chauffeur—

well, he hollered so I was almost getting scared myself. That Marvin hates his guts, I tell you. Some day, if Sol is ever found with his throat cut, Marvin will be the one who did him in."

"Well that's what I mean and—"

"As a matter of fact Sol is pretty rough on everybody except important people, celebrities—that kind of thing. That's why he's a success in business. You know what else he does? He keeps pretending he's going into television—says he's going to back a show—but what he does is to keep people rehearsing, showing him their stuff, making them wait for his answer. They wait for months sometimes—he keeps promising—makes them work and work. You know he's been almost a kind of gangster in the past. I guess if you have anything to do with trucking you have to be kind of rough."

"Yes, sure, that's just what I mean. Sol is really tough—Sykes is just somebody putting on an act with women. He couldn't get to first base with men."

"Yeah . . ." She was excited now. "Yeah, that's right."

"And in a pinch, if I'm not mistaken, I think old Sol could even push you around some, m'girl. I don't think he is quite as tame and gone as you think he is. He definitely has an eye for attractive dames."

"Why?" The interested look disappeared, giving place to a look of fear. "Who did you see him going for—Daphne?" I said, "I doubt that," but she went on as if she hadn't heard. "I know I was a fool to bring him anywheres near that one. She's murder. I've been having a funny feeling ever since last week end when he saw her here—and I wouldn't be surprised right now—listen, did you notice how suddenly he left us this afternoon—or didn't you?"

"She's in Palm Beach!"

"Is she? Are you sure? Jesus, maybe that's who it was that was calling him on the phone! You remember when he was paged he went downstairs? Oh my God! I'll bet anything that's who it was."

"Of course not. Daphne wouldn't be interested, and besides—"

"Listen, last week when I was in his office the same thing happened. A call came in for him and he talked onto a hush-a-phone—that just goes to show he's hiding something. And what could he be hiding from me but Daphne?"

"Forget that for a minute. You told me of a particular fantasy of yours, remember? You're a rich man's wife living in the country on a fine estate—acres and acres with a long winding road. In this fantasy of yours, your husband is constantly leaving to go on trips—"

"Sure, I remember. I find out he has different girls he goes to see. Nevertheless, when he returns he demands his marital rights and when I refuse on the grounds that he has been unfaithful, he punishes me until I finally give in. Yeah, that was great—but that was a *fantasy.* If that sonofabitch of a Sol ever pulled anything like that on me in real life—I'd ruin him. What made you bring that up?"

"Well, I think it's possible—I mean, it's not probable but it's possible—"

"You think it's possible he's made a date to meet Daphne in Palm Beach? I know she's going to do something or other before she gets married—if she ever does. And now she's in Palm Beach—she probably told Sol—and he's impressed with any kind of social atmosphere, that's for sure. That's what you were going to say, wasn't it?"

"No, of course not. He's not Daphne's type."

"Are you kidding? She hasn't got any type."

"He's an East Side boy, and you know what a snob she is—"

"She's a man-eater." I asked her what she meant by that, the word had always interested me. "I mean she eats men. She'd kill her mother to get next to a man as rich as Sol. I'm worried now. With a girl like that nothing counts. Listen, I'm going to call him up right away and if he says anything about having to go out of town *I'll know.*"

In the dark half-hours that followed, as Toni chased the evanescent Sol by telephone from his brother to the servant at his country place and back again to his brother's apartment without reaching him, she was alive, fighting, and Sykes was as forgotten as last year's book. As luck would have it, Daphne was equally impossible to reach over the long distance telephone. Afternoon wore into evening without a word from either of them and it began to look as if old Sol was taking on the wolfskin cast off by Sykes. If only he would show up once again and claim it, there might be a happy union.

It kept coming to me over and over again, like a telegram from my deep self. There's nothing more to be had up here with this doctor. It's time to jump off the pier and take the sprint in the deep cold water.

3 0 1

We discussed the possibility of ending the analysis and Dr. Silvers said it was up to me, that I could always come back if I needed more help.

I had my last session with him early in September, terminated the one good analysis and said good-by. I hadn't expected it would be so difficult. Walking out into the street from his office was something like walking over the Grand Canyon. Fortunately I was going away for the week end and there would be something to do with the hours up in the air. There was even the possibility I might come out of it, a situation I looked forward to with considerable interest.

Back home I found Toni walking around downstairs in a pink slip, packing for her trip to Maine with Sol. The place was littered with shorts, slacks and bikinis, with shoes, jodhpurs and organza dresses. "You see what I've been going through!" Toni groaned. "I've just got to get all this stuff into two bags and one hatbox." I suggested her using one of Daphne's. "After all, Daphne's boxes are the biggest in the entire world," I said, and threw myself into helping her get packed.

Toni finally got off, with Sol the protector, offering sympathetic last words about the terminated analysis and saying that if I felt very depressed I could always call her long distance and receive still more of her sage advice to help me over the difficult passage of time.

By Monday of that endless week end, coming back to the empty place, I was inclined to take her suggestion about calling long distance, but decided to wait it out. The mood didn't last, but for many months it kept coming back. I felt like an elevator running up and down the shaft but stopping at no floor. The doctor had done a good job, plunged the knife carefully to cut out the bad tissue, wiped the gangrene off the pieces and showed me what he'd done. "Those are removed from the machine that once was you," he said, in effect. I thanked him and went home to find a dry spot for the discarded pieces.

I went around those days feeling exactly like an empty clock. I still had a face and a body, a covering for the interior from which the machinery had been removed, but I wasn't ticking. Oh, occasionally a gust of wind passing through me caused the minute hands to move and sometimes the hour would strike. Ha, I'd cry, I'm still here. I know I am because I laughed or I belched. And even a stopped clock tells the correct time once a day.

Occasionally I'd find myself feeling around for my old pieces as the amputee feels for his lost legs, and then I'd remember, they'd been removed. Those poisonous old drives were no good anyway, I'd remind myself, and you should be glad they're gone. Yes, I know, the tickless me would reply, but they moved, they made a noise like living, and good or bad, they were me. Since I was able to carry on in my small way I went empty clocking on. What will I do today? I'd think sometimes, and this would change quickly to, What will who do today? The doctor had run over me with his tractor leaving a stretch of land flattened out like a pancake, full of the gaping holes and scars of introspection. Since nothing had started to grow here, I kept on walking over the turned-up earth like a ghost, looking for the way—forward or backward into life. Wait a minute now, *backward* —back to the frog pond? Maybe the frog pond was not so goddamned, after all; at least there were other frogs in it, croaking their lives away, whereas here there was nothing and no one. A wasteland.

So the long months passed, and I was still in the same state, still in the pond. Everybody else was getting ahead, getting out. The first one out was Toni. She had gone off and married Sol Meyers, while Daphne was still engaged to Tom and still going out with other people. Toni insisted she'd seen the Texan sitting downstairs in the dark when Daphne was having visitors upstairs. "He was sitting near the stairway, listening. Gives me the creeps. That's why they're not marrying so fast," she said. "Like I told you, Joyce—a man gets to be fifty hasn't loved a woman, he starts to stink." Sol himself was at least that old but he was a widower and that was "something entirely different."

During a hot spell in June Toni called to tell me the happy couple were leaving for Europe. "Sol's got business in Paris and then more business in London and Italy. We're making drizzlers and jodhpurs now, in addition to slacks and shorts. He's opening a new plant in Venezuela and we'll have to be there for a while. One trip after another—"

"You won't have your dream about the man who leaves you alone and then . . ."

"Stop it, will you?" *Laus Deo,* she was off the stuff. "Now listen, we're leaving next Saturday and we're having a party on the boat. You can tell Daphne. It was going to be just a few people but Sol's gone and invited everybody he saw last night at Sardi's. I don't know how to entertain that many people but Sol says the stewards will do all the entertaining, we just have to be there and pay."

It was nearly six when I finally walked up the gangplank of the *Queen Mary*. I knew from the number of handsome people protruding from every inch of the great ship that Sol's party was in full swing.

We finally made it upstairs to the Meyerses' suite, where Sol's loving eyes, slightly weepy with the excitement and the drink, were the first objects I saw clearly in the crowded sitting-room, his big damp hand the first object I felt, his warm voice the first true sound I made out. "Here, Joyce, you sweet gull, I want you to meet my friend, Mr. Muller." I met a smiling little man who, for some reason known only to himself, wanted to show me around the boat and I was just extricating myself from his unholy persistence when I spied Toni, trying to get through a fresh crowd. I couldn't make out what she was saying, the people were all getting drunk and talking at each other, but finally there I was standing beside Mr. and Mrs. Meyers, listening to one of those travel talks. Toni was afraid of airplanes, the sightseer Muller was trying to persuade her that flying was a wonderfully relaxing experience. Sol said they would have to fly to Italy. He had just hired two new engineers, they'd have to be in Caracas next winter, and "that little gull'll be spending half her life in the air. . . ."

I found Toni in the bedroom combing her hair. "Do I look all right, honey? Tell me the truth, you like this new kind of thing?" It was new all right, Toni was dressing down these days, and the soft muted pastel tones of the gray and yellow ensemble were perfect with her new light hair. "Because you see some of Sol's most important connections are coming to say good-by—I mean like partners with money—and you know it's a strain meeting business people. Most of them can't talk, Sol is practically a conversationalist by comparison with some of the others. Did you know Sol can't read or write, he just never learned, I guess he didn't have time."

She sat down at the vanity and started fixing her make-up. "Sykes came down last night to say good-by, I thought Sol'd be sore but you know, he didn't seem to mind at all. Sykes said something funny, he said I'm embracing an effigy. Isn't that a funny crack? I tried to look it up in the dictionary but I guess Sol didn't have the right one, anyway I couldn't find it. And he talked about the way Sol looks at me. He says there's a word in German that describes the kind of a man who marries an actress." I told her not to mind what Sykes said, he was already a thing of the past. "Oh I know. I told him maybe I am but just think how far I've come. I've come a long ways, haven't I now, honey?" I said, "You certainly have, there were times when—" And she said, "I know, I never thought I'd make it either. Just think, only a few years ago I couldn't stand to have a man staying overnight in the same apartment—and there's no use a girl wanting to be married if she feels like that. Remember how I used to say it would be all right to get married if your husband would stay hanging out the window all night?"

"Yes, everything has changed. The men are all in from the windows."

"Jesus, that's one to think about in the long winter nights."

"Now, now, there won't be any long winter nights from now on. You'll be too busy having fun."

"There'll be short winter nights. Like my mother says, between the theater and parties and restaurants and week ends, I won't have time to get bored. And then these trips. You know, I think even a bad marriage would succeed if people kept taking trips. Oh, trips, dear trips—I love you, trips."

"And his poker night—he says he's a poker genius."

"All night sometimes. Sonofabitch lost twelve hundred smackers last Thursday. I just can't get used to people gambling like that. But I wouldn't even mind that—Oh, Joyce, if only he didn't think I was so wonderful because I'm an actress. I mean if only he knew what happens—the half-men all around, the crazy commercials, all the cheap, depressing stuff goes on. Imagine a man as smart as Sol, he swallows anything when it comes to the theater. I've started to tell him but it's like trying to take somebody's religion away from him."

This was the kind of conversation I didn't want to hear any more, it was getting dangerously near to the old broken record. Someone had opened the door now, carnival sounds came through from the deck outside, the orchestra was playing a rhumba. I wanted to get out, back to the party. "Come on, let's get back." She got up from the vanity reluctantly, she always hated to leave a mirror. "And here's to you, darling—the first one out of the frog pond!" I lifted a glass to hers. "I hope you're the next, honey," she was just saying as the door opened wider and Daphne appeared, pushing through a group of people, causing a mild sensation in a tight-fitting white jersey with a Grecian drape and a white cape lined with brilliant Chinese red. Daphne disappeared into the crowd, and there we were again, with Toni going on where she had left off. "I'm just lonesome is all, the married loneliness is better than the other, I know, but—well if I can just tell this to somebody. I'm envious of Sol—now wait—he's hit the jackpot."

"But that's great. You don't want to string a pants-manufacturing empire around the world, do you?"

"I don't mean success or money or anything like that. I mean he's got this thing. Like we used to talk about. Love from the one who is unattainable. You remember how we used to say what we wanted was impossible to get. Like hot ice, like snow in August. What we want is the bad one should turn good, remember? Well that's what Sol has. The old unattainable comes to life and moves around the house and gets into your bed."

I got it then. "You mean you. Sol's attained the unattainable because he has you."

"Who else? Not Marlene Dietrich. Me, Toni, nogoodnick. Can speak English too, can read and write, know people in the theater."

With the door open the bridal suite soon filled to overflowing, forcing the crowd to burst out onto the decks and eventually to emerge into the greater party downstairs in the bar. The sounds had grown into one great continuous screaming when the first whistle for the guests to leave pierced the air, after which, into the raucous medley of the loud-talking chorus, came the strains of the orchestra playing *Auld Lang Syne*. I wanted to speak to Toni but the noise was getting worse by the minute, with greetings and frantic promises to keep in touch being passed around, so nothing seemed to matter.

We were being pushed along in the crowd as it moved en masse toward the first deck. I was beginning to despair of saying good-by to Toni when suddenly there she was coming out of nowhere, grabbing me by the arm. "The thing to do is get everything solid first," was what she was screaming in my ear. "I mean after you've got a solid basis with a man why then you know already it's worth the effort, see what I mean?" She was screaming, "The solid thing takes time—you can't count the minutes," as the last whistle blew its deafening roar into the fracas and it was time to go.

CHAPTER THIRTY-FOUR

· · · · · · ·

I ALWAYS REMEMBER TONI'S FAREWELL PARTY BECAUSE ON THAT
bright June day I actually believed I was "getting somewhere." I
didn't know then, as I was to discover later, that I was going ahead of
myself: trying to pick flowers off my new psyche before a single
sprout had grown. And I remember John, the Britisher I'd met at
Sol's party, to whom I confided the sexual part of my secret, and who
confided in his turn that some of the more prominent ladies in London
had been doctored with his loving embrace, after which the problem
had disappeared like magic. It wasn't their fault, he explained, it was
just that the chaps they'd known just couldn't quite cut the mustard.
I listened with interest but when my turn came I found that not even
John's sorcery could exorcise my devils. It turned out I was still a
department store dummy. I was still a bisque woman.

I often thought of John afterwards as I wondered, Why couldn't
I like this nice man? Why does this creature inside keep pulling me
back and ever further back? Why, I would ask, trying to reach my
other self, trying to persuade it as a mother might try to persuade a
wayward daughter to go ahead with the marriage plans. What is there
you don't like about John? And straightway the craziest notions would
flood my mind. His lips were too far from his chin, things like that. I
knew they were ridiculous, and I knew where they came from. This
pygmy self, the one I call Devman, he who turned blushing from those
who loved him and ran toward the ones who didn't, he was still
pulling the strings!

Months, almost a year later, after the good therapy, I would wake
up, start to work and—bang!—there it was again. The *thing,* the

damned *thing*. Fantasies bursting in on my conscious mind. No matter how hard I fought to keep my thinking on the matter to hand, the curtain in there would rise and there was I—watching that other I, until the words on the paper would fade into nothing as the great Technicolor movie took over. I noticed as I watched from day to day that these movies were increasing in power and potency, growing wider and more colorful, wilder and more complicated. (This is the goddamndest thing for a writer who requires the entire use of his own mind. I wished I were an actress, I'd had a fling at that, not bad, either—or a laundress—anything where I didn't need such absolute concentration!)

The main characters were always the same: I was the passive pitiful heroine and the strange sadistic prince was the active hero; but the situations and scenes changed daily, and often as not new characters, equally cruel but often amusing in a macabre way, appeared suddenly.

When the pictures started I would see them coming up, and try to push them down and go on with my work. This almost never worked and at last I, the unwilling but compelled observer, would yield to this powerful other self, put aside the work and watch the spectacle. Only for fifteen minutes, I would promise my other self, then back to the "real" world. And suddenly I would be transported into that familiar medieval city where I could see the market place lit with that unholy Technicolor sunlight as clearly as I could see my own living room. It is morning in there, the slave girls are waiting for their prospective buyers to arrive. Naked and beautiful they stand with the glaring light shining on their hard young bodies and prying into their frightened eyes. I can hear their whispers above the voices of the market place, a medley rising higher and higher as the prince's horses are heard crossing the hill and entering the gates, and then arriving at the inn near the slave mart. The carriage draws up, the prince himself is not present, it is the prince consort who will barter for the slaves and as he alights to begin, the naked girls crowd together for comfort.

Sometimes, as the movie was driving toward a climax, with the terror scenes coming on apace, I would deliberately get up and walk around, in an effort to stop the damned thing. Sometimes this worked temporarily, more often it did not. The fact was these fantasies were sexually enjoyable and were taking over more and more of my waking mind. Since the good therapy, my working hours were being more and more invaded by the theatrical obsession. What was the good of trying to work when the most energized part of myself was back in that medieval township—awaiting the delicious tortures of the prince?

This was discouraging, to say the least. Remembering how I had rejoiced over the cure of the yielding compulsion, believing I was now ready for fuller living, I began to think my entire expectation had been premature.

Then, one day, I would wake up free and clear! My mind was my own. *It* just wasn't there. I was "normal" and happy as a lark. In these spells I usually managed to do all the work that had been held up and then some more, as first my normal thinking rhythm would be restored and then a wave of new creativity would come sweeping in. Ideas, themes, characters, plots, entire concepts complete to the last detail would come pouring in—first in small bits, a sense of a character, a feeling of a live situation, and then this would grow into a complete scene containing more people and moving in a continuous way, all highly charged with life and reality.

I would yield gladly, take it all down, let the entire movement come to fruition, and as I worked I realized I had something I could not possibly have planned consciously in this absolute and often breathtaking perfection, all so full and ripe and ready as to need no change whatsoever. Sometimes it would come through forcefully for ten or twelve hours for days on end. I would fall asleep from sheer exhaustion with the words still pouring through me, and awaken to find them waiting there to claim me.

This was not entirely an unmixed blessing. Often toward the end of one particular piece, before it was finished, just as I was receiving it full blast—bang!—another one would be there pushing and screaming at the door, taking precedence over the first while the first was still going on. I would try to avoid the new idea but it would become so complete and fascinating in the end I would have to give over to it, take it down and, being fortunately a fast typist, I would often get most of it. But, like the first, it would ripen with such completion I could think of nothing else, and just at this point, the first would intrude again and keep coming in. Or just as often another entirely new one would burst upon me full-blown!

And then the fantasies would return. I didn't know what to do.

I was not a compulsive yielder any longer to people, but I was indeed a compulsive yielder every day in my dreams. A conditioned reflex, only how to recondition it now seemed imponderable.

Imagine being locked in a dark theater for hours, days, years on end, being forced to watch a drama you really despise. Out in the bright streets the life of the world goes on. Now and then the door opens, the sunlight streaks in, you hear the sounds of the other life. Or opportunity knocks while you sit still, your energy being drained out as the minutes tick away, never to return, lost in the lure of the unwanted dream. I learned to work, of course, while the play was going on, but after the task was finished, there it was starting up all over again. Desperately, I would think, if only I could take this record going on inside my head and smash it with an ax, how gladly would I do it.

There was a time when the fantasies suddenly took on such a fierce life of their own I would see them going on no matter what I was doing. In the office talking to people, in the quiet at home when I was trying to work. I shrugged and went on, watching to see how much worse it would get. My mornings, especially those week-end hours I cherished for my own work, were now being devoured. For some reason I still cannot fathom they never came at night.

One bright morning I sat down at my typewriter and started writing what I saw. Before I realized what I was doing I had covered fifteen pages of what might have been the outline for an historical novel except that it was screamingly funny and, of course, unprintable. I read it, laughed heartily, and had my first relief from the fantasies. To my amazement and delight, they did not come back the following day, or the next or the one after that. A week or more later, there they were again. Once again I sat down and wrote out what I saw, coming up with *Mathilde and the Prince,* and coming once again into a spell of relief.

Now at least I had a method of dealing with the obsession. This was a promising business at first but after a while I seemed to have written it all out. The fantasies kept on coming—sometimes weaker, sometimes stronger, and sometimes, God be praised, they just were not there.

"But of course you're still busy with your fantasies," said Toni, in one of our rare confidential chats. "You will be until you meet up with the prince—or a facsimile thereof." As to where such a priceless object could be found she couldn't say. "I'm having my own difficulties pinning my fantasies on to Sol."

That finding the prince sounded like a good suggestion but, like many another hot tip, totally impossible of fulfillment. I would take the chance, if I knew where the chance was. Where could I find the cruel prince and still play it safe? As far as I knew, he didn't exist anywhere outside of my own head.

It is cool and dank in the frog pond. The leapers wallow at the bottom in an arctic anonymity or rush through the smoky waters to the scorching sunshine at the top. And there are times when the oblique musk-root memory of the human world out there titillates their heartstrings, times when some quivering sound or redolent scent causes one leaper to recognize his kin. And kinship being that which causes warmth and glow in all living things—even, I suspect, in the indifferent slime where vertebrates and Vermes share the mystery of being—for a while everything is new, the fetid pond seems sprayed with mint and cinnamon, and there is little difference between frogs and men.

One day a man named Cy Bergson came into the office and one of those warm spontaneous friendships sprang up between us. A successful businessman, he was nevertheless desperately unhappy, but amusing and active about it. Few brothers and sisters are ever as intimate with each other as we were in the months that followed. We had been over much the same path—seeking help from doctors—and had much in common. Whatever it was I did for him, he brought me a fresh masculine point of view on the whole picture.

I remember one hot September evening I had a conversation with Cy that opened the doors on a world I hadn't thought existed. He had just finished reading one of my fantasy manuscripts, this one called *Elmira and the Whips*.

"Wait! I've got an idea." He started walking up and down the room as he elucidated. "You haven't had any *action*. You didn't really get your trouble out of your system because you have never come face to face with it—except when you were a baby. Why don't you come face to face with it now? Go out and get the cruel prince." He hollered the last, as if impatient with someone who hadn't done what the fantasy paper implied I wanted to do. "You can, you know."

"How?" I hollered back.

"Look, they've been selling you health. You're not in the market for it. Now do you really want to try it the other way? You really want to go the way the current is moving you?"

"Of course. I don't like this obsession."

"What you need is to get the whipping."

"All right. But how? It's impossible on the face of it. I don't know of any place where one could go and be whipped—and even if I did I wouldn't want it that way."

"Of course you wouldn't. You want it the real way. From someone who needs to give it to you—just as much as you need to get it. Now listen to me, and listen carefully. Don't you know there are hundreds just like you who want the same thing—but who want to play it safe —just as you do?"

I had never even heard of these people and I certainly didn't know what they could do about it. "Most of them do nothing, I guess, but just about what you're doing. But others go out and get it." I started to ask how and where again, but he was talking fast now and not to be interrupted. "Just as there are females who want it, so are there men who want to give it. You know, by now I like to whip women—cold models in particular. Last night I flogged an awfully nice woman named Victoria. She came to New York all the way from Idaho to get whipped—she makes this pilgrimage twice a year, stays two to three weeks, and then goes back to her husband and children. She's a respectable matron married to a banker and a pillar of society back home. I gave her quite a beating—my arm still hurts."

"Where did you ever meet her? And how did you ever find out— that was what she wanted?"

He went on to explain how these whippers and whippees met each other by code advertisements placed in certain periodicals, and so found fulfillment of all kinds. It sounded funny—and horrible.

"What on earth kind of people are they?" I asked, fascinated.

He chuckled, and walked some more. "Some pretty famous and wonderful people, as a matter of fact. I've been in the club for six months and I've never met a dud. Some of the women are a trifle too mature for me—I like them around eighteen or nineteen—but they're all highly intelligent people."

"But wouldn't that be dangerous? After all, my dreamboy, old Prince Hildecrantz, is under *my* control."

"Of course not, silly. Joyce, I tell you, these people are experts. They know just how far to go. Now listen, I'm going to introduce you to Vicky. She knows them all. She's been at this thing for years. Gets around among the best. You don't seem to understand, this is a fairly swank group. Sophisticates, not dullards. She's in town now. I'm going to call her up right now—"

"Wait a minute!" I screamed as he went to the telephone. "Give me time to think this over."

"That's what you've been doing all your life," he said, as he dialed the number.

After a few minutes talking he began beckoning to me frantically and grinning from ear to ear.

"She's free this evening. She'd like to meet you for dinner. You talk to her and make a date. She'll fix you up, I know she will, she knows them all."

After the description Cy had given me of Victoria Bassford I had to look twice at the woman I found waiting for me at a table in a restaurant in West 46th Street before deciding to approach her. She was young, about thirty-four, with beautiful yellowish-red hair, big sea-green eyes, and a lovely smile. I found her friendly, sophisticated and gracious. We took down our back hair, talked about everything under the sun, being only obliquely honest with that peculiar appearance of absolute frankness common to women, in which the big secret card is always kept up the sleeve.

She talked about her home life out West where I gathered she was a leading figure in her town, her husband the banker and members of her family, including her mother and father, two rather vague high-class Southerners who had not resorted to corporal punishment. She cheerfully admitted she and her sister both had these movies running in their heads and on this score, since it was all impersonal and only-in-the head (that was the assumption, anyway) we both told each other the truth. Here for the first time the conversation became for me full of surprises.

"My fantasy life is as corny as the worst old silent serial movies—say the *Perils of Pauline*," I began, eager to get to the subject to hand and off the social nonsense.

"Like a whole lot of other people's," said Victoria. "Grade-B melodramas. Go ahead. What role do you play?"

"I'm a slave girl—beautiful, of course—purchased in the open market by a ruling prince. After this—"

"Wait a minute!" Victoria interrupted. She put down her coffee cup, lost all interest in the dessert and talked. "The Prince is now your master and he takes you home to the palace. Henceforward through thousands of reels in as many different situations, climes and countries, he whips you with every implement known to princehood—dependent on his mood."

"How did you know?" I was always struck with a funny feeling whenever I heard how other people, who had certainly never shared my experiences in my very special past, had the same damned daydreams.

"Have you ever had this one?" She went on to describe a fantasy in which the ruling prince meets a slave girl from a neighboring province, and is charmed out of twenty years growth by her great beauty and tremendous wit. The two are dining in a small suburban palace when the prince, suddenly fearful of the girl's charm, orders the musicians to seize her, undress her and whip her. She must be punished for the power she is exerting over him.

"Yes," I admitted in a slightly lowered voice, "I have had that one, too. But how on earth did you ever have it?"

Victoria smiled, and played with her dessert. She wasn't talking.

"I wrote that one out," I went on. "It was a tough nut to crack, by the way. It seems especially difficult to write a sadist's lines."

"I haven't found it so. They are exceptional people, my dear."

I didn't go along with that. "I suspect that all sadists are mamma's boys. Weaker than water, and show up badly in a crisis. Just can't take the jumps."

"I don't agree with you at all," said Victoria. She wasn't smiling, and I had a funny feeling that I had somehow offended her, though I certainly hadn't meant to. This was my first inkling that there might be some fundamental difference between me, and my own attitude, and the other members of the club to which Cy had so generously referred me. But as time went on and I became more intimate with Victoria, I saw there was this difference and at first it baffled me.

In a nutshell, to Victoria the sadists and their antics were sacred. She had found a way of life which nothing could disturb: therefore any humor about this matter was entirely out of place and fiercely resented. And the desire to get over it, indeed the very idea that it might be a diseased part of life one might even want to get over, was totally inconceivable. But I didn't know this that night of our first meeting. It dawned on me slowly over the hours, and as it did I was somewhat baffled to see that these people were on a totally different psychic level from me, that they were actually living out, and mistaking for real life, what I considered to be a damned nuisance that I would do almost anything, including becoming a member of the society, in order to get over.

But I am getting ahead of my story. As we finished coffee and dessert and ordered liqueurs, Victoria told me of the wonders of the man—Walter something, she called him Von—she had come to the big city to see. He was intelligent, celebrated, cruel, and she was in love with him. He consistently insulted her and made her feel inferior, he was forever punishing her unmercifully for this or that misdemeanor—her dress was soiled, her pronunciation was poor—he had an ideal of perfection, she explained. She was afraid of him, it was never possible to predict just what he would do. I tried to hear more about this but she became evasive. She withheld his surname—I gathered names were kept in strict secrecy among members of the group—many of whom occupied high places. As she talked on about their meetings, week ends, dinners, and evenings together, the general impression was that Victoria was involved in a violent and unhappy love affair with an intellectual scoundrel, and only occasionally, just as I was about to offer sympathy, did it flash over me that she was having a wonderful time.

But for all the inconsistencies, Victoria was a warm and genuine person, and I enjoyed every minute of my first session with her. Dinner over at last, but the conversation still unfinished, we repaired to her apartment in a smart East Side hotel where we sat picking up the loose ends. The first loose end Victoria picked up concerned me.

"I don't believe you've never had it!" She made a flat statement it seemed useless to deny. "Feeling the way you do I don't understand how you could get along."

I was trying to get rid of it, I tried to explain. I had work to do. She took a dim view of people who "wanted to get rid of it." She couldn't see that there was anything so bad about it, as a matter of fact it lent drama and excitement to existence. People without it seemed flat as pancakes to her. I started to remonstrate, after all these people without it probably included the whole of the rest of the world that I regarded with envy rather than disdain, but I quickly thought better of this as the demon intuition threw me a line: If you go along in that direction, you'll never get into her club.

We talked on into the small hours of the morning, and just as I was about to leave I asked her point-blank if she wouldn't introduce me to one of her whippers, but, to my great disappointment, she became "ladylike" and elaborately evasive.

"I'm going to think about your problem," she promised, giving me the impression I was wheedling something out of her. "I'll get in touch with you in a few days."

One afternoon, to my surprise and delight, the telephone rang and a man speaking in a faintly Viennese accent introduced himself as a friend of Victoria's. We talked, he made some rather amusing remarks, and we agreed to meet for dinner that evening. I called Victoria to thank her for setting up my initiation, and incidentally to check a bit on the soft-spoken Mr. Harry Bense, but found to my chagrin that she had gone away for the week end. Next I called Cy, but he was out of his office; it wasn't until ten minutes before my date —I was beginning to wonder if I were doing the right thing—that he finally called me and reassured me at once.

"Joyce, these boys are experts," he repeated. "You don't have a thing to worry about. They're not amateurs, remember—they're professionals. They're making this thing a career, they live for it. What are you wearing?"

"Oh, I'm dressed to the hilt," I told him. "My highest high heels—the works."

"Good. Because remember you're not moving in on some suburban punks. This is the real thing, baby. Well, happy monster-dom."

The man who rang my bell at seven o'clock couldn't possibly be Mr. Bense, I decided, although he assured me—in that same soft, faintly foreign accent I had heard on the telephone—that he was. He stood just over five feet, I was over a head taller than he. He had pale eyes behind horn-rimmed spectacles, grayish-blond hair, and what I can only describe as a pathetically eager little smile. If this was a sadist, I decided, nature had certainly loused up his physique —but of course he was a sadist, the club consisted only of sadists and masochists, and since I was the masochist he had to be the sadist.

I promptly concealed my disappointment in his appearance, of-fered him a highball, which he accepted, and we sat down together to get acquainted. Mr. Bense worked in Wall Street, he had never been married, had been disappointed—he was going to go further into that, I could tell. After the second drink he told me.

"You are everything that Victoria said. She didn't exaggerate—not by a half inch. I asked her how tall you were and she said over a head taller than I am, and that's exactly what you are."

At the third drink he came out with it, all at once. "You're just like her—the one I'm going to tell you about. Tall, blond, cold, efficient —and cruel—oh so cruel." To my absolute amazement the little man was getting down on his knees. "You won't hurt me too much, will you dearest? I promise I'll try to be good."

"I can't make any promises," I said, picking up the cue from him. I knew instantly Victoria must have mixed up her cards and sent me a man who wanted the same thing I wanted. There was nothing for it now but to go through with the evening as tactfully as possible, al-though I knew at some point I would have to inform poor little Mr. Bense that I was not the cruel stepmother but just plain Cinderella, and that was a moment I was not exactly looking forward to. "Let me call you Brunhilde!" he was saying as we taxied out to dinner.

I must say he knew his way around. He was an excellent host and took me to a Viennese restaurant that was the best I had ever eaten in, including some in Vienna. Over the chilled wine and excellent schnitzel he told me the story of his last Brunhilde.

"This is how I discovered the way I really am," he began. "I was going out with her daughter—a young girl of seventeen, not very

3 1 8

interesting, I liked to dance with her so we often stayed out late. She told me her mother was getting furious, but we didn't pay much attention. Then one night we came home, and found her mother waiting. She grabbed Eloise first, turned her over her knees, pulled up her dress and gave her a hard thrashing with a hairbrush, then sent her along to bed, crying. I started to go over to her when the mother grabbed me and did the same thing to me. My, how easily she handled me. She had arms and hands just like yours—the same blond hair—and I'll bet you make magnificent noodle soup."

Poor Mr. Bense's love affair had started right on her lap that evening and continued for several years until she had left the country, leaving him miserable indeed. All these months he had been dreaming of a big blonde to take her place, and now at last, thanks to the tender intervention of dear Victoria, he had found another Brunhilde. As he went on, not very subtly describing his desires, I found him so pitiful and so repulsive, I wished the evening were over. I hated to let him down, but when the time came I decided things had gone far enough and told him the simple truth about myself. His little face, a mass of smiles and joyous sounds all evening, seemed to go into a mess of sad lines when he heard the verdict, but he recovered quickly.

"You must have cruelty in you," he pleaded. "I've seen it in your face. You like to whip," and the tears came to his eyes at this, "You just don't want to whip *me*."

I felt compassion for poor Mr. Bense but not enough to grant his wish, and I went to bed thinking that the members of the whipping club were all unpredictable, that there were people in the world worse off than I—as I envisaged this poor little chap looking vainly for another Brunhilde in order to complete himself.

Victoria called early in the week. She was just going on, "You made a great hit with Harry," when I interrupted to tell her how she had mixed up the cards. She said, "Oh," and muttered some kind of apology, "I didn't know," or "I wasn't quite sure," and found nothing the least bit humorous in the situation. She would get in touch with me again, she promised, as soon as a certain man came to town, one could never be sure just when that would be.

CHAPTER THIRTY-FIVE

· · · · · · ·

ONE DULL NOVEMBER AFTERNOON VICTORIA CALLED ME JUST AS I was leaving the office and asked me to stop by her place for a drink. I came immediately and after a couple of rounds the dank November evening took on a softer hue as Vicky confided some of the brighter spots of her recent vacation with her paramour who, it seemed, had insulted her continuously. As we talked on I began to level with her, having decided that if I were ever going to get into the club I had better find out how to do it on my own. With this end in view I started out letting Victoria know how greatly I envied her "adjustment."

"I seem to be stuck with this thing—this nasty black part that smudges up the whole white part—whereas you . . ."

"Who wants the white part?" she interrupted. "Why do you think there is any white part?"

I heard myself go on. "Maybe there isn't. Anyway, some people like to eat rotten bananas and why shouldn't they, if that's what they want—it's probably the best thing for them—and may actually be the most healthy thing for them in the end. After all, if what passes for love to me is elixir of razor strop . . ."

Knowing by now that these people loathe words like sickness and therapy with all their souls, I carefully avoided any mention of these, and as the evening progressed I began to feel I was getting back on the right foot—although it was taking longer than I had expected. At one point, encouraged by her new friendliness and the whiskey, I sailed in once again. Surely the happy old members of the club might share their joys with a hungry newcomer, I began. In a word, I was after meeting one of the sadists and enjoying the elixir of razor strop, and what I wanted to know was, how soon could it be arranged?

"If you make fun of it, Joyce, if you don't understand this is a sacred thing, I don't know what to tell you. Those wisecracks of yours—elixir of razor strop and all that—do you realize you are making fun of love itself?"

I hadn't—after all it wasn't real love—but I quickly apologized. "I didn't come here to talk about it, Victoria. I'm like a drug addict who's been off the stuff too long. They've been trying to sell me health but I'm not in the market for it, Cy says. It's all because of these damned words. Who knows what health is and what sickness is? I've drunk five thousand quarts of milk—and I'm hungry and thirsty as when I started. This Von as you call him—couldn't you just once—let him operate on me? I could go in your place and—"

She reminded me again that this was love. "I don't even think he'd care for you. In fact I'm sure he wouldn't."

The telephone rang and Victoria went to answer it. I was lying on one of her twin beds, waiting for her to come back. And thinking. Nearly twenty thousand dollars in cash money, my bank account was way down now, and here I was, still with a lion eating inside my chest. At that minute Vicky seemed smarter than I. She was able to settle for the nice white prison walls—hell, she was enjoying them, making friends with the other prisoners, carrying on. Why did I have to keep looking for the key to get me out? For now at last I suspected that here was a door that had no key and what I had done with the years of trying to find it had been to wear down my hands to the bleeding bones. And all the time I hadn't even wanted to get out. All the time I liked the poison they poured down my throat when I was new in the world—all right, so as not to die of it, I had developed first a toleration and then a desire. Right now this very minute here I was trying to get another swig of it.

Then I was telling some of this to my new friend Vicky. And then Victoria was asking, "Have you finished?"

"Yes. Why?"

"Because I have something to tell you."

"Go ahead."

"He's here!"

"Oh no!" I jumped up. "You mean *him*—the one you said . . .?"

"Just blew in from Chicago. Mr. V. And he'll take you."

"My God! When?"

"Tonight."

"What time?"

"At eight o'clock."

I looked at my watch: it was six already.

"Where?"

She named the apartment house and the number of his suite. I was to go up in the elevator and . . .

"What did you tell him about me?"

"Nothing much. I didn't tell him your right name, of course. You are simply Miss R and he is Mr. V. You are to knock at his door promptly at eight o'clock. I advise you to be on time, dear—because if you aren't, it may be very bad for you."

I didn't quite get this last. All I could think of was, I'm going to get it now, I'm going to get it at eight o'clock, and maybe after that . . .

"How do you feel?"

"Fine. Wonderful. It was kind of you, Vicky."

"That's all right. I wanted to do it for you—but we had to wait until just the right one came in."

"What's the procedure? Will he give it to me right away?"

"No, certainly not." She gave me that surprised, slightly disgusted look. "He'll punish you first. But not even that at the start."

"What then?"

"These evenings usually begin with getting to know each other—drinking champagne, talking. If he likes you, he'll give you the best. But we haven't too much time to talk. You'd better start dressing soon."

"Dressing? Why, I thought—"

"You're not going to wear that awful dress?"

"Why not?"

"My dear, he would loathe you if you dared to show up in anything like that. He's very style-conscious."

"Well then, in that case, I'd better run home and dress."

"Wait a minute." She went to her closet. "Let's see, maybe I can lend you something. It will have to be something new—something he's never seen. If he even dreamed you were wearing something of mine, it might be pretty bad for both of us." There were implications here I didn't understand. Of course Mr. V and Vicky knew each other, but why the clothes mattered so much was difficult to comprehend. "Oh well, since I've gone so far I might as well go completely overboard. Here, you can wear my new white wool. I haven't had it on since I tried it on in the store. I know you'll look wonderful in it, you lucky little bitch."

She was lifting a bit of white wool cut on extremely simple lines with a single fur pocket of shining leopard. I took it and got into it quickly. It fitted me pretty well.

"I'll call downstairs and see if we can get the beauty parlor—wait a minute—Hello . . ." From what she was saying I gathered the parlor was still open, and by now I was just as interested as Victoria in making myself perfect in the sharp eyes of Mr. V. And what would he look like, I wondered as I started combing my hair.

"The girl will be right up and do your hair and nails," Victoria announced as she began looking over her various lipsticks—she had quite a collection of them. "Your underwear isn't quite right, darling. Take off that panty girdle, for God's sake—"

"But I thought—"

"Don't think. Here, you'll need a slip. You can wear this."

She handed me a beautiful new slip and helped me to dress as carefully as if I were going to meet my bridegroom. The beautician arrived shortly, and started to work on my hair and nails. The progress toward perfection took on pace and excitement. By seven-fifteen I sat before Victoria's long mirror as Vicky and the beautician worked on my face, making it up within an inch of its life. "Delicately," Vicky kept saying as the girl gently streaked black dye on my blond eyebrows, "Discreetly. Only the faintest trace of eye-shadow," and in a whisper, "V likes clear eyes and clear skin. I know he'll love your hair—you ought to always wear it in a long bob." So as to flow freely during the whipping, I'd assumed, as I wondered what the beautician thought. I felt grateful to Vicky as I obeyed all commands, like a younger sister being decked out in her trousseau by an old hand at the game.

Besides, I was enjoying my role, and the keen anticipation of meeting Mr. V was very exciting. Imagine meeting up with a good, hardworking, high-class sadist under circumstances that were safe, with no aftermath such as I had supposed might happen in the form of a story on the front page of the tabloids. "These men are experts," Cy had said. Now and then I wondered about Mr. V, what he would look like, whether he too was looking forward in equally keen anticipation to meeting me, but all questions, How old is Mr. Vee? and, What does he do? were brushed aside by the noncommittal Victoria.

When I had finished dressing, the beautician gone, I stood before the mirror once more and this time Vicky examined her handiwork with a critical eye.

"You're all right," she said with satisfaction. "Now wait just one minute."

She disappeared again, going into the vicinity of her closet, and came back with a white cashmere coat lined with leopard which she handed to me, saying, "This goes with the dress. It's too bad about the rain but you'll take a taxi—and anyway, I want you to make an impression. I know he'll be mad about the clothes—and that's half the battle." By the time I had put the coat on and gathered up my bag and gloves it was ten to eight.

"For God's sake, hurry up!" cried Vicky in a slightly panicky voice.

She held open the door for me as I went out and walked the long way to the elevator with me.

"Grab the first taxi you see," she cautioned me, "and tell the man to hurry."

I said, "All right, I will, but why? Is he so impatient?"

"That's not exactly it," said the evasive Vicky, "but I'll tell you this much—it is sometimes dangerous to arrive late. It's likely to go much worse for you."

I started to say, "Worse—you mean better, don't you?" but quickly changed my mind as I remembered the no-humor edict. The elevator arrived, Vicky muttered a tight-lipped "Good luck," as we kissed good-by, and I went down to the lobby and out into the street.

It was pouring down rain. I waited outside under the canopy for a taxi for ten minutes or more, then gave up and walked up the street to the avenue. Another three-five minutes, and I was on my way. But I was late arriving at Mr. V's apartment. I saw by the clock in the corridor downstairs it was 8:25 as I made my way to the elevator.

Then I was standing outside his apartment. I rang the bell and waited another five minutes before the door was opened by a man with sharp black eyes, thick black hair and a small black graying mustache. He behaved with such impersonal civility, I had the impression he was the butler. A sharp voice said, "Good evening, come in." I came in, and he closed the door promptly behind him. I noticed I had entered a poorly lighted foyer as I saw him opening the door to the closet. "Put your things here, then come inside," he said, adding as he disappeared something that sounded like, "He'll be with you shortly."

It must have been Mr. V's butler, I concluded, as I came on through the corridor and entered an oversized oblong living room with dark wood-paneled walls. The place was furnished in excellent taste with heavy antiques and was faintly Oriental in feeling. I came further in and sat down on a sofa at right angles to the fireplace, in which a coal fire was burning in a grate, the sole item of cheer in the slightly forbidding room. As I waited, I remembered that butler, wondering what Mr. V would do with him for the evening. He was easy to remember—especially his eyes, the sharpest, smartest eyes I had ever seen. And his voice, the way his words came out in commands—why, he was like someone commanding a servant instead of it being the other way around. I couldn't remember anything else about him—his mouth, for instance, completely eluded me—except for the mustache, but I had felt those eyes behind his horn-rimmed specs, the way they seemed to leap partway out of their sockets and bite into mine, as if he were annoyed that I had appeared to distract his master. And that voice, low-pitched but decisive, impersonal as all hell; he was just about the last man I would pick for my servant.

I heard a door close, and wondered if he had gone out the back way for the night. And now about Mr. V—what was he doing in there? I listened but I couldn't hear a sound. I turned around once to look at the rest of the place but couldn't see anything, and once I got up and looked through the shadows behind the draped oval in the wall, but there was nothing to be seen except a large hallway with a table, an enormous Oriental lamp, and some chairs. This must be an expensive place, I concluded, as I wondered if he actually lived here or just rented it for his experiences. I came back and sat down again, watching the fire. For some reason I had the idea Mr. V was a businessman, and now was perhaps attending to some last-minute office matters.

Fifteen minutes came and went, then twenty, and then twenty-five.

I was uneasy now. What on earth was going on in there, I wondered, as I considered every possibility. Was he undressing, perhaps—or dressing? Or preparing the champagne—or the implements? Perhaps another whippee was keeping him busy—but no, it couldn't be that— that would indicate an assembly-line deal—and from the way Vicky talked I concluded it wasn't like that. I smoked my third cigarette. I felt slightly self-conscious as I waited—as if someone were watching me—that sort of thing was possible, after all. If he was getting the implements ready, that wouldn't take long, or would it? They didn't have to be heated? And what would they be? "I hope he won't give you the cat," Vicky had said. "I'm terrified of the cat."

He kept me waiting so long, it seemed like nearly forty minutes, I began to get worried, going in a circle from curiosity to fear of what was going to happen to fear that nothing was going to happen. I even thought of leaving—was it possible the door was locked and that I had gotten myself into something bad? I trusted Vicky, I trusted Cy too, in a way, but no one could tell what would happen in a thing like this. Cy didn't really know her, had met her through an advertisement, and . . . Or was it possible Mr. V had seen me from some place where he was peeping, and changed his mind about the whole thing? Sadists were unpredictable, and maybe . . . I was just about to get up and go to look for him when I heard a movement somewhere back there and decided to wait. I did wait, and when he didn't appear I did get up and go to the living room alcove. This time I called out, "Mr. V. Are you there?"

He didn't answer at first, but I heard movements and went back to the sofa. After a few minutes the same man appeared who had opened the door.

"Did you call me?"

"Well, yes, I did—I've been waiting for Mr. V and—"

"Don't do that again!" he interrupted me to say.

So that man was Mr. V himself, not the butler, I knew that much as I said, "I'm sorry, but I thought perhaps—"

"That's beside the point. I'll be with you shortly."

He disappeared quickly, and I lit another cigarette. My, but he did seem angry. Not exactly a sweet-tempered gent was this. I was slightly afraid of him now. Nothing was going as Vicky had indicated. He hadn't seemed the least bit interested in my beautiful clothes, the white-and-leopard coat was off in the closet, the magnificent new dress and expensive make-up was lost on that busy angry man who seemed hardly to have seen me, and certainly to have been annoyed by my calling his name. I was getting pretty uncomfortable about the whole thing when he appeared again out of nowhere, this time bringing with him a silver tray complete with glasses and a bottle of champagne in a bucket of ice which he placed on the table before the fireplace. He settled on the other sofa and I sat there watching him uncork the bottle and start to fill the glasses. He said nothing; I smiled tentatively when I saw him glance at me, then settled into quietude in which I could hear the burning of the coals and the sound of the steady drizzle of rain outside.

And suddenly he was talking, still attending to the glasses and without looking at me. "That's a good color for you, that white. I noticed the lining of the coat and the coolie neck. It's too long though. Where did you get it?"

"I had it made," I lied.

"Design it yourself?"

"Oh yes."

"You have fairly good taste then. Women seem to be able to pick good clothes that are almost alarmingly unbecoming. Do you like champagne?"

"Yes, very much." He passed me the glass without saying anything more. "I'm about ready for it, too."

This time he looked at me. "You were the one that was late."

"Was I—well, not very much."

"Is your memory poor?"

"I suppose so, if you say I was late."

"You suppose. Don't you know?"

"My memory is pretty good," I said.

"How late were you?"

"About fifteen minutes, I'd say."

"Then your memory is poor. You've lived with your own mind a long time—twenty-eight years, I'd say."

"Thirty next week," I corrected.

"Yes, thirty next week, that's long enough to be quite sure of many things."

"I guess it is at that," I agreed, thinking what a clever way he had of making me confess my age. He looks sad somehow, I was just thinking, as he smiled.

"Well, my dear, your vocabulary is surely not your long suit—but here's your health. That's a suitable toast, you seem to have plenty of that, at least."

"And yours."

We drank. I sipped mine, but Mr. V drank off his whole glass. The minute he had put down his glass he stared at me, I looked back, and for the minute I felt his hard eyes coming out again at me with that black bite. A locking sensation, it was rather exciting. I looked away.

"I do like your neck," he said. "A long full neck is a pleasant thing to look at. These American women, so many of them with pretty heads have these awful necks. It's a mild obsession of mine."

"Aren't you American?"

"Yes, in a sense." He smiled and shrugged, as if to say that which we are about to do is not exactly American, it has no name and no nation can be blamed for it. What he said was, "I was born here, if that's what you mean."

We drank for quite a while, and talked and talked. My, the wise things we said! He quoted Sophocles, I quoted Confucius—that kind of thing, none of which I can remember. We were on the second bottle before he picked up my hand and pulled me over—I thought to place me on the loveseat beside him. Instead he sat down, leaving me standing foolishly before him, and looked at me, in fact watched me while he drank, this time without offering me a glass. He was talking when I went back to the other sofa, feeling slightly rejected.

"Well, little girl in white, brave little girl in white—you have brought your charm along with you, haven't you?" I muttered something, "Thanks," and he continued. "I've no doubt you find it a protecting device, most women do—even those who do not have it." I thought this was rather amusing, asked him, "How's that?" and he replied, "Oh come now, surely you've seen women making eyes and putting themselves forward, presenting themselves, as if they were charming and attractive—when the fact is they are not at all." I said, Yes, I had noticed that and often envied it, and pitied certain ugly women, too—although now that I came to think of it, they seemed to be the ones who often had the most security presenting themselves.

"Never pity an ugly woman!" said Mr. V. "Sometimes ugly women become more attractive than pretty or charming women. Remember too, some men absolutely detest beauty in women. Charm, too. But of course you know that."

I said I hadn't noticed it, thinking to myself, from the way he said it, that possibly he was one of those. He laughed. "No, I'm not one of those," he said, as if reading my mind. "You have this charm, of course. You had done better to have left it outside— under the circumstances—but since you prefer it this way, you are the one who dictates the evening."

I didn't understand what he meant, it sounded promising and slightly frightening; it couldn't be what I thought, however, because now he was smiling. "You may use your charm, it is delightful and useful to you, no doubt—and I, in turn, will use my powers on you. All human relationships are tests, are they not? And each must use the weapons he likes the best."

He refilled the glasses. On the third bottle, while I was still wondering what he had in his mind, he showed me his more cultivated side. We talked music, he was immensely learned, and not snobbish about it; we talked art, books and philosophy. Sometimes I almost forgot what I had come to receive, I was even wondering vaguely if possibly he, too, had forgotten, when suddenly, in the midst of a discussion about opera—I had said I didn't respond to opera, he was explaining why other people did—he continued in the same voice, saying, "You were warned that your charm would require to be punished—but you weren't listening or remembering! I must attend to your memory, my dear—and as for that charming way you have, you'll find I am not vulnerable. I have my own line of defense, my own way of putting the veil over the female face when it is being used *against a man*."

I said, Oh, but I wasn't meaning to bring about any such situation, thinking he was joking or flirting. He continued to look at me, I had the feeling he was almost hypnotizing me, perhaps these were merely Victoria's suggestions, "The sharp concentrated way he looks at people often has a hypnotic effect," and other such. Anyway, without knowing what I was doing I got up and came over to him.

I remember thinking, perhaps he wanted to kiss me and was self-conscious (obviously I was a novice at this business, and did all the wrong things), but that was not what he wanted at all. He took hold of me suddenly, half-leaping from the sofa. Seemingly in one stride with panther lightness he had encircled my waist with his free arm, and in a flash I was stretched over his knees face down. I couldn't think how he did everything so fast and with such astonishing deftness, he was like a man with ten hands, my arms were pinned down, he started thrashing me with a thong of leather that resounded in the room. (Jesus, this is it, I thought, as I wondered with some fear how far he would go and remembered Victoria's, "I just can't stand the cat, I hope he doesn't give you the cat." Then I forgot to think as the old desire came back—the old memory of being overpowered, completely helpless.) The lashes were beginning to sting and hurt, the pain-filled pleasure, when he stopped suddenly, grabbed me tighter in his clutch, and talked.

". . . must teach you what to expect when you try to charm me . . . You'll find I'm not the soft man you think I am . . . You'll see what it arouses in me—and then you may remember."

He reached for something else and went on talking in exactly the same voice, hitting me now with something smooth and flat that hurt badly, a hairbrush, I thought. (So this is it.) The whacks stung and hurt, growing slightly more painful and slightly less pleasurable, they had nowhere near the thrill they had in my fantasies. I heard him talking in that even voice, it had been kind of scary at first, but was growing less so as other sounds came in. I noticed he wheezed as he whipped. In fact, the more excitement I engendered the more he wheezed. He was having at it now, going round the bend, wheezing very hard. Was he slightly asthmatic, I wondered, as I caught a quick vision of his having a possible attack, and my having to call a doctor. That would be awful, having a doctor arrive to attend a strange man I knew only as Mr. V. He talked on now between his heavy breathing, then he reached for something else—the implements Victoria had mentioned were coming on apace. This one swished, it felt something like a switch from off a tree to which something had been added, some kind of tape, and it stung badly. He was slowing down now. What was he saying? Even his talk was giving out. There for a minute it gave out completely. He was whipping with much less elation and breathing rather queerly. That funny old boy up there, I thought, as I felt his grip slipping, I hope he isn't having an attack of some kind. So this is all it is, this thing I've been dreaming about, avoiding, fearing, desiring. This queer sick little man in his locked-up rooms . . . with his stertorous breathing. He had let up now and dropped me as quickly as he had picked me up, though not for the same reasons.

My dress repaired, I glanced at my wrist watch. It was nearly two a.m. He had stopped, exhausted; I noticed he was in a perspiration as he went hurriedly out of the room. He ought not to be doing this, I thought, as I stole a glance at him on the way out, deciding he didn't look much like a fiend. He wasn't looking at me as he went out, he was staring before him, a look of anger and irritation on his face. So I've had a licking at last, I said to the dying fire. So this is all it is, I said again. I took out my comb and combed my hair. This was a preliminary, I assumed, and now there would be something else, something more sensible and loving.

I waited for Mr. V to return. He was the most going-out-of-the-room and making-a-woman-wait type of man I'd ever seen; however this one seemed to be in a good cause, to freshen up for the finish. This time Mr. V returned sooner than I had expected, drawn back to the scene of the crime, bringing with him a fresh bucket of ice and another bottle of wine. I was just powdering my nose, ready now for a friendly chat, the chips were down, but to my amazement he sat there saying nothing and ignoring me completely. (He probably just has to treat a woman badly now and then, I thought, just as I have had to be treated badly. But now that we have both gotten it out of our systems, it seems like a foolish business, keeping it up, just playing mad. Or is it that he is embarrassed at the entire nonsense?) With this last in mind I started to talk and found myself blurting things out. I had enjoyed the experience, I said, but seeing the look on his face I added tactfully, I had of course been thoroughly frightened, neglecting to mention I knew I was stronger than he and could have gotten away at any time. He poured us more champagne and thus aided and abetted he told me of other women he had whipped: his big moment in recent times seemed to have been the daughter of some old flame of his—for not learning her lessons, wearing soiled underwear or forgetting things. And others whom he had not whipped but tormented in more subtle, and more revolting, ways.

I must have been drinking too much on an empty stomach; I had been hungry there for a while, I don't know what caused it, but I heard myself talking, telling him the simple truth. "All my life I've had this goddamned fantasy. From childhood experiences. My father —It's taken up hours and hours of my time—precious hours of life. An awful nuisance. Some people enjoy this kind of thing. I would give anything to get over it—obviously I would—that's why I came here—and you have done me a great favor. I'll be everlastingly grateful to you and to Victoria . . ." I was about to finish up with, "That is, if I've gotten over it," but stopped, seeing an icy cold grimace on his face. My, he was a one with the queer glances! Perhaps he was waiting, calling me to him. This should be about the time. . . . I got up and came over toward him and seeing no move on his part I sat down beside him and tried to kiss him, but he gave me such an awful push, holding his head far from my face, I landed back on the sofa. (That was when I found out for sure, what I had been told by Victoria and by Cy, and forgotten in my incredible naïveté: that there is no love in this club, that the whipping is the whole entire experience, and this is not to be trifled with or changed in any way. A hate club. Love turned into hate. The whole damned thing now seemed outrageously funny, but I knew better than to laugh.)

"Well anyway, Mr. V, I'm glad about all this . . ."

"What's to be glad about?" he shouted. "These things happen, that's all, but who's glad?"

Somehow I knew he was furious, and this time I honestly didn't know why. He got to his feet.

"Your coat is in the closet," was what he said.

I got up to go, intending to say a proper good night, but seeing his eyes decided in favor of the closet where I quickly found my coat. He didn't follow me to the door, but turned as I was leaving.

"Good night, White Dress!" he shouted. "Good night. And *get out!* Get out—and go quickly, please!"

It was two o'clock when I left. The rain had let up, a bracing cold winter wind came blowing down the street, so I walked instead of hailing a taxi. I didn't know why—I hadn't of course had time to digest the experience—but I felt greatly relieved and highly exhilarated.

Something had gone wrong up there, at least for Mr. V it had, I knew that much—but it didn't seem to matter. It hadn't gone wrong for me—no, not at all—but somehow it must have gone wrong for him. It really wasn't much of an experience, come to think of it, yet somehow my heart was gladdened, I could see ahead. I thought of calling Victoria to tell her of my undying gratitude, but decided it was too late. Besides, I couldn't tell her the truth, the whole truth was unknown to me, and such of the truth as I had in my hands was not to be divulged to her, although I enjoyed it privately. Actually I had been pretty much disappointed in Mr. V as a monster. He wasn't much of a monster in my book. Just another lost little human being, somebody who had strayed off the road. I thought of him up there in that dark place with his implements and his wheezing, and suddenly I laughed like mad. Here I was again acting crazy, laughing on the streets as I shed another skin, and looked back at it.

Was it possible the fantasy was gone? No, I couldn't quite believe that—you don't get over an obsession that quickly—or do you? I would soon know the answer to that, and I was deeply curious. I would never again seek out another Mr. V—that was at least a certainty. The thought of going back up to the dark apartment and waiting for that phony sadist to get going with his implements was too much. The whole thing was a charade, a caricature of some terrible old rotting reality, including all that elaborate anonymity. But by walking back into the past through this foolish current duplicate, something was released to laughter, the only whitewash my soul would accept.

But it wouldn't last. It couldn't possibly be the end of a lifetime obsession. Of a whole emotional conditioning. *Or could it?*

Only time would answer that, I knew, as I went home and fell soundly asleep.

CHAPTER THIRTY-SIX

• • • • • •

I MADE A DIARY ENTRY. IT READS: THURSDAY. IT IS NOW THREE DAYS since my evening with Mr. V. I have been waiting, apprehensively, for the visitation, and am at last beginning to relax, and believe it. No whipping fantasies for three whole long marvelous days. A funny thing happens instead of the regular Technicolor movies. The old medieval city appears, but now it is shadowy and stained like an old postal card about to fall apart and, when the prince appears, over his face comes the wheezing Mr. V. Everything fades in laughter. I wonder if it is gone for good, and think perhaps it is.

Today, Friday, is the fourth day since Mr. V. I went up to see Victoria to return her clothes and to thank her for her goodness, and to bring her a gift. I told her, "Vicky, you did me a very good turn, I'll always remember it," adding, "I wish I could do something for you."

"I don't need to have anything done for me," said the smug Victoria. "You're the one who's in trouble."

I decided to give it the tactful treatment. "Maybe you're right. But now that I've found out—" I was going to say "how ridiculous the whipping obsession is—" but quickly swallowed the *verboten* words, and continued, "where relief can be found, I feel much better."

"I don't think V will ever see you again!"

"Oh no!" I was remembering those last quarter hours when I must have blurted out things I couldn't remember, as I added on a hunch, "What will I ever do without him?"

"He gets into town so seldom," Victoria was saying, "and when he does of course it's me he wants. He's amazing, isn't he?"

I agreed that he was brilliant, a cultivated man. It seemed kind of odd that Victoria should be jealous—that was the emotion she was registering—since Mr. V was not her big moment. I wondered about this as the conversation began to lag, then decided to ask her, "What does V do for a living?"

She was blushing. I wondered why this should embarrass her so, as I watched her hem and haw. There was something about his being "a professor" out West somewhere, it was all very vague, and I knew I shouldn't have inquired.

"Well, maybe sometime when I get the urge again, you'll be good enough to find me another spanker."

"What do you mean—when you get the urge again?" She was frowning. "Don't you have it all the time?"

"God no! If I did I'd go crazy. I haven't had it since the estimable professor helped me out."

She followed me to the elevator and pressed a piece of paper into my hand. "Now at last you've found a way of life. You call these numbers when it hits you again." We kissed good-by, she promised to get in touch with me when she came back and I left, feeling about a thousand tons lighter of spirit.

The days stretched into weeks. I would wake up wondering, will the old obsession be here this morning? Will it be waiting for me, always in the background, as it has been, lo, these many years? At the end of the first whole week, when it had not come back, I began to feel more relaxed, but I was still not certain it had gone. I decided to keep count of how long it stayed away "this time" as I remembered unhappily that after all it had disappeared in the past for weeks, sometimes even for months, only to return unexpectedly and stronger than ever.

After six weeks I awakened one morning thinking about it. It wasn't there the way it used to be those days when I would awaken knowing "this is going to be one of those days," but the idea was there. I got up, had breakfast, and then thought about it again. It was there, but it was more static, less affecting. The market place was lighter in color, reminiscent of an old faded movie, the people moved more slowly, the prince's carriage was coming along at snail's pace. I thought about the prince, but the minute I did I thought about Mr. V, a more current sadist, and found myself laughing. The minute

I laughed the whole picture disappeared. Just remembering V, the way he was up there in the hotel suite making like a sadist and me making like a masochist—those hard bird-eyes of his, the squeaky knees, the wheezing in his chest. He appeared over the prince and the prince receded into nothingness. Good-by, Prince! Good-by, Dream-life.

One afternoon I was passing Victoria's hotel. On an impulse I went in and called her from the lobby, but getting no answer I went on up in the elevator and knocked on her door. I saw the *DO NOT DISTURB* sign at the same time as I noticed a streak of light coming from under the door. She hadn't checked out, she was probably in there, but why the silence? I knew her to be a person of some discernment who would never indulge her whims in a hotel suite, yet a feeling of uneasiness crept over me as I knocked again, then called, "Victoria, it's Joyce. Are you in?" After some minutes I heard a clicking sound as the streak of light disappeared from under the door. Then the knob turned, the door opened, I found myself entering a darkened room in which stood a woman I knew, of course, was Victoria: it had to be Victoria, she was wearing Victoria's red robe and she had Victoria's beautiful long hair, but there was something so different about her she was almost like another person.

"Didn't you see the sign on the door?" Her voice sounded hoarse. "You didn't have to make such a racket in the hall."

I didn't answer at first. In the gray light coming through the windows I could just make out her face—pale in spots, red and swollen in other spots, with vast dark areas in her upper cheeks that made her eyes seem like pinpoints of pain in the distended flesh.

"Victoria, what happened?" I gasped, quickly assuming she had been in a motor accident. "You should be in a hospital."

She walked heavily towards the sofa—there was something the matter with her foot—and settled in a corner under the unlit lamp. "Sit down," she said, this time her voice was so low I could barely make out the words. Still in my coat I sat down on a chair near the window. I asked her if she wanted a cigarette and she said No, and after that I knew better than to ask any more questions. I don't know how long we sat there not saying anything, then suddenly Victoria seemed to come alive. She asked me first what time it was, I told her Five to six, then she asked if it was raining and I said No, just damp and misty, and thus encouraged she asked what day it was, and I told her it was Tuesday. Next she suggested that I get us both a drink, which I did, and later she let me bathe her face with witch-hazel and ice, and even prop her up in bed with pillows, cigarettes and ice-packs. She still wouldn't let me turn on the light but as I helped her into bed I caught a glimpse of one leg. I saw a mass of welts and bruises and winced as the full horror of what had happened to this endearing woman came over me with a chill. It was too much for me, I had touched the bottom of the barrel and now, sick with identification and fear, I found myself wishing I hadn't come by to see her.

Three drinks and many iced soakings later she talked. "Don't keep looking like that, Joyce. Don't make such heavy weather of it. All right, so we went too far."

"How can you say *we?*" I remonstrated. "The man who did this is a fiend—"

"Oh stop, you little moral fool. I say *we* because it was *we*. We both wanted it. We just forgot ourselves, we lost count, we just didn't realize how far we were going. I lost my head, I guess, and so did he. I've never had the cat before. I wanted to try it just once . . . to see what it was like."

The telephone started up and as she answered I noticed her voice pick up. "Hello . . . Oh, Hello . . . Yes . . . Yes, I've been waiting. No, I haven't. . . . No, honestly I haven't. I've been waiting for you. Yes, of course. Eight o'clock? Of course I will—I mean I shall . . . I shall be right here waiting. Good-by."

As she finished she completely recovered her voice, and with it her spirit. She sounded excited, expectant, almost joyous with anticipation. To my absolute amazement she got up out of bed, took a negligee out of her closet, then crossed to the bureau and began making up her face.

"I'm afraid I'll have to ask you to excuse me, Joyce," she said. "It seems I have an engagement."

But I managed to speak my piece. "Victoria, you ought to be in bed—under a doctor's care. You shouldn't be seeing people."

3 3 7

"You ought to know, we never see doctors. And it isn't people. It's him."

"You can't mean—the man who did this terrible thing to you? This criminal—"

She stopped brushing her hair and looked at me.

"You!" The sharp edge of contempt made her voice sound louder than ever before. "What do you know about anything? Go on back to your safe little daydreams. You've never lived—never for a minute. You'll never know what it's like to go all the way to the edge—real danger—with real people. Not a silly movie inside your silly head."

She laughed, and there was contempt and merriment and something else in her voice, some wild half-animal sound.

"If you want to know the truth, Mr. V hated you. That little phoney, he called you. The experimenter. Go on home. Have a cup of cocoa and dream some more fantasies and see another doctor. You don't belong with the real people. You just haven't got the right blood."

I started once more. "But Victoria, this thing gets worse and worse. You keep needing more and more. It's like taking dope. Apparently there's no end until—"

But Victoria interrupted me.

"Good-by, Joyce," she said. "This conversation ended some weeks ago."

CHAPTER THIRTY-SEVEN

. . . .

AUGUST 21, 1949 DAWNED, A BRIGHT HOT DAY, THE FIFTH OF THE heat wave. At noon I turned on the radio, heard the temperature was over 100; and glancing down at the paper I noticed the date. *August 21.* There was something familiar about that day—and the heat. Wasn't it just about this time—good God, seven years ago— that I cracked up? I found an old date-book stuck in my file and there it was, sure enough. August 21, 1942. Dr. Ramsey. 2 P.M.

He was the first, the psychiatrist. The old wife-tier and the case-forgetter. Seven years ago. Seven years in the frog pond. Summer and sun—and disinterment. Now where did that phrase come from, slipping down off my mind like a piece of loose skin? I took down the dictionary. This is a day to look things up.

"To take out of a grave or out of the earth," I read. "To bring from obscurity into view." Why that's exactly what I started doing August 21, 1942 and have *not yet finished.* My, but those last three words were hard to put down! Not yet finished. Why not *yet?* Why not just *not finished?* The *yet* is such a friendly open-hearted little word, implying the finish is just around the corner. Why can't I lie peacefully to myself, I thought, as so many other people do? "The disinterment is finished, oh long ago, it's over now and I'm well," when all the time we know the creatures we disinterred are still stalking the graveyard.

I am still in the thick of my seven years' war, I wrote in my note-book. Some symptoms appear dead—but are they really dead or do they just resemble corpses because I've looked at them for so long? Are they more likely *waiting?* How often have I felt these corpses lifting their dead hands and pulling the strings once again—and when this happens what good are all the names we have called them? And when this doesn't happen, when they remain dead, where is the fresh new life that's supposed to rush in?

The fact is, the current is still off. The *elixir vitae* is not yet turned on. I brace myself and cling to the cure—formulas, interpretations, insights. Wondering, is it still the uncure? I don't know. I don't want to know. All I know is I am still athirst and even the poisoned waters feel cool in this "land where every weed is flaming and only man is black."

Sometimes I can almost hear this other self, this one that holds me back, howling like an animal way down there at the bottom of my soul. What's the matter with you? I ask of the silence. Why can't you act like other people? Why won't you get up and live?

And sometimes I can almost hear the answer coming back. *Because you didn't get me what I wanted. The doctors didn't have that elixir vitae . . .*

Imagine being controlled by this kind of creature! Imagine hating the strongest, biggest, most mysterious part of your own self! But it's all true, what this crazy self is saying. But where is this thing it needs? And what can I do with it now? I haven't got this nectar . . .

So the insights didn't help very much. I remember now, I left Dr. Five because suddenly I saw these insights could go on until death, but what I needed to heal my wound was something else, *something that wasn't there*. What was it—this thing I wanted so much and was so desperate without? It had to be a penis, Five said. Everything always came back to that. But I said no, it was more like—well, like a connection had gone wrong somewhere and the current had gone off. The current. Now if I could just get this connection fixed somehow, the current would be on, and the fountains would start flowing.

One summer evening I went to dinner at Irene's. A pleasant experience, but toward the end, even in those big rooms, the air began to feel dead, vitiated of all buoyancy. I mentioned it to Irene, reluctantly she turned on the window-fans, then came back to inform me, it wasn't the warm air, it was the wish for denial, and there I was listening to a discussion of old Portzweig's theories. As I listened I had a chilling sense of a circle that has come full, closing in on the victims. Move now, I thought, or you may never get out from under this double-talk! Move almost anywhere, take any exit but don't be caught, fixated, frozen in this maze!

We talked about it later—Cal, old friend of Toni's and mine, I hadn't seen him in a long time—after we had left the party and were sitting in a half-empty village espresso shop.

"That's just what it is, baby," Cal was saying. "A maze—the rats just keep running back and forth. But as long as you know it's a maze you're not caught yet."

"But what good is all this talk? Where's the free-flowing warm new life?" I asked.

"That's involuntary. New theory. You can't interpret your way into it." He had saved himself, he told me, because of a doctor he'd found who understood "the bio-electrical nature of pleasure and anxiety." I listened, thinking to myself—another doctor, another theory. So human beings were bio-electrical. At least Cal looked different—yes, quite different than he had in the past. "Somehow I found my way back to biology."

The current, I thought, *the connection*. And I listened now with more than a passing interest. But how on earth could any doctor bring this about? Why, it sounded impossible on the face of it! Yet someone or some *thing* had brought about a change in this man. He was calm, it was as if his inner powers had been mobilized, allowing him to canter through at his own speed. A change all right from the harassed frightened man I'd known. I pressed him to tell me what the doctor had done.

"You couldn't even get him to tell you," he said. "This group tries to stay away from *theories*." They believed in the bio-electrical nature of life, that people were armored against nature and life within themselves, and this led to the extinguishing of life. A living organism contained electrical energy in every one of its cells and kept charging itself from the atmosphere—by the process of breathing. Considered as a phenomenon of bio-electrical discharge, the word orgasm took on a whole new meaning. The idea was to restore bio-psychic motility.

It was different from "the word therapies," Cal explained. There was no thinking back into the past to understand the present. It had to do with physical functioning. With tension and discharge, energy in the air, and the current in living things. His doctor had had some

3 4 1

spectacular cures but, *laus Deo,* he didn't want publicity. Besides he belonged to a group that was "experimenting" and that was frowned on by the other groups.

We were still talking as Cal drove me home in a taxi. He wanted to come in and talk more, but was going away early in the morning. He wrote something hastily on a piece of paper. "You just stick this in your bag—in case you ever want to use it. From there on you can make up your own mind."

I didn't quite believe what Cal had been telling me but I kept the piece of paper just the same.

All the next day I kept remembering Cal and that afternoon took out the piece of paper and dialed the telephone number. In his hurry, Cal had forgotten to write down the doctor's name. All right, can you stand it, so it's Dr. Six. He couldn't take me for two weeks, he said, but if I got into "hot water" I could call him and he'd make the time. I said No, the hot water days were over but the cold water days were almost as bad in their way. We made an appointment, then I rushed to catch the train for Connecticut, and the week-end with the Richards, wondering what Daphne would be like in her final metamorphosis as Mrs. Tom Richards, and whether or not Toni would come.

"I'm only invited for dinner," she complained on the telephone. "Who wants to drive three, four hours just for dinner in the country? She must be desperate—asking us. Still and all, I'd like to see how she's making out in that house to end all houses, so I might just drive by for a drink. Said I must stay for dinner—she's having fancysmancy stuff—roast beef with Yorkshire pudding. After all, a Fourth of July week end—who hasn't got roast beef?"

I hope Toni comes so I can see the two of them together with husbands, I wrote in my notebook. And take a peek at the third act —or is it just the second? Whereas here am I still in the long, long first. Would like to see how it is with us all together—The three fates, "daughters of Necessity . . . Lachesis singing of the past, Clotho of the present, Atropos of the future."

Here I am sitting in one of Daphne's pleasant sleeping chambers— the next entry reads—furnished with beautiful things, rich textures, a great comfortable sofa and chair, and a red lacquer antique Chinese coffee table. The background is serene. Walls of gray and white, gray and blue silk upholstery, a gray Moroccan rug, white over-curtains with a red and gold geometric design, and a marvelous deep fireplace cut into the white-paneled walls upon which Daphne and Tom have hung "family mementos"—mostly from Tom's side, etchings of relatives and horses. Daphne has thrown in a gloomy-looking woman she says is her grandmother.

The place is full of surprises. Plants and fountains come out of the dining-room table, reflecting pools appear in the floor and the fireplaces are circular. Who'd believe it was handed them by a clever decorator a few weeks ago? And how do the happy people live in this Arabian Nights house that was designed to lift the spirits, as Daphne keeps saying? I must put it down right now while it's still just above my head. A swarthy man with piercing blue eyes and a self-contained smile—Daphne calls him Yule as in Yuletide—was working on the pond in the loggia when I arrived. Must be one of the workmen, I thought, he looks so full of sun and sweat—yet there was that in the way she introduced him that made me wonder. "It's all Yule's, this whole place," she said later. "The builder went crazy and the decorator was a queer—but Yule made things happen. Funny kind of man, likes to work."

I'll never forget seeing Toni come treading across the highly polished white floor like someone walking on eggs, stopping to stare at a collection of photographs set in the wall lighted from above. "How about a swim?" I asked, but she shook her head and continued staring, then started that creepy walking-on-eggs again.

"Where are you going?"

"God knows." She stared from the photographs back to me. "I've been trying to find my way out of this mortuary. Jeepers, Joyce, you mean to say it doesn't scare you?"

"No, not any more." I'd had a few hours over on her.

"I keep thinking somebody's looking down at me." She seemed to be more frightened of the house than the situation required. "All those awful plants that look like your grandfather—and water coming up out of the floor. Listen, a place like this I could go crazy in. And look at those!"

We looked up at a gallery of theatrical photographs—of all the handsome men Daphne had ever known (the plain devils were left out), some famous, some not so famous, but all young and beautiful rather than handsome, and just one woman at the center, Daphne herself. I asked Daphne if she thought it wise to have those pretty boys up there gaping at Tom over his coffee, but she shrugged it off with, "That's part of my charm."

"I tell you, honey, she's a regular Bluebeard," Toni wailed. "Imagine collecting heads like that. What a woman! I don't want to stay here long, Joyce. I just don't want to stay here very long." I said I thought she was being foolish. "Oh, I guess I just feel uncomfortable in a place like this," she finally admitted. "I saw them setting the table . . . it looks awfully fancy—all those funny knives and things— I might do the wrong thing and I know Sol will. And anyway Daphne always makes you pay a price for anything she gives you. She asked us here for a reason—it's something she wants."

"Have you forgotten—she's rich now! What on earth could she want from us? She has one too many of everything."

Toni went mincing on across the floor, hanging on to me and whispering. "I feel like something can happen—something bad, I mean. We're the only women—don't you think that's funny?"

"Of course not. We're the only women she knows very well. She can't be having all men all the time."

"Oh, can't she?" Toni was just asking when the subject of the discussion appeared, barefooted and golden tan in a flesh-colored Bikini that gave her the look of being nude.

"How do you like the house? Come on, tell me the truth."

"It's beautiful," we cooed.

"Wait till you sit around the pool. You're both coming for a swim, aren't you? Come on, Toni—you've got to—we have drinks and appetizers around the pool. And talk. The talk gets good around here sometimes."

As I went off to get my bathing suit, I heard Toni wailing. "I'm not much at aquatic sports, Daphne, really I'm not. And I didn't bring my bathing suit or anything—and anyway we have to go soon, we really do." But Daphne had her by the hand and was pulling her determindedly across the floor.

The first object I noticed as I came toward the pool was Sol's round stomach spreading cheerfully above his trunks. With those big cocker-spaniel eyes and sunburned skin he hovered over the green water like a warm brown smile. He was talking to Tom, whose heavy leonine face inclined toward him with an expression of distant benevolence. Toni, she'd just come to the end of a long drink, left her husband and came on over to the poolside bar where she sat down between Daphne and me.

"I think our boys are talking about money," she told Daphne. "It always gets kind of complicated, I mean when they start talking deals. It's like some foreign language, I guess—Chinese or something. What do you do, Daphne, when Tom starts making deals?"

"Just amuse myself till he has a lucid interval. I don't let it worry me."

"But don't you feel kind of left out—I mean like as if he was in the army or something?"

"I'd feel more left out if he didn't make deals," Daphne said.

Yule was sitting two stools removed from Daphne, sipping a long drink and laughing to himself. I couldn't help noticing his expression of great good-humored self-containment, as if he were looking down from a distance and from some mighty comfortable spot.

"Well now, Toni, don't you feel too bad about that," he chuckled. "You just tell them you've got the exclusive rights to the Gerson tractor in the Eastern hemisphere and they'll take you right in."

"She wouldn't even know how to pronounce it," said Daphne.

"Cement stocks. Tell 'em you've cornered the market on cement stocks."

"Sol wouldn't believe me. He's the gambler in the family. I'm still too scared about things like starvation."

Daphne moved over next to the Italian. We couldn't hear what they were saying, but she laughed at whatever it was with genuine gaiety. "How do you pronounce his name?" Toni whispered, and I told her "Graciadei." She pronounced it after me, correctly too. "Did you notice how she swallows the name when she introduces him to anybody? It's like she doesn't want you to know . . . Well, listen, honey, he's no handy man around the place, I know that much." She would have said more—Daphne was now engrossed in the conversation she was having and laughing gaily and loudly—but the butler appeared with a second round of some delightful concoction served in frosted glasses garnished with mint. We both took seconds, and began sipping.

"Say, what's in these drinks?" I asked Daphne.

"Don't ask—just drink and everything'll be all right."

Yule got up from his stool and strolled over to us, leaving Daphne sitting there by herself, leaning on the bar. "Those are called Suffering Bastards," he explained. "I'm responsible for them here. They have gin and cognac and some other things in them. Sophisticated kind of drink. Didn't you girls ever have one in the old Shephard's Hotel in Cairo?" We admitted we hadn't. "Where's that hotel?" Toni asked. He laughed at Toni, those high squeaky questions, and I thought what a big round laugh he had, very pleasant to hear. "Oh, Cairo's down the road a piece. Have two more and we'll spin down there."

Toni, she was halfway through her second, looked suddenly worried. "Wait a minute, you mean gin and cognac in the same drink?" she screamed. She'd been drinking the second in gulps. Daphne got down off her stool and stood beside us, putting her arm around Toni, something I'd never seen her do before; she liked everybody that day. "It won't hurt you, I promise. I've had as many as four before dinner. You have two more and you'll like everything better is all. You'll put on one of my bathing suits—say, I've got an adorable new bikini and if it fits you can have it—I know you'll love it, too. You want me to get it?"

"No, not yet, please—I have to think about the water for at least an hour before entering."

Daphne put down her drink, glanced at Yule and ran off toward the pool. We all watched her taking a graceful dive from the board. Words and phrases floated over from the two men. *Capital gains, specialty items, yield of 42 per cent.* Toni went back to her drink, smiling up at the new man. "You tell us what it means," she said.

He listened for a minute. "Something called American something is the best prepared mix. And . . . I think consolidating warehouses is great. . . . Wait a minute. Neither Mr. Meyers nor Mr. Richards believes in litigation. I don't think it's necessarily because they're humanitarians—but there are other elements involved—like time and money."

Toni felt she should resent his making fun of her husband. "Business is a great source of excitement to Sol," she explained. "I don't know what he'd do with himself if he couldn't make deals. Sol gets nervous when he's home sitting around. It's absolutely terrible when

3 4 6

he has a temperature and has to stay in. It's not exactly the money, I think it's the excitement."

The men were talking loud now, and getting louder and faster. Tom, looking like a weary lion, the eyes still sharp as if he could never stop listening, and with that hard pained smile, was watching Daphne swim in a race against a handsome young actor named Alvin Hammond who had arrived as if by magic at the opening of the bar, had two quick ones and gone off to change for a swim.

"No, I don't think I'd better have any more of those depressed bastards," Toni told the butler who was now making the rounds again, this time with appetizers which he pressed upon her. But she was skeptical of the paté—it had to be taken out of a jar—and withdrew in open hostility from the magnificent pink shrimp centerpiece. "That's aspic, isn't it?" she stage-whispered, as the tray was moved on. "Jesus don't you hate that stuff?"

The Italian laughed, Toni's antics seemed to delight him. "It's photogenic. Reminds me a bit of jello—a loveless food that's also photogenic."

Two of Tom's business associates drove by. One completely bald benign little man couldn't take his eyes off Daphne. The other, a middle-aged man who looked something like Einstein, went into such a jet-propelled conversation everything at the bar quieted down in favor of his hocus-pocus about "nonstop direct mail" and the importance of "acquiring companies." Even Alvin, the easy-to-please actor—who seemed perfectly happy as long as he could drink— jumped into the pool to escape. Soon the screaming and diving sounds, mingling with dog-barking and radio playing, began to drown out the hullabaloo about profit potentials. Graciadei and I went for a swim, after seeing Toni on her third drink drift resignedly over toward Sol.

A last round of drinks was served at the bar, where the entire party gathered before dinner, and stories rolled on and on, all with the same point, it seemed to me. We heard that Tom had lived a fabulous life, having made his original twenty million in Louisiana and Texas oil fields "without putting any cash down." This going around with no money, "borrowing quarters," had been a keen source of pleasure to Tom.

"Why as recently as twenty years ago, I borrowed money for meals from a truck driver—just for the hell of it!" The businessmen all thought this was remarkable and exclamations of admiration rose everywhere. I heard Graciadei whisper, "I'll bet he never paid it back," and Toni giggled. Then Tom told about the time he heard of a new oil well being drilled somewhere, rushed to the location during the middle of the night, looked it over and promptly bought it. "Strictly on credit without putting down a cent." He then waited until the news leaked out and sold a fraction of the land for half a million.

"Friend of Presidents," commented Graciadei, as the party finally broke for dinner.

CHAPTER THIRTY-EIGHT

· · · · · ·

ALVIN, THE ACTOR, A YOUNG GREEK-GOD TYPE WITH TAN SKIN, GOLD
hair and heavy eyelashes over blue eyes, called to me as I hurried
toward the house. "You're staying over, aren't you?" he asked. I said
yes, why?—there was such intent in his voice. "Oh, nothing," he
laughed. "I can see it's your first time here. Thank God she's brought
in a girl for a change." He went ahead, leaving me wondering what
that was all about. The place was full of innuendos.

Then Sol came padding heavily across the white marble loggia.
"Toni don't want to stay. I don't know any more what's the matter.
Wanting to go home—a time like this! She's going hurt people's
feelings—running out. She's invited to dinner. It's too fancy she says."
He walked on beside me, grunting disconsolately. "A little *goisha*
festival—Fourth of July stuff—so they're showing off. Me, I'd do the
same thing I had a house like this. Mansion of a place, couple hundred
G's if it cost a cent, but Toni's got to go home like she's sick or
something."

"She's just jealous of Daphne's house," I told him.

Sol smiled. "Maybe she's jealous at that, I wouldn't know—women,
who can figure? But wait till you see that penthouse I found! I tell
you, Joyce, it's something from a museum. A beauty. Listen, you
talk to her and maybe she'll change her mind. These are fine men—
big people. Tom Richards—he's being written up in *Life* magazine,
did you know that?"

Toni must have changed her mind at the last minute. She was
there, that's the main thing I remember about the dinner. The food
was wonderful, magnificent to behold and delicious to taste. The

guests were, in fact, dwarfed by the lavish table. I remember at one point deciding I rather liked the house-fixer, now the prized guest, this Yule Graciadei, who seemed for a time the most alive and by far the most amusing of all the guests.

The party picked up after we left the table. The seating arrangements in Daphne's living room forced people into small groups. There was the window group, the round-the-water group, and the sofa group, with no group having to mingle with any of the others. Toni stopped watching Sol, who was in the water group. She had been waiting for him to come to the end of one of his rolling stories and join her in the sofa group—and smiled at Yule.

"You're very witty, Yule," she said, smiling up at him. "I guess I'm not a very good conversationalist. I'm kind of a dud at dinner parties I think."

"I wouldn't judge myself by this one," the Italian said cheerfully. "It's not exactly the flowering of Athens."

We three were just settling down when Daphne came over to claim him.

"Tom's been driving me crazy about the pond," she told him. "He says I've done everything wrong. Yule, take a look at it now, won't you?"

"I can't make him out," Toni announced, the minute they had gone. "He's kind of calm for a place like this. I wonder what he does for them—"

"Or doesn't do," I suggested, not quite knowing what I meant.

"Daphne's gone on him, you can see that, can't you?"

Sol had come to the end of his rolling story and had thrown his arm around the bald benign man. "Everybody has to promise to come to our New Year's Eve party. You have to come, Eddie. You give me your telephone numbers—everybody here has to come to our penthouse New Year's Eve!"

"He's drunk," Toni whispered. "We just found that apartment. I don't think we've got a chance of getting it. . . . I wouldn't care but Sol would. Oh, Joyce, we've been trying to have a baby. Everything's so hard. You've even got to try for that."

"But it's fun, isn't it?"

"Oh no, it's very depressing when you don't get the baby. Every month you wait in such hopes—especially after thinking like I have all these years, that all I had to do was get married and lie down and the baby would be there in nine months to the minute. I've been going to this clinic, you see, and the stories the women tell up there—you wouldn't believe what people go through to have children. It seems like that's all there is to living to hear them talk. They feel so inferior when they don't have any children. I guess I should have started earlier."

Daphne came over, she was alone this time. "Want to see my fish, you two—they're kind of beautiful."

"Are you going to have a baby, Daphne—now that you're settled and all?" Toni asked.

"Hell no, I'm the baby," Daphne snapped back. "Are you?"

"I hope so," Toni confessed.

"Well, have one, two at the most—but for God's sake don't go having half a dozen. I'm so sick of kids I know going in for litters." We both asked why, and Daphne explained, after glancing around to make sure the men weren't listening. "You mean you don't know about this new baby-having-at-any-cost craze? It's always after a war, I guess. But it's revolting. I mean kids going to school and just having a baby without thinking and then having two more babies . . ."

"I know what you mean—they don't seem to relate to their offspring." Alvin had overheard her, he was standing near the sofa. "The idea is to escape in a great big group, and feel important."

We wandered out to the pond to see the fish, then came back to the sofa. It was some time before Toni got a chance to whisper again, beginning just where she'd left off before. "Takes all the fun out of sex. It's fantastic. I think maybe it's Sol's fault—but he's scared to go to a doctor."

"Hey, sweetheart, there are eight people here, eight telephone numbers I've got for you!" Sol called across to her. "Everybody here gets an engraved invitation to the opening of our new apartment on New Year's Eve—I'm telling you now you shouldn't forget!"

He was drunk and happy when they finally started for their car, talking loudly to Tom and the two businessmen. Toni and I walked behind them, with Graciadei and Alvin beside Daphne.

"It's on Fifth Avenue—remember now!" Sol leaned out the side of the car, beaming joyously and hollering at the top of his lungs. "December thirty-first, nine o'clock! Good-by, Daphne, you're a great little kid. Good-by, Tom, and thanks. Good-by, Eddie and Horace."

Toni was sitting beside him now, leaning out of her side, saying good-bys. She had just time enough to tell me, "I still don't dig her asking me, but I've got her asking you, Joyce. Call me the minute you get back."

We were all converging on the pool for a moonlight swim before bed. It must have been near one o'clock. Daphne and Alvin, the Greek-god boy, were already capering in the water, Graciadei was watching from the diving board, and Tom seemed to have disappeared—when last seen he was entering his cabana. It was just as well he wasn't around, for Daphne and Alvin were going in for some rough-and-tumble aquatic numbers which included every grope, grapple and manipulation possible in or under water, combined with piercing screams, gurgles and convulsions. After a while Graciadei took himself off, leaving Diana and Neptune to play the scene alone.

I was just thinking I too should leave them alone and was making for the cabana when a sound startled me, and turning I saw Tom standing just behind me—in his bathing suit and looking strangely tense.

"Wait!" he whispered. "Don't go—please—not now."

His mouth was open, those long buckteeth were shining in the moonlight, and he was breathing heavily. He stood there watching his wife and the actor, his head lowered, causing chunks of his cheeks to be pressed together, and there right over my shoulder was that mouth pressed open in a hard and mirthless grin. He looked as if he might be biting on a nail. I said, Hi, but there was something unpleasant about the apparition and I started to move away. I was, in fact, ready now to run back to the house, passing up any idea for a swim, but he caught my arm in a tight grip.

"Stay a while, dear. It's early. You're not going in—a beautiful moonlight night like this." Now he was talking through his teeth as he continued looking toward the pool where the squeals were rising louder and louder. I wondered if there was something the matter with him, too much to drink, or, possibly, the beginning of a heart attack, then quickly decided it wasn't that. And if it wasn't, what then?

"I'm kind of tired," I said. "I think I'll just call it a night."

I might have made it too, but just at that minute Daphne came out of the pool and went running off into the stretch of woods behind the house, with Alvin following fast behind her. I felt Tom's grip tighten on my arm. This time I tried hard to pull away. I heard him say, "Wait! Don't go, not now." He was gasping. Something had him worked up. Was he jealous—that must be it!

"She'll be right back," I said quickly.

"Oh yes, of course she'll be back. She likes to run and dance—and so does Alvin. Two such handsome people—on a moonlight night like this. Early autumn is very exciting in the country. It's even thrilling . . ."

He was talking casually now but there was something tense and slightly furtive about him, standing there like an animal that has seen or heard that which causes it to be disturbed. He was not looking at me, in a sense he was hardly talking to me, but I knew he was using me in some obscure way for something he wanted. His hands felt hot on my arm, his breath came out in warm little gasps, he was like a dog straining at the leash—but there wasn't any leash, or was there? And he went on in that even voice, all *sotto-voce,* as if this were some secret between him and me.

"You've known Daphne for a long time, haven't you, dear? You must have known about Daphne and Alvin, didn't you? Just tell me the truth now, Joyce, please dear . . ."

Jealousy, that must be it. A little spell, something that would pass . . . "Of course not, Tom. I didn't know anything at all about them. Don't think there was anything to know."

"Now, now, you don't think I'd scold Daphne, do you? Quite the opposite, my dear. I just want to know—to reconstruct. You've seem them together. You must have. He was in love with Daphne. He still is, that's obvious."

I said, "Everybody was in love with Daphne."

"Ah, now we're remembering. There's the girl. Here, sit down beside me, please, dear." He pulled me over toward a chair near one of the small poolside tables. "Now we're getting somewhere. Everybody was in love with Daphne. Now just tell me, Joyce—tell me what you remember—about Alvin and Daphne."

I said quickly, "I can't remember anything in particular." I meant it, too. Where the hell had they gone to—running off in the woods like that! Leaving me here with this sticky man pouring oily words into my ears. "Now, now, I think you can remember if you try. The first time they were together—why, I remember that myself. Daphne wore a yellow dress, you must remember that dress, girls always remember dresses. I know because I saw her being fitted in that dress. I remember very well. She left the windows open—as she promised she would. She had the lights on too, so I could peep in at them. I tried to get her to let me hide in the apartment. I would have been very quiet, my dear, oh very quiet—and of course Alvin would never have been any the wiser, but she said no, she would do that some other time. You know how women are. You know very well. But anyway, there I was—and it is true I could see into the apartment. I saw quite a lot that night, my dear." He was laughing; he seemed to shrink up as he laughed. "Oh yes, I saw quite a lot . . ." He was pinching my arm now and moving in a jerking manner, as if the memory was somehow convulsing him. This would be a good time to make a dash for the pool, I thought, as I tried moving my arm, but found his grasp had hopelessly tightened.

Then I heard sounds—voices calling through the trees. Was it Daphne and Alvin coming back at last, or some damnable strangers? It didn't matter as long as I got away. "There's Daphne now," I said eagerly, expecting the news to work like a charm. "They'll be here any minute. I'd better run along and have my swim."

He was still off in that special world of his own, but holding on to my arm for dear life. "Oh yes, dear girl, they'll be back soon. I can hear them calling to each other. Daphne, my wife, and Alvin, the beautiful boy, the Greek god." He was talking faster and faster. "Now tell me, Joyce dear—you must have seen them together—didn't you ever see them making love? I'll bet you saw it, I know you must have. You saw him kiss her, didn't you? You saw that—tell me, didn't you, Joyce? Tell me about it, dear. Tell me all about it. Quickly now. You know I told Daphne, before Joyce goes home we must give her a present. Now what would you like, Joyce dear? Think of something—a bracelet—anything you'd like—I want to give you something pretty. Now tell me about Alvin and Daphne. You girls like to peep on each other. Now the night you saw them kissing. She herself told me how it was the first time, but I want to hear it from you. She took the rouge off her lips because Alvin said he liked his girl's mouth naked. Wasn't that an idea now—Daphne's naked mouth—and Alvin's naked mouth? You must have seen them coming together many times, didn't you, Joyce? I have seen it myself. I was there too, even though outside in the street. After all we are all a part of each other, you know. I am a part of Alvin and he is a part of me."

I kept remembering those success stories. I could see him gleefully borrowing money from the truck driver, smiling to himself while collecting on the million-dollar oil deal, keeping all the money, even the borrowed quarters. The voices were calling again. Then there were flashes through the trees over there in the woods behind the house. They must be coming back. Now I could see them chasing each other. Why, there was Daphne running toward the house with Alvin after her.

The rest happened so quickly it left me breathless. Tom let go of my arm and took to his heels. He must have reached the house at the same time as Alvin: it looked as if the two men had collided. Then, almost at the same time, Daphne and Tom disappeared as if the very place had swallowed them up.

I sat looking gloomily at the water. I was thinking vaguely of jumping in when a sound hit my ears. It must have been Alvin diving from the board. He went under the water and in another minute he was coming up in the moonlight, the sparkling water dropping from him. "Hello, chum. Why aren't you swimming?" I said I was thinking about it, but now I was afraid of waking the inmates and somehow this idea threw Alvin into paroxysms of laughter. "Not them!" he finally managed. "The place is soundproof as far as they're . . . I tell you they're gone for the night. I mean they're way out, chum, but it's great your thinking about waking them up. It panics me."

Daphne! Even now, remembering that week end, she bursts into my vision like a thunderstorm: excitement, beauty, uneasiness, trouble. . . . A car starting up in the driveway directly under my window awakened me in the morning. I ought to be going home soon, I thought, as I remembered Toni's advice from the night before. It was Tom's car, with Tom himself at the wheel. There was Alvin coming out of the house, suitcase in hand, running to the car to join his host. The door banged to and the car headed down the driveway.

I had breakfast at a table near the pool. Daphne had gone shopping, and the place seemed almost empty. From somewhere inside came an intermittent sound like the operation of some electrical machine. Making my way across the living room I saw Yule Graciadei—a workingman again, in deep concentration, his eyes squinting as he cut across a large piece of glass with an electric knife. So this was the source of the buzzing sound! He was working in torn old house pants stained with paint, and beads of sweat stood out on his forehead. A heavy-set man, not tall and with a cumbersome body, yet he was remarkably agile. The knife stopped buzzing as I watched, he had finished cutting the glass which he now placed carefully against a wooden horse set on a soiled canvas spread under his feet. As he moved about carrying the glass he seemed to glide, his heavy body almost floating as if its solid weightiness were an illusion.

He heard me and stopped his work. We talked. He was driving back in the afternoon and would be glad for some company. "Wait till I clutter up this place some more and I'll take you for a real swim—down to the lake. You haven't seen the lake, have you?"

We went through the woods in back of the house and across a wide meadow, and eventually there it was, a sure-enough lake with a deserted summer house and a rowboat. Graciadei was in the same state of quiet amusement he'd been in last night. He had an honest way of talking, not dull, and he was mighty attractive when he turned his full face around with those blazing blue eyes.

We sat down on the edge of the lake and threw a stick for the hound dog that had followed us across the meadow.

"I heard old Tom going on at you last night," he said. I didn't answer; up to that second I'd had no idea he had been anywhere around. "Oh, you couldn't see me," he went on. "I was sitting way back on the lawn. I just hope you didn't have too bad a time."

"He wanted me to tell him things about Daphne."

"Oh, I know, I know . . ." He sounded impatient of the whole thing, as if it was some old familiar problem, and something he didn't want to hear anything more about.

The dog began barking; he had caught his leg in the branches of a bush. Graciadei jumped into the water and swam over to him. I watched him moving the bush carefully until the dog was free. The poor animal had hurt its leg. He picked it up and held it in one arm and swam toward shore with the other.

"Poor fellow's got a bad splinter. There's a knife in my pants pocket, hand it to me, will you please?"

I got the knife and watched the operation. Now his deft fingers worked steadily, one hand hypnotizing the animal with its slow caressing motion, the other lifting out the piece of wood with a careful flick of the knife. In a minute or so the dog bounced up and was playing again with the stick. We swam across to the other side of the lake and stopped to rest on the opposite shore, then swam back and began walking slowly toward the house. He asked me again about driving home with him and I said that would be fine.

We were just coming through the clearing in the woods when Daphne came out on the lawn. She stopped dead still when she saw us, then went quickly back into the house without saying a word. She was standing near the aquarium when we came in.

"You haven't done anything you were supposed to do!" she hollered at Yule. Graciadei chuckled, without answering. I said Hi, but it went unnoticed. "You haven't touched the aquarium!"

He came slowly toward the glassed aquarium, a lush world of water and sunlight, of green foliage and graceful fish, and stood there, his head pushed forward, his eyes squinting in the sun, still smiling that private darned smile.

"The rocks aren't heavily enough planted—otherwise it looks all right," he said.

"What about the fish you were supposed to put in?"

"I have a scarlet Characin I'll give you."

"What kind of fish is that?" I asked, just to say something.

"Well, the female looks something like Katherine Hepburn," he began, "around the snout, anyway. She's inclined to eat her own eggs and fry but she's a picture."

I could hear Daphne hollering as I went upstairs, and the last glimpse I'd caught of her scowling face told me I'd better take the train and let the Italian come home by himself. But I ran smack into him as I came down, all dressed and packed to go, and before I could call about the train he had taken my bag and pushed me down on the seat built around a tree, and then those piercing blue eyes of his were blazing down at me as he said, "Wait here, I'll go get ready." I didn't know what to expect from Daphne now but when she finally came out of the house she was smiling.

"Ever been to a country auction? Listen, darling, there's one five miles from here. I know the woman who's selling out." She rattled on, rather hysterically, I thought. "There's some fascinating stuff coming up—you'll see things you didn't think existed. Please ask Yule to take us. I know he'll agree, if you just say you'd like to go. . . ."

The auction turned out to be kind of interesting. An elderly woman was selling out her family farm. We stood with the crowd—shrewd city-eyed antique dealers and smart suburbanites and sober-faced farmers. It was fun watching the gambling fever that gripped the bidders.

I was by now keenly aware of an attraction I felt toward this Yule Graciadei. This man with those thick coffee-colored legs I'd seen gliding over the fields in the heat. What had happened in the hours between that now, standing near him, I actually felt drawn toward him by some almost physical force or influence? And this, in spite of Daphne's tantrums, her quick changes of mood, her interruptions as he inquired what I thought about things—the furniture, the auctioneer's chatter and jokes, the people, anything.

Something was going on with Daphne, all right. By the time we reached the inn she insisted we stop at for luncheon, she was back in the snob-to-handy-man mood. "I've never been in a public place with him before," she whispered as we got out of the car, "and I don't know what he'll do." I reminded her, "But you've had him in your home, and he seemed to know how to behave—better than most of the guests." But she was amiable as all hell during the meal, the atmosphere was jolly for a change. I liked the way Yule laughed —not because he felt he had to, but as if some great delight was gathering force within that finally burst into the open. If I'd known him before, I thought, a healthy man like this, things might have been different. . . .

It was past midnight when I finally got home. The telephone was ringing. It was Toni. I dropped my suitcase and told her all of the above. . . .

"Go on. You're at this inn. What happened then?"

"Daphne kept drinking. Ran the bill way up and then didn't have any money and no account at this place, so I had to give it to her. She waited until Yule came back to the table and paid the bill—"

"To humiliate him, of course. Go on!"

"But he wouldn't let her do it. He said no, he'd give them a check, and he did and nobody seemed to question it. But Daphne was furious, especially when he made her give me back the money. Drove all the way back to the city with us and then she wouldn't come in—made him drive her somewheres uptown."

"She was sitting you out," Toni said. "And all that stuff she told you—she's afraid to be seen in public with him, he's just a workman, that kind of thing, I just don't believe it at all. She's dead gone on him. There's something masculine about that cookie and it kills her. It's a wonder she didn't tell you he was a spy or he had syphilis or something."

It took me a while to realize that Toni was also attracted to Graciadei and that made three. He must be a bad lot, if the old rules still held. And if he wasn't, if he was the "healthy masculine" man Toni had him tagged, then that meant I'd never see him again because he just wasn't in the old pond.

CHAPTER THIRTY-NINE

• • • • • •

DAY BEFORE YESTERDAY I SAW HIM, THE ENTRY READS. DR. PAUL Halsted, Dr. Six. I shouldn't be calling him that, it groups him with the other five, whereas he is unique. *Sui generis.* But wait till I tell you.

I pressed a bell on a door in the East Fifties. The door was opened by a tall light-haired man in a gray sports shirt open at the throat. From the way he looked and the loose easy way he moved, he might have been the janitor on his way downstairs after fixing a leak in the kitchen sink. And then from the casual way he asked, "Is it still so warm out?" I thought maybe he was just somebody helping the doctor out. "You can change your things in here," he said next, opening a door into a small room that looked something like a laboratory. "Come in here when you're ready—it's right next door—" I went in, changed quickly into the leotard and shorts he had suggested I bring and hurried on into the designated room.

Already I had the feeling of something off-beat, of having strayed off the beaten path, and no wonder. Imagine a doctor dressed like a plumber, and now five, ten minutes gone already and all he's said is, Is it still hot? and, Change in there. A man of few words.

My second glance at Paul Halsted, in a larger and brighter room, gave me a slightly different impression. This time I saw his face more clearly and felt a mite less skeptical. An open, calm face, with clear gray eyes and a tender, inquisitive smile, as if he were watching something pleasant and interesting. He was standing beside a black steel table covered with a sheet. "Sit down here," he told me, and I sat on the long table with my back to him, while he settled in a chair beside me.

"I want to see how you breathe," he said. "Just breathe normally, the way you do all the time." So I sat there in an upright position with my legs stretched out and breathed normally as he'd said, and this went on for quite a while. Look at me, sitting here breathing, and him sitting there watching, I thought. What kind of crazy carrying-on is this? He next pushed a board behind my back which made me more comfortable and said, "Now try to breathe more deeply and more slowly. Just fill up your lungs as it comes naturally to you. Don't force it. Breathe deeply and slowly, slowly. Just fill 'em up and let it out through your mouth." So now I did this, feeling only slightly less silly; this second one required some small concentration. After a while he said, "All right, now you can start to talk. Keep on with the breathing, as I told you, and tell me your troubles."

"How can I do that and this deep breathing, too?"

"Try it and you'll see."

So I went on inhaling slowly as he said, and talked during the exhalations and between breaths. I began listing my symptoms, the ones left intact—dear God how long! Insomnia, the apprehension, increasing now that I was alone, and then the sexual fantasies—they'd come back hard and heavy, and the sexlessness in real life, the other horrors of this night before living, a seven-year night.

He told me, "Describe the apprehension," and I did.

"Where is this anxiety now—right now while you're talking about it? Keep on breathing deeply while you tell me."

I had to think a minute. "I don't seem to have it now."

"Try to remember when you do have it, where is it?"

"Gosh, I don't know where it is. That's like asking me where's my mind."

"Think some more about it. Keep on with the slow breathing. Where does it seem to center itself?"

I thought, Hell I don't know, and then it came to me.

"It feels like it's centered in my chest."

"In your chest, all right. Go on talking while you're breathing. Seven years, five doctors . . ."

After a while I noticed this deeper breathing seemed to hurt somewhere near my throat just above my chestbone, and then this area seemed to clear, the air came through and the breathing became more rhythmic. "Keep on talking. You get these fantasies in the morning . . ." After a while I thought I noticed something else. The whole damned story I'd been going over felt as if it had *moved further away*. Now wasn't that crazy? I thought. I was temporarily estranged from it, and as I talked on it began to seem less painful and somehow less important. It was as if a machine of some kind, say a boat with a motor going, were carrying me further and further away from all that old life out there and toward *something down here*. Away from some cold old block of shadowy darkness and into some nice warm here-now living physical being.

"Where's the trouble now? Keep on with the breathing, deep and slow."

"Well just now, I thought it was in my head. Or above my head. Right this minute I don't know. It seems further away. That might be because I'm with somebody."

"Might be," he agreed. "Now see if you can breathe still more slowly. Just inhale slowly, fill 'em up, and then this time see if you can hold it a few seconds, hold your breath, then let it out more slowly and keep on talking. Keep on telling me the troubles."

So I kept on, and the trouble seemed to be in my head, or outside my head, and then maybe it was over my head. I couldn't tell any more. This is crazy, I thought. *Cr - a - zy*. But temporarily pleasant. The more deeply and slowly and rhythmically I breathed the less attachment I felt to my terrors, to my head altogether and the entire thinking process up there. And my body began to feel warmer and more alive, as if new life was awakening down there and had begun pulling me or drawing me into it.

"You've been talking about your problems to doctors for a long time. Can you remember how you used to feel? Not what you used to *think*—just how you used to *feel*?"

Yes, I could. In the past, listing these damnable symptoms, my body would start feeling cold and my head hot. This time it was the other way around. My head felt light and cool and my body warm and tingling.

And then it was time to get dressed and go back to the office. Dr. Halsted made only one suggestion. I was to stop the Benzedrines I took in the daytime to wake up and feel better, and the Seconals I took at night to put me to sleep. If insomnia troubled me I should use the second breathing exercise. "See you Thursday," he said, by way of good-by, and I went on out, feeling kind of light and kind of funny—light-headed, as if slightly drunk on champagne. My body still felt warm and tingling, as if the blood was coursing faster through my veins.

Cr - a - zy, I thought, as I walked out in the hot street. Breathing exercises yet. As if I haven't been breathing all my life. And locating the anxiety—now wasn't that loony? So I'd come to this. . . .

My, my, that hot little September day, unimportant, uneventful, for by now a new doctor was more of an incident than an event. Looking back I can see that day with its homely sweaty sunny face, and I see now—what my nascent self saw then—that was the day I fell off the calendar. That was the day, and the very first day, the terrified pygmy who had me by the umbilical cord actually *began to let go.* For the breast he had been after, lo, these many years was finally put into his hot little mouth.

But I'm getting ahead of my story. Walking back to work with this warm tingling *I'm here* feeling in my body, almost as if some new liquid life had been poured in, I thought, at least this feels all right, it can't harm me. I was, of course, not taking it too seriously. Physical sensations, something new, and this physical location of the terrors, that was new too. I didn't think much about Halsted. I'd picked up an impression of someone immaculately clean and exceptionally light—I mean almost light in weight, although he wasn't thin, and possessed of some great quiescence. A forest with not a leaf stirring, I thought, and a miser with words. Yet what he'd said stayed with me. Especially that toward the end, when he gave me the one about insomnia. "Don't accept anything you can't prove. It has to work immediately or it's no good."

Maybe he was all the way crazy. As if anything could work immediately! Now there was a challenge. He'd thrown down the gauntlet with that one all right, and I was the first to pick it up. That night when I went to bed, if I followed his advice about no sleeping tablets, I'd have my chance to try the second breathing exercise on the insomnia. Oh I'd try it all right, and what's more—oh hell, maybe I wouldn't even bother to tell him how it turned out. I knew already. I'd just say it didn't work with me and call off the next appointment. One more experiment.

As the afternoon wore on I began to think maybe this therapy did have something. (I had read about Yoga and had even had a hunch about it for myself. During the period after Silvers and the good analysis I'd looked patiently for a teacher to give me the Yoga training, and found in New York City only people I knew at once were phonies.) This Halsted therapy had little resemblance to Yoga as I had read of it and heard it described, except for the emphasis on breathing exercises. But what he had done with me was certainly not proper analysis. Attempting to locate the anxiety in the *body* of the sufferer, as if it had a physical place of residence, that was entirely unorthodox and unlike anything I'd ever heard.

Crazy, sure, and yet the damned thing did feel as if it had a location, and that in my case was in my chest. Crazy, undoubtedly, and yet something had happened up there: a tremendously depressing anxious feeling was dissipated, destroyed. And something else: a new good feeling had come in. It was only temporary, of course, a bit of phenomenon, possibly, but I had experienced something. The conscious thinking process diminishing in power whereas with the other doctors it had grown, the ghosts in my head receding into far corners whereas before they had come forward. And now life seemed to be centering in my solar-plexus. Why even as I worked at my desk that little old apparatus kept on, a subtle feeling of life rolling around like a water wheel. I felt as if I'd just discovered a sweet new friend who liked me very much and we were going to do some good things together. Then all of this receded and I just forgot about it, except I did seem to feel more at ease in my work and accomplished the mundane tasks with greater facility.

By the time the day wore out, and I was undressing for bed that night, the little flash of life had long since given out and I'd lost all interest in the entire experiment. I remembered Dr. Halsted's suggestion about the insomnia with some contempt as I saw the precious Seconals peeping out of my bathroom cabinet. I didn't take any, deciding at least I'd try this ridiculous breathing technique, and then when it didn't work I'd just come on back to the Seconals. And finally I was in bed, and desultorily I remembered about the second exercise I'd learned that day, and so I began to do it.

"And what was the result?" he asked when I came back again on Thursday.

And so I told him. "Well I started inhaling fully and slowly and letting it out as you showed me. I guess I must have fallen asleep, sometimes I do anyway without a sleeping tablet. Anyway next thing I remember the telephone was ringing and it was nine o'clock in the morning and I was late to work."

As I heard the telephone ringing I remembered clearly what had happened preceding sleep. After about five or ten minutes of this rhythmic breathing—it took a bit of doing just to get it going—I started yawning uncontrollably and that was when I must have fallen asleep. It wasn't too bad, I thought. Of course it won't work all the time but even if it works sometimes it's well worth the trouble.

On this second appointment I was curious to see if I mightn't have imagined that warm feeling in my body and the other sensations. Heretofore, sensations had been produced by thinking or visualizing—those damnable fantasies, for instance—but they were largely destructively erotic, certainly not plain healthy happy earthy stuff such as I'd seemed to have had up there. So I went back determined to keep my mind on what was happening and check to see if anything actually did take place.

This time as I breathed according to directions and talked about my troubles I began to feel again the warm feeling in my abdomen—yes, there it was all right, an actual physical sensation as of a new substance stirring in my blood. I'd just been telling him about old Portzweig and how the hollering had affected me but as I did I began to feel the sense of inner currents coursing through more strongly and lost track of the entire matter. Suddenly everything else in the world seemed trivial by comparison to this simple delicious inner warmth, and then there was just nothing else in the world, nothing but this.

I was to practice one of the exercises at home, Halsted told me, the particular one I'd just learned, and to alternate it at certain intervals with the first, both to be preceded by an exercise for muscular relaxation which, while it seemed quite simple, took me a long time to master. I asked him about the price which, to my absolute incredulity, he seemed to have forgotten completely. "Oh that, yes, well how much can you afford to pay? Let's not bother about it now, though, you can let me know some other time."

This time as I went out I was conscious of a deep new physical contentment and I knew it was real. I hadn't imagined it, there it was. It lasted longer than before, perhaps an hour longer, and then it went, leaving a kind of afterglow. I had a queer impression, as I worked, of seeing things more clearly. My desk, the typewriter keys, papers I was working on, the street outside the window, all of it seemed more still and larger and closer to me. It was as if everything had been moving or quivering before as from an earthquake. Now it had stilled. And with this new stillness I felt more of a physical relationship to the things I touched.

This was a queer kind of therapy all right, but it certainly wasn't harming me any. I hadn't actually told Halsted anything much, that was his fault for making me learn those queer breathing exercises. And that other muscle-relaxation one, that was a dilly. I'd keep on with it, I decided, for a while anyway, but I wouldn't take it too seriously. After all, what I was experiencing was probably nothing more than the phenomenon accompanying any unusual intake of air into the lungs and, once my body had become accustomed to the increased amount of oxygen intake, very likely the phenomenon would disappear, and the troubles would come back as they always had.

It's one chance in ten this Halsted might actually have something, I thought, and with this idea in mind I kept on with the therapy. The first two months were consumed in learning the breathing techniques and the body and mind-stilling techniques. After about six to eight weeks had passed and I had mastered just a few of the exercises, I found my body taking on an involuntary life of its own. Everything was being stepped up, as if a secret intravenous feeding were taking place. I felt nourished, and content. Often I would be aware of actual currents in my body, and sometimes I would have the sensation almost of melting. I would go away from Halsted's place feeling light and warm, with these little currents running around inside me like a bunch of playful animals, and without knowing it I'd find myself smiling or laughing, and people, men especially, would smile back. The South Sea Island feeling, I called it to myself. I was aware of a re-centering of life from my head to my solar plexus, and this was a mighty fine feeling. Now I could live more comfortably in my own house for the furnace had been taken off the roof and removed to the cellar where it could heat the house.

It was all too good to be true, I knew that much. It couldn't possibly last. The doctor seemed to agree with me. "A common windfall from fresh oxidation, don't you think?" I would ask. "Yes, maybe, I guess so," he'd reply. "I don't quite understand how these effects are brought about or your theories," I went on. "What kind of analysis is this, anyway?" And he'd say, "Haven't you heard enough theories? The only thing you need to know now is this training—how to do it. It's nothing you have to think about. It has to be lived, not learned. It's in yourself, not in me or in any book. All I can do is give you the mechanical means, a walking-stick that may help you weather the storm."

I was doing something more than merely weathering the storm. I was living those days without anxiety. Sometimes as I'd go away I'd feel that I had lost something—my purse, an important package, something familiar and heavy that I'd been carrying around. But no, I'd go over my belongings, everything was in order, it just felt lighter. I felt lighter. I'd forgotten about sleeping tablets. The fantasies had stopped completely.

Toward the end of the third month I noticed some pleasant by-products of the new therapy. I was smoking less or not at all, eating and drinking much more lightly. Apparently the craving for consolation by putting things in my mouth was leaving me in favor of the deeper nourishment coming in through the respiratory system.

The connection is turned on, I wrote during the fourth month. I had been noticing, with the slow perfection of the breathing techniques and the other exercises, I had begun to feel an increased sensation of life in the lower or pelvic part of my body. With this kind of physical good feeling, it was just about impossible to feel anxiety. "Anxiety is the negative of sexual pleasure," Halsted said. "You've been short-circuiting the discharge of tissue electricity most of your life." This caused the feeling of being blocked, cut off, not connected, he told me. It's reassuring to hear of a physical or biological being. He says the good feelings were cut off because I was so afraid of breathing deeply, afraid of letting go, afraid of melting, afraid of disappearing, afraid. . . . Lately I've felt a wave or current extending itself—running from my neck over my chest and going down to my abdomen, warm and pleasant. Sometimes it lasts a long time, sometimes it recedes and no amount of effort brings it back. And then suddenly I feel it coming back on its own.

3 6 7

There's no transference between Dr. Halsted and me. He's on the level, a man in his shirt sleeves who talks frankly about himself, whenever I question him, that is. He says he has girl trouble. His girl has problems, they apparently love each other, he hopes they'll get together soon. He doesn't pose as a god, doesn't put on any show of mystery. I like him and I am of course deeply grateful to him. Even if the stuff gives out I'll still be grateful for the happy interim, but I'm not particularly interested either in him or his theories. "Why should you be?" he says. "I should think you'd had enough of that stuff to last you five thousand years."

In the fourth month I began to realize how utterly unorthodox his therapy was.

"We've hardly even discussed my case," I said.

"Oh yes we have. You have anxiety. You're afraid of being murdered. You think someone is coming to get you."

"But shouldn't we be working this through?"

"That's just what we're doing."

"How?"

"You know how. With your physical being. A little matter you've been forgetting for seven years or so. After all, you're an animal."

"Oh you mean with these breathing techniques and these other exercises? I know . . . but I mean, why aren't we talking about it? I was taught to associate—and verbalize."

"Keep on taking in the breath. Inhale slowly, and then hold it. Let it out slowly. We can talk just the same. Go ahead."

"Verbalizing," I repeated. "After all, I've had a traumatic experience and . . . that's what we should be reaching."

"Yes, you did have a traumatic experience. And that's just what we are reaching. It occurred in a pre-verbal era of your life and can only be reached by pre-verbal or physiological means. What good would it do to try to talk to a baby in a convulsion?"

I thought that over. "But remembering what happened—wouldn't that help?"

"You can't remember it. Even if you could it wouldn't give you what you need to make you feel good."

"But this deep breathing stuff—after all, I've been doing that all my life."

"Oh no you haven't."

"What have I been doing?"

"You've been unconsciously holding your breath, breathing in a shallow way. You saw yourself you were holding your breath when you were trying to go to sleep, and that was what was keeping you awake."

At another time, "You were starved on a physiological level. Psychology might give you some temporary help. The insights are stimulating if they don't become a habit. People often become obsessive with them and that leads to more life-negation. But they wouldn't feed you. They wouldn't give you the nourishment you need."

I told Dr. Halsted about the fantasies having disappeared, for now they seemed to be gone as if they had never been. "The old theater in there is locked up! I can't even see inside any more. Wonder what's happened to the prince—he must be lonesome as all hell by now. Do you think he'll return? Do you think the theater will open up again one day?" But Halsted shrugged that one off. "Wait and see. Maybe one day when the current turns on full, the theater in there will burn right down to the ground."

Some other phenomena began occurring early in the practice of the exercises. A kind of inner sight was starting up. It usually began with my seeing something that resembled an empty television screen, with moving black and white lines. This would fade and give place to a continuous stream of sights—dancing girls, rooms opening into other rooms, people, flowers and streams and hills, trees and roadways, sometimes immense and varied and beautiful, at other times smaller and more enclosed. All of this was either coming to me with a quick flowing movement, like the scenes in a moving picture when the camera pans back to show you a long view, or else I, or the seeing part of me, was passing through all this. Sometimes I would have the sensation of going completely out of my consciousness and taking off in a flight. I remember seeming to fly over traffic resembling the East River Drive and seeing the tops of cars moving bumper to bumper, and then passing over them and seeing how small they looked. And I remember the sensation of climbing up the side of a very steep, almost vertical mountain, brilliant moonlight about me on all sides, noticing the odd foliage shining in the light, and again flying toward a brilliant lighted city.

"What on earth is all this about?" I asked Halsted. "And how come I suddenly see all this—with my eyes closed."

"It's physiological," he explained. "This inner sight is being released from centers in your body that the exercises awaken. Part of the infinite capacities you have—not too well understood in this country. But let's not discuss this now. Your endocrine system is being nourished—stepped up. How do you feel afterwards?" I told him I always came back from these trips greatly refreshed, with greater clarity of mind and ease of being. I noticed a marvelous freedom from any aches and pains, and increased powers of concentration.

And there was something else. "This place looks different somehow when I come back—or I feel different about it. Everything seems more clear and bright and close, I enjoy it more. After the glimpse I've caught of the whirling infinity out there—I feel more tenderly about everything in my current life. Every false feeling or idea seems to have been blown out as if it had never been. It's as if something way inside—like a weather vane on the roof of my soul—had been set right after a hurricane."

CHAPTER FORTY

. . . . . .

TWENTY-ONE DAYS TO CHRISTMAS, THE NEXT ENTRY READS. DAY BE-
fore yesterday Daphne called me at the office to say she was in town
for some Christmas shopping and would like to pick me up later in
the day. I said all right and she came by to drive me home in her
station wagon. "I've got just one stop to make," she announced as
we headed toward Second Avenue. "I guess you know where we're
going though—don't you, Joyce?" I said no, I thought we were going
home. "You mean you haven't seen him since the Fourth of July?
Come on."

"Seen whom?" I screamed over the traffic noises, as a chill memory
of husband Tom smiling in the moonlight rushed up before me.
How long ago it seemed, how far away and long ago!

"You know *whom.* Yule Graciadei."

I said, "Yule the furniture man?" And she said, "Yes, Yule the
furniture man. Just so." And now I remembered the rest of that
week end, with Daphne reaching out toward something healthy yet
evasive in the Italian, and me being used as some kind of cat's-
paw for her needs. "No, I haven't seen him, I'm not in the market
for any furniture and would have no reason. . . ."

Good old Daphne, always one for surprises, was suddenly friendly.
The greeting had been a slightly cool mink-coated Hi but now she
was chatting away. "You ought to know him, Joyce. He's kind of
a genius—in his way. Why don't you do over that awful old place?
You're in a new mood—what is it, anyway—a man?" I said yes,
and let it go at that. "Well you'll tell me all about it later. What
are you doing for Christmas? We're having a Christmas Eve brawl.
I know Tom would like you to come, he asked me particularly about

you, and Yule is coming. I hope he is anyway—and he could bring you out." I was quick to say No, I was going away for Christmas, remembering the Fourth of July complications and finding the prospect of a sequel not too festive. The tendency I'd had to accede to anybody's demands having left me, Daphne's request for company on her treadmill was easily averted.

Daphne parked her car in front of Graciadei's furniture plant and looking through the windows we could see people moving about inside. She honked her horn three times and Yule came out. It was good to see him, a big good-natured male child with graying black hair full of raindrops, still in that same state of secret amusement as when last seen so many months ago, wearing overalls and an old shirt full of sawdust. "Hello. How are you, Joyce?" He reached over and shook hands. "Want to come in and see the shop?" "What's so funny?" Daphne inquired, as we went in, but he excused himself saying he'd join us later. He went over to an office partitioned off to one side, while we wandered around looking things over. Some of the furniture was interesting, other pieces were conventional, I thought, but the place itself had a personality of its own. The two floors made a duplex of great height, combining so many objects, finished and unfinished, it was difficult to decide where to stop. We looked at lightly scaled angular tables, at low high-styled sofas, at elaborate desks and breakfronts—before coming upon the screen he was making for Daphne's bedroom, a series of paintings depicting the flora and fauna around her home.

She kept muttering about him as we moved around, rather disconsolately, I thought, almost like a complaining wife. ". . . Never gets anything finished on time. What's the good of people like that having talent—you could almost snatch it away from him. Just look what he's doing now—there he is, as if he had all the time in the world."

The place did seem to be in a state of confusion but the boss himself was calm as the jade Buddha someone had placed on a mantel near the door. The workmen were apparently waiting to see him while he went on talking to an agitated couple about something that wasn't yet ready. He seemed to have forgotten all about us so we wandered on upstairs and found a skylight studio where all kinds of objects had been shoved together, including some interesting wood carvings and many canvases. The walls were lined with paintings, mostly modern and looking as if the paint had been dropped or thrown or sprayed from a distance, or measured into strong bold unintelligible lines and circles. One of these—it looked like a huge mouth floating in space—caught my eye. "Well what do you think?" Daphne asked me. "God knows, but all together it has something." We played a game to see who could identify the most objects or ideas in the canvases—discovering eyes, rims of glasses, butterflies, dishes, hands, feet and ectoplasm. I thought it was fun but Daphne was exasperated. "It's just Yule—in his own little world!"

I said I had to be going but she pleaded with me to wait. "He'll be along any minute. Why don't you ask us down to your place—I know he'd like to see it—just for a drink? He'll design something wonderful before he knows what he's doing." I said I couldn't afford anything at all, besides it sounded crazy, but there was no stopping her. "He likes what he's doing so much he can't stop once he's started. That's how people can get things from him. All kinds of people come down here from all over the place. He's got so much, he's overflowing. That's how it was with my house, he just got interested and he couldn't stop." This "couldn't stop" business seemed to fascinate her.

We were examining a painting, an enormous red, white and black long-division that seemed to have happened on a bare tree, when the artist himself burst in again. "Well, how do you like my little brother's paintings?" We didn't say anything, he had come in on us too suddenly, but he burst out laughing. "Evoke no response, huh? That's good. That means you're both normal." He had changed into a business suit and was still smiling at that secret joke he had as we went out.

Daphne seemed glad to see the old place. I felt rather attracted toward this Graciadei again. It's the way he moves, I thought, a certain gliding motion. He does seem to have a bountiful spirit. He said he'd like to help me with the place, but Daphne obviously had him earmarked for herself. She was on one of her kicks about color and vibrations. She said there was something ghostly about the place, something positively pallid, discolored and practically cadaverous. It seemed color went moving like a train at a special rate that affected people, that was why she and old Tom had spared nothing

3 7 3

in the house in Connecticut which was now vibrating at just the proper speed to attract only perfect people.

"That girl should find something to do," Graciadei commented, when she went downstairs to telephone. "That acting all the time—she can't even enjoy the water—and that's a helluva note." For some reason this seemed funny; we were still laughing when Daphne came back. Toni and Sol came by on their way home, we heard how Sol had invited so many people for New Year's Eve they'd had to hire detectives to watch over the valuables. Just once before the party broke up I found the furniture man looking at me. "You've changed since I saw you." I asked, "How was I then?" He said something like, "I don't know, the way people get when they have to think all the time," and I asked him, "Don't you?" He smiled a nice warm smile. "Oh I used to—but not any more. The damned thing gave out on me and I haven't bothered to put it back."

I am *connected,* the next notation reads. That's the only word I know to describe the new feeling. The current is on. The clock is ticking. The old life-force is coming through, the way it is in a great many people and the way it is not in how many others. The problems I face now are real, they're not from somewhere outside. I don't have to hang on to words any more—and other people's old words at that!

It's snowing. A deep white blanket a foot thick covers the streets and the back yard, suggesting plenty—a full cupboard, a large bank account, good friends, holiday—all of which, except the last, I seem to be fresh out of. Maybe I can get some of the others. A genuine experience, this with Dr. Halsted. The techniques have brought me down to earth, connected me up with my own deep unknown self. Sometimes I feel like a South Sea island maiden (is supposed to feel): at ease everywhere in my body, fluid in my involuntary movements. . . . Have dropped the Freudian pattern of analyzing everything, a dulling process at best, destructive of spontaneity. Now that I am actually doing these breathing exercises—they aren't mastered quickly—I know where the healing comes from: in that silence, right in the tunnel that leads out of the conscious self and beyond the subconscious into the subliminal self.

"Those are just words," Halsted says. "But now at least you see this deep part of you can't be reached by thinking or talking or imagining or even concentrating. Now still more slowly, hold it, and count." I find more and more when I do the exercises properly I go off to where there is nothing of me, not my mind, desires, longings, fears, memories, just nothing—yet in the very going in there, into that nothing, is some tremendously revitalizing and creative experience, not to mention it's the first time I've been *out of the cage*. "And afterwards, what are you feeling?" I try to explain: these days I'm aware of a new unity, hard to describe, as if all the conflicting selves are being brought together, drawing in, under the control of some powerful, more sublime part of me I never knew till now. "I wonder if this is the He of the twenty-third psalm, the Lord of the deep unknown," I say. For so it seems, this is the He who "maketh me to lie down in green pastures, He leadeth me beside the still waters, He restoreth my soul."

"Maybe," says Halsted, and goes on with the teaching. "What else? Keep on with the results." I have a sense of balance, of having reached some center in myself which seems to have restored the inner scales. The fantasies have stopped cold, I wonder about that. "Maybe the theater in there has been burned to the ground." He smiles. "Maybe it has for the time being. But maybe it can rise again."

Now what? How soon will I meet up with Devman—and what will he say to all this? I'm almost eager for the encounter. . . .

CHAPTER FORTY-ONE

· · · · · ·

AT FIVE O'CLOCK ON FRIDAY, GRACIADEI ARRIVED. I REMEMBERED HIS promise to stop in and help me with the place, but was almost certain he wouldn't make it, what with the snowstorm holding up traffic I'd had a hard time finding a taxi myself, arriving home only a few minutes before he rang the bell. So there he was—red-cheeked and full of snow, wearing old rubbers and a cap with earmuffs and carrying an oblong carton. "Hello, well here's that furniture man." I said, "Hello. Come on in." I thought immediately his smile wasn't so big today. He seemed reserved, almost irritable. Oh well, in this snowstorm, and having to cart that big package. Besides, I wasn't in much of a mood myself. He'd come too early, I'd hardly had a chance to take off my wet coat, and I found myself resenting the bumptious way he dumped the carton in the middle of the room, throwing his wet overcoat on top of it. I'd just give him a drink and tell him I'd decided not to do anything about the place, which was true enough. What with my two tenants gone to fairer climes and being fresh out of money, I didn't know whether I'd even keep it.

Those goggles he was wearing made his eyes look funny, and his hair, which had looked so rich and thick in the summer, now seemed merely wet and unkempt. He reminded me of a certain con man who'd been appearing on the front pages these days for manipulating the stocks of some big Chicago corporation. I looked closer as he moved the carton against the wall and decided this Yule Graciadei—his real name was Ulrich—and the con man might almost have been twins, especially around the mouth where each had the same supercilious grin.

"Would you like a drink—or coffee?" He was standing near the front window looking things over as if he owned the place. "Coffee'll be all right now—maybe a drink a little later." For some reason he made me feel uncomfortable, I was glad to get away. By the time I came back with the coffee he was in the dining room, this time looking through the window into the yard. I said, "Nice out there, huh?" and he said, "Yah, all back yards are nice—even the ones stuck up against buildings like yours. Who's the old boy up there? Seems to like your place." I knew who it was before I looked up at the building next door. "He's still looking for another glimpse of Daphne. I wonder if I should drop him a note and tell him she's gone to another state." He shook his head. "I think I'd just keep closing the drapes in his face." He did it for me, leaving enough of an opening to show some of the new snowy beauty of the yard. We had our coffee, sitting opposite each other at the big table, and after a sticky little interval in which I desultorily went on more about the snow he came out with the big thought.

"What did you decide about your place?"

"Oh nothing. Just to leave it alone."

He shrugged. "It's quite a thing for some people—changing things around." After that he relapsed into a state of calm desuetude interrupted only by the sipping of the coffee. Now the calmness which had seemed attractive in company began to seem desultory. I wished I'd asked Toni or Irene to come by—or even old Daphne, and was just determining to call one of them when he asked, "Aren't you cold?" and I said yes, I'd been planning to make a fire, and he got up quickly and began making it for me. The only trouble was he did it so deftly it was blazing much too soon, and there we were again sitting around drinking more coffee, listening to the logs crackling in the fireplace. Once I glanced up and felt embarrassed to find him watching me. His eyes were good, I thought, as I moved uneasily from their piercing blue question. By the circuitous route of mundane remarks—first Daphne and Toni, then Sol and Tom were seized eagerly by me and put quietly back in their corners by him —we got back to the place.

"You say you bought this stuff from the guy that had it before you?" I admitted I had and asked him what he thought of the whole deal. "I'm not thinking. You're the thinker—remember? Women writers are always thinking and trying to find out what other people are thinking." I said, "You can't make me mad with that one. I don't like them any too well as a class." But I resented his saying it. He lit a cigarette. "I'll bet the goon who owned this stuff is kind of dull." He was looking through the rooms. "There's nothing warm or nice about him, I'd swear to that. A square if ever I saw one." I thought about B, wondered how this Graciadei knew just from the furniture left behind. "Oh it's so proper, a copy of stuff you see in bum magazines. I knew it wasn't yours. Some low-grade boy scout dumped it on you, I figured. What about those wooden boards out front?" I hold him they belonged to the super and asked, "How about that drink of Scotch?" He said he'd like it.

He's definitely not for me, I decided, as I went to get the whiskey. I remembered how he'd seemed in the country, deciding that while the blunt honesty stood out in a group, it was a helluva thing in a closeup. Oh well, now that I knew he was destined to be nothing to me, not even a friend, I felt more relaxed about the visit. He wouldn't stay long, anyway, and I'd never have to see him again. I had everything ready on the tray when I noticed I'd forgotten to change into dry shoes and decided to let him wait. I must have taken longer than I thought, when I came back the dining room looked entirely different. My visitor had swept everything off the mantel, placed the super's boards against the wall like panels, closed the draperies completely and was just moving the table out of the room. I wondered uneasily whether he'd have time to put the heavy pieces back before he left as I placed the tray with the drinks on the window sill.

When he came in again he was carrying a sofa from the living room into the dining room. He placed it carefully beneath the window, cried, "Hey now, look at that!" and stood admiring his handiwork. I looked, and with the draped window for a background, the niche had a decided new appeal. "Very pretty," I said, busying myself picking up the stuff he'd moved onto the floor. Meantime I found myself with nothing to do except watch this busy man who seemed to be enjoying himself at last. He hummed to himself as he worked, I noticed again a certain gliding way he had of walking, almost as if he were skating. He was more interesting to look at in the concentrated working mood—probably just wasn't much of a talker, I decided, one of those men who was hard at work most of

3 7 8

the time and needed to be doing something in order to enjoy himself. It was just too bad I didn't want my place changed around.

He kept at the moving, most of the time he seemed to have forgotten me altogether. He's probably just lonesome, I decided. Has nothing but his work and that awful painting he does, and with that homely personality, what could he expect in the long hours ahead? But what on earth had Daphne *and* Toni seen in him? Now there was a mystery. . . .

The telephone rang, and a soft feminine voice said, "Hello. . . . Is Mr. Graciadei there?" I called to tell him, "It's for you," he was carrying the small upright piano on his back. "Tell 'em to wait," he said, between grunts. I resented his giving my number to his girl friends. Besides, now it appeared he'd be leaving before he had a chance to put things back. "Where did you get this number?" I asked, but he was still busy with the piano. Daphne was the only answer, but why? I felt suddenly annoyed at the whole foolish business. He finally got the piano off his back and into a corner beside the fireplace where to my surprise it fitted perfectly. "Get that stuff off the buffet, will you?" I reminded him about the telephone call.

"Hello. Oh hello, Eloyse. Yeah—sure—I see. You mean *now?* No. I don't think I can—not tonight—I've got a job to do." I looked at my watch and saw it was quarter to seven. I'd left the evening open—and now there he was tying up my telephone. I wanted to hear the rest but just then I heard a pounding on the upstairs door and went to answer it. It was the super who'd come to deliver a stack of logs. When I got back Graciadei had finished on the telephone, swept a great many objects onto the floor and was now busily moving the buffet into the front room. As soon as he finished this last, flushed and perspiring, he came in and took his drink.

"Look, why don't you do something for a while? Go on upstairs, huh, and then when I finish up I'll call you."

I decided I might as well be good-natured about this odd procedure and went out to shop, but when I finally returned I could tell from the awful rumbling noises the furniture man was still busy with his obsession. After a while the sounds became almost pleasant. I wondered which piece was being moved where each time a new rumble started up. It seemed as if they'd never stop but they finally did. "Come on down and see your new joint," he called.

It was new all right. The front room was so filled with leftover furniture it was almost impossible to move. The dining room was barely recognizable and very attractive. With the piano moved to one side of the fireplace, a shelf improvised from the super's boards on the other, logs piled neatly under and two old pewter mugs on top, the room had space and charm. "It's marvelous," I cried, delighted, "but what will I do with the stuff out there? And where will anybody eat?" He shrugged, amused at my travail. "I don't know. Don't worry. When a room gets right the other pieces usually fit."

He had another drink and started moving things again, this time singing *How Long,* catching the phrasing of the blues song in his mouth between movements of his body as he lifted the various pieces of furniture. Once he asked me, "What you got upstairs in those files?" I laughed. "Oh all kinds of things—mostly unfinished. Why?" He didn't answer but went back to his singing—*Baby, how long? Baby, how long? Baby, how long?* "You'll finish them sometime," he said, after a while, then went on singing, *If I could holler like a mountain jack, Go on up the mountain and call my baby back.* "What kind of stuff is it?" he blurted out later. "What you saying? Is it funny or gloomy—or maybe you're mad?" I tried politely to give him an answer. We went into one of those involved conversations, going from Dante to Yeats to Herman Melville to Kafka, and then from Joyce to Dostoyevski to Shakespeare. So much fiction was weak in spirit, he said. American writers hadn't found out much except the difficulty of getting *things.* By the time he'd finished downstairs, everything fitted into place as he'd predicted. We ended up good friends.

But upstairs a new mood opened up as I saw he seemed bent on changing things still more. "This room frowns at you," he commented absent-mindedly, standing in the middle of the front room. Some of these decorating people were mad, I thought—remembering something about an upholsterer who'd murdered one of his customers. Those long-fingered hands of his—what was that abominable ring, a signet ring?—and that hair over his arms—red hair, at that! "Not any more now!" I screamed as I saw more furniture being pushed into the far end of the room, and then there he was spreading the big chair opposite the sofa with a bolt of Chinese red satin I'd bought for a New Year's dress, and letting it run over onto the floor. I was so irritated this time I lost track of what he was saying. ". . . wouldn't have all this colorless stuff around any more. Whole thing looks like a water tank. Nothing for a blonde, kind of place'd show up that beat look you had last summer. Sit down and see what I mean."

Those crude comments—but honest, and not mean. He had seen into me with those piercing blue eyes. I fell into the red chair and watched him moving, now quite conscious of that fascinating ease he had, that gliding motion. A man with some good ways about him, a plain unvarnished male man—or was this another mirage I was seeing from the long thirsty walk in the deathly dry desert? He wasn't a killer, he wasn't a thief either, but it flashed over me he had come here for a purpose. He is after something, I felt—possibly even something innate and almost coeval with birth, that he wanted to get away from me. And if it wasn't love or a job, then what was it?

"You poor girl, you're having to think again."

"And you don't, I suppose?"

"Not much any more, I told you. But you're mad now. Go ahead and tell me what's on your mind."

"How much you remind me of that crook they've just caught— the Chicago stock manipulator—the Hungarian with that obnoxious smile. My God, I'm glad they caught him!"

"He won't be moving anybody's furniture around for a while."

And suddenly we were laughing. And he was saying, "I'm hungry. I know a French restaurant on Third Avenue." And we went out quickly like old friends, talking continually as we walked through the snow.

The bistro he knew turned out to be an excellent restaurant, I was surprised, having rather expected him to pick a poor place. We settled on a window seat. "I live right up there," he said, pointing to a brownstone we could see through the windows. An apartment nearby was something I hadn't counted on. "Don't worry, I wasn't going to ask you up there," he said, with a burst of genuine friendliness. "It's an awful damned joint. Let's go to the bar." As he took my elbow and we started toward the bar, I felt he really was a friend: he had not only spared me from having to face a test but he had shown delicacy in blaming it on his having a poor place. We settled at the bar and smiled at each other as peacefully as a couple of old pals, meeting after a long separation.

The drinks tasted good, much better than the ones I'd mixed at home, and now communication between us began to flow more freely. He was talking about me—my place, my books, my job on the magazine, questioning me with such eager interest I began to see I was a personality to him. In fact, catching the view he had of me reflected in his impulsive raw expressions, I began to feel a glow of identity such as I'd had as a very young girl in high school when my first work was accepted for publication. That's me, and look, it's rather nice, I thought.

One sticky little question buzzed like a fly in the bright ego radiance: was it because he wasn't much himself that he found me such an Interesting Personality? Then I thought, No, this particular power is never found in inert masses, and moved a step forward. A whole new wave of ebullition swept over me as the waiter showed us to a corner table, the best in the small dining room, and looking over the handwritten menu I felt a rising curiosity about this man, the stranger whose honest admiration was awakening my slumbering sense of myself.

Thwarted thus far in drawing up my case against him I was aware of some gnawing questions—such as who indeed was he, what manner of work was this he actually did, was it true, what Daphne had said; and if all this still failed to file him away, then was he, very likely, someone else's husband or lover—possibly Eloyse's, the shadowy owner of that well-groomed voice over the phone. Or Daphne's, that was a possibility, or the wife's or even the ex-wife's. Anyway, they were all there. He had his own codification going on. "Are you laughing—in those things in the files?" I parried, "Sometimes, why?" And he gave me his unexpected opinion.

"You're going to find you give yourself best with your funny bone. You wait and see now—that's my idea, anyway." Meantime, he ordered dinner—"Mussels first, with that fresh bread"—and we stayed on the big general stuff. Existentialism, what did I think about that? He had a friend who was a writer, not very good but he made money, and somehow this philosophic refueling seemed to help him. I said philosophy wasn't exactly my dish and he seemed relieved.

I asked about his work and now the blunt answers ("A furniture maker," "I'm a lathe man," "Fellow likes to cut up wood"), showed me he was being modest or evasive, or both. "Not enough status for you? I'm a designer then, says so on the window." I noticed as I went digging for the roots that other people show so easily, this Yule had a novel way of parrying my thrusts, answering just enough to cover the question. "You can tell people I'm an artist if you have to. That's what Liana calls me—when the guests come in." He chuckled, as if the memory amused him no end.

"Why do you call Daphne *Liano?*"

"Lian*a*," he corrected. "It's spelled with an *a* at the end. It's the name of a plant." I had to pry the rest loose. "A murderous plant . . . climbs by wrapping its arms around a tree—until it gets to the top and reaches the light. Then it slowly stops the sap from flowing —until the tree dies."

"Well. . . . Chilling little picture you make." He probably has slept with her, I thought: this sounds like a conclusion after the fact.

"No I haven't," he said, so suddenly I was taken aback. "I haven't made a chilling picture. It's just nature I'm talking about."

"You sound as if you loathe her."

"Oh no, not any more than I loathe the plant. I like plants. So they're dual like people. Some of them like to kill and plunder, quite a few do, you know. The liana's a bit different. She holds the corpse in her arms—and looks exultingly over its head while it's dying. Yes, she's quite a plant."

No, he hadn't slept with Daf: whatever else he was, this Graciadei was nobody's corpse. What now? I was discovering each time, just as I thought I'd got onto the door to his secret closet, where I could now look inside at the ogre heretofore concealed and walk coolly off, he stepped aside saying, no, it's not there, leaving me still on the trail.

"Hilda thinks Daphne is colossal. Spends her time trying to be Daphne. She calls it her Americanization."

Hilda was his former wife, a German girl. He'd been in Germany with the Occupation Army, that was where he'd learned the hard trick of not thinking. His closest friend in Germany, Arthur, was always quarreling with Hilda. "The more Arthur hated her with her German ways, the more I couldn't help thinking about her. I can't explain it, she began to interest me. I kept thinking, no one could be that bad, there's something wrong." They finally met, Hilda wasn't at all as Arthur had pictured her, nor was he as Arthur had pictured him. And before long they both knew Arthur had served a subtle purpose: he'd been the messenger of love.

As we walked back home through the snow I wondered what Daphne had told him about me. Whatever it was it didn't really matter, for this was a man who didn't resent a woman being a little wacky, who had in fact no preconceived notions of how anybody should be. We would be good friends, I could sense that. I felt the slightest pinpoint of sadness because that meant we wouldn't be anything more—but a friend meant there would be no more strain. It would be easy to ask him to put the furniture back, and I was relieved on this score.

Things went wrong the minute we got back. I had no sooner put the key in the lock and turned on the lights when I stumbled over a chair out of its regular place, and would have fallen hard but for quick arms picking me up, a pleasant sensation. "Ah, I'm sorry— I knew I should have come in first—I remembered about that chair. . . ." I said, laughing, "It's all right. Thanks." I'd enjoyed the experience, especially the way he'd said Ah, with genuine sorrow.

But he was watching me after that. I could feel his glance as I started putting things away, and for some reason I resented it. I even wished he'd go now. The conversation had come to a sudden halt. I felt caught—so much so it was hard to keep moving. "Would you like a drink?" I looked up and felt the impact of those bold honest eyes riding—like the muzzles of two gleaming blue pistols— straight into mine, and a warm thrill, exciting but slightly painful, swept over my flesh like a hot summer wind. It was embarrassing, I wanted him and he knew, he with that awful con-man smile. After that he pulled me toward him. When we came out of it we both laughed—with relief was it or pure joy? And in the lively minutes that followed I unbent more and more as I sensed the delicious absence of responsibility: here was a man who enjoyed taking over in the act of love, who moved eagerly, passionately, joyously—and damned gracefully. And (as a result) I myself felt equally inspired with grace and without fear in the sweet thrilling receiving role. And who wouldn't, I thought, as a vague vision of that soft-voiced woman who'd called him on the telephone and was now being kept waiting indefinitely flashed through my mind.

It is hard to tell what happened right here. I remember we moved in unison as if to some secret music. There was a hushed time but with no awkwardness—we were hooked, caught up. I remember marveling at how inevitable, then how easy, love moving on male feet, so different from that sad phony athletic stuff; and then I stopped noticing because things seemed to stop in my head.

I stopped noticing he was a man, a supreme fact (recently repulsive and stirring only to the horror sense). Why, it felt perfect and right, here and now with this new awakening spirit in my body, alive to receive and give back and receive again; there was a certain mad bright wonder at the delicious pain thrill, then a rapturous lightness that seemed at first almost to elude all sense, only to come back more fully into the senses—like flame, like light, like wine. A new animal life was stirring gently, first rising then receding and then rising further until it stretched and reached way up. And I knew it was him, I could feel him for a while and then my body taking over and I, even the feeling I, melting into the new living animal life in there as it started to go into its dance on its own—leaving me a stranger rapt in surprise at my host's loving hospitality. Climbing climbing climbing, losing all sense of time and place in the warm nebulae of semiliquidity that is like the flaming mist in the isinglass of love, then parting and breaking, the rippling spindrift breaking into new wellsprings—darting into hitherto unknown places, from here to there and further up to there, a delicate silver snake climbing the primordial chiasma and taking me all together with her; an animal on its own to whom I now belonged, climbing in her own neoteric rhythm to the top of the feathered mountain and there, in fatal whirling shuffle, in time to the baton of her being, she starts—breaking herself into a shattering mass as she falls over the high feathered top, then shaking herself free and letting out the sweet lifeblood that falls over the feathery mountain in a line of fire and light, of water and snow, and then fire and light again.

Dear. The word flashed a light in the hill of algae down which I was tumbling into an ocean of red snow and blood rain, rocking me back and forth in its smooth moss-animal eternity, rocking me slowly back toward the sudden hard lines of my apartment. . . .

I was in my apartment, I remember waking up and seeing the window in the bedroom but I must have been in a daze because I couldn't remember putting on my clothes and going out—yet there I was standing outside my apartment and looking at the familiar building with the two lower floors that I called home. I turned and looked up the street, only it wasn't the street but instead a country lane, and here was I walking uphill toward a house I knew was mine—but, my God, what was happening to it? Smoke framed it on all sides, yellow smoke that climbed and twisted around like the gold locks of some giantess. The two big windows were lighted up with blue and white flames, there was something staring about these flames, as if they were looking out through the windows, as if they could see. The house had a two-door entrance, but the doors were oval-shaped and flaming red, and they were not standing vertical like proper doors but were instead horizontal.

I was being catapulted up the hill toward my burning house. I felt as if I was flying and as I came closer and closer the outside of the house began to resemble a human face, especially with the golden smoke in rings like the hair of some wild Medusa. And as I came nearer the face began opening up, the horizontal doors gave open as if on signal and I saw the inside of the house. It was burning up and hot, dangerously hot. Why there was nothing left inside but the white-hot skeleton of the foundation! I knew I should stay outside but I couldn't stop myself from flying in. And in I went. Now I was trapped in this burning building that had no proper doors, only those crazy horizontal doors and I was standing vertical, thinking how would I ever get out with only that opening that was made all wrong for human egress. And the whole house was going fast, I even felt I was actually smoking, why I was burning in unison, in rhythm with this house, we would be burned down together! The studdings were already quivering. If I was to escape, it was now or never, and it was life or death.

Yet I felt I ought to stay in this house and go down with it, the captain going down with the ship, and at the same time I could not. This was a fire but it was more than a fire: some event was taking place that had been coming on for a long time, that had about it the terrible unpredictability of nature and I was being forced to move along with it. And I was afraid. Everything was dark and unknown outside, whereas within this small area, now in flames, at least I knew the rules.

But it was too late now. Whatever I should have done to make this place habitable was not done and now the fire had come. It was no longer my house, or anybody's house; it was a dangerous white-hot burning skull. And just ahead was the only exit, that crazy upside-down exit, and even it was in flames. I thought, I can't possibly make it, how could anyone walk through those doors. But suddenly I was flying. After all this was my house, my old home, I thought, it must have been built to accommodate me in my flying role! I put out my hands and went swimming or flying forward to my death. But it wasn't to my death, it must have been forward into freedom, for in that wild minute of flinging myself through the flaming doors I must have wrenched them open and gone straight through into the open air!

I had made it alive. I was outside now. But I realized I had been carrying something. It had felt like a live creature—a dog or a cat or a baby—something I was trying desperately to save, but whatever it was had been dropped in my flying exit. It is lost, I thought, gone forever, the thing that is so close and so familiar as to be a part of me. It was killed in the terrible minute when I flew through the door into the open air. An awful sense of desolation came over me, now I will have to go on without the only thing I really love.

I heard a soft swooshing sound and there before me I saw the house, it was falling and settling on its foundation, its great head lying down in the grass as a last gasp came through the red doors like a sigh. All right, let it go, I thought, it never meant much to me anyway, with everything upside-down like that. But oh that creature, that thing I was carrying that was so alive and precious, my love, my little life, I must have lost control and dropped it, and now I must go on without it. So I started going wearily on and as I did I heard something running in the grass around me, laughing or grunting joyously. Ah, that's it, I thought, the precious little animal, I couldn't be sure but there was something joyously familiar about the sound.

I looked up at the sky and saw a fierce red hand in the gray clouds, and it was lifted as if to stroke an animal. Suddenly I saw a remarkable sight: a small black horse with its mane unfurled ran up the hill leading off from the house and leaped right up into the sky over the raised hand. It moved so quickly as it went over it was hard to follow, but I saw, I saw it was laughing and looking back at me, oh there was no mistake about that. I could see its bright white teeth and flashing eyes. I had a great feeling of joy about this horse, and simultaneously a feeling of resignation, such as one might have about an animal that has run away and then later turns up in some place where you can't reach it, having itself one hell of a good time. I knew it was looking at me and laughing, Look at you down there, and me up here, it seemed to be saying, and it awakened in me a feeling of deep intimacy.

I had hold of the clue as I awakened from the dream. The horse, now who could that be but that crazy pygmy self of mine I called Devman? He had written me a letter and there he was signing his name. I figured it out later. All right, go ahead and have your orgasm, you'll lose the familiar house you've been living in, you'll be going off into the unknown but it's all right with me. I'm having fun. And he was laughing at me for trying to control him.

A sound beat into my ears, it was somehow pleasant and consoling. I thought vaguely, maybe I am in the country and there's a cow outside eating its way across the lawn. Then bright light filtered in and my first thought was to escape back into bed, but there is never any escape once you've seen outside. Yule was right there, big as life and far more alert, sitting under the lamp eating hard crackers—chewing, chewing, my what a clack-clacking he made as those crackers went through his teeth. Yule, that crude thick-legged furniture man, he was the one who . . . Oh no, it wasn't true—and even if it were true—I could still slip out the other side of the bed, grab my clothes and pretend nothing had happened. . . . There was a way of doing that or there might be a way, though it required some careful moving about, that is if it was still last night.

"Hello." The word was so vigorous, I knew I'd better move fast. Then, "Baby, what are you doing—crawling away like that? I'll bet you think you're invisible!" He leapt across the bed and caught hold

of me in one of those easy lithe moves of his, and was now caressing my hair. "You're not a bit invisible, honey—honest you're not.
Now tell me, are you all right?" I said yes, I was fine, and why was
he asking. ". . . had me scared last night. Do you usually take off
in those swoons?" I said no, definitely not and how long . . . "Were
you out? About thirty minutes on the drop last night—then you
mumbled—since then you've been asleep. Are you sure you feel all
right? There's a spot of brandy left in a bottle downstairs—I turned
it down myself!" His bluntness was somehow perfect, so much better
than compliments, I was laughing—why even the terrible truth was
funny. . . . "It's ten o'clock in the morning. I've been out buying
groceries . . . nothing here but crackers in jars. . . . Waiting for you
since seven o'clock." I asked, "What day is today?" And he told me,
"Saturday. And now if you're all right . . . calls to make, be right
back. But look, before I go do me a favor?" I said yes, with some
misgiving, I was still planning to move away, move on. "Tell me,
do you hate me very much?" I looked and saw that damned male
grin, it was oddly reassuring this time, and said slowly, "No, but you
do look like that con man. You are a thief, too." But we kissed and
he was chuckling happily as he went away.

CHAPTER FORTY-TWO

. . . . . .

WHAT'S THIS HAPPENING TO ME? MY NEXT NOTE READS. AND WHEN have I been so *busy,* with everything humming and buzzing so I have to pinch myself to remember the days—this is Saturday or this is Sunday, nineteen days to Christmas, gifts not yet bought but I don't have to work today, I can just walk out of my past life and enjoy myself doing all the pleasant ordinary things I've never done before. Like making a "country breakfast" from Yule's outlandish grocery purchases which included tomatoes, cornmeal and nutmeg and mace, smoked salmon and caviar and cheese and champagne. And devouring it hungrily before the fire in the made-over dining room. And then driving downtown in his station wagon, his "Let's get you some new china," leading to a descent on the downtown china-goods section where two hours disappeared in selecting china. And then coming home at five o'clock with a dinner set *and* a tea set and having tea on the new tea set upstairs. And then opening the carton he'd brought (I had to go back to the unpleasant half hour—a thousand years ago or was it yesterday?—when I so resented seeing it coming into the house) to find it contained a beautiful grow-ing Christmas tree. "It'll do fine just inside the window for three, four weeks, then it should be planted in the yard." And by the end of the first day the place that had seemed so distressingly forlorn, especially since I'd been in it alone, looked as if it was just lonesome and waiting eagerly to make friends, with the corner gobbling up the bright tea set and the long window proudly showing off her new Christmasy dress.

Sundays are big full days now. There's something about this work Yule does, this making beautiful things, and the way he shares his incredible knowledge, so different from the secretive way writers and "operators" work, hugging their short cuts to themselves and fearful of running dry—but more as if it came from some boundless source within himself and you were doing him a favor by taking off some of the excess. I've found out so much from him and through him, there's more and more in there, in the vast corridor with those doors opening, there's nothing closed off or closed up. We talk, in half-hours snatched in the off-beat restaurants when we are suddenly hungry and questions are answered and remembered. About his former wife. "Hilda's a good girl. A baby girl, she wanted her mother, so I brought mother over and now she's happy in her way." I say, "It sounds rather bad for her." But he shrugs. "You might call it a poor way for a woman but it's her way, so it's not poor for her." And I, "Are you still friends?" And he, "Oh yes. There wasn't any bad feeling. I just saw there wasn't much place for a man—except as a father." And I breathe a sigh of relief.

A man who feels good about women, a man who truly likes women. A rarity? I think I love him most when he sees into me, and laughs with that animal wisdom he has. "You still filling in that brief against men?" he chuckles. I, of course, deny this but he knows.

And at his shop with his work. How every piece of wood is an absorbing problem, almost as if each slab has a nature and life of its own which challenges him to use it to its fullest capacity, like the half dozen plump blonde beauties with the pink bottoms he's making for the lovely Mrs. H. who keeps dropping in to see them or him. This deep satisfaction he feels in the work—was this why he quit the big industrial concern which awarded him the five-figure salary and status, to open his own shop? He couldn't get the feel of things, he explained. Couldn't develop craftsmanship. "I'm un-American that way, ask Liana, she'd tell you about my revolting conduct. Only crazy people get pleasure from learning. I was a cabinet-maker and a carpenter and a painter, remember, and I learned more than I did in the four years I spent at college or three years in industrial designing. A waste."

There's something about it, those hours he spends working harder than the workmen, he seems capable of deeper concentration and enjoys what he's doing more keenly. "If it lures you so, why don't you make something?" And I did: it took me three hours to make a tiny flower holder from a piece of cherry wood, pressing the wood in the lathe with the tool he gave me and seeing the splinters fly off, and then increasing the pressure as it slowly took shape, it wasn't as much fun as I'd thought from watching him. I was admiring my handiwork—a perfect miniature, I thought, with not a nail in it—and wishing for another, and one of the workmen made me the other—only he did it in fifteen minutes. No use for me to be lured by this world, a place where lasting objects of beauty and usefulness are made by people's hands, but I'm glad he's only casually interested in the totally unimportant little corner of the word town I occupy.

Occasionally I notice, I'm happy, an accidental by-product of shared experience and work. And I see the smile that irritated me so is just the relaxed way his mouth falls when he's pleased. Even visiting those vast impersonal male emporiums filled with strange objects of brass and steel, or driving out of town and walking in ugly little towns with the ocean hiding off in the back, where we talk desperately or are quiet and then begin talking again, I notice this welcoming feeling in my chest that comes from some richer rhythm of the inner senses, undulating through as if from some coiled being hidden under a stone and now slowly awakening. Sometimes I can feel it rising, threatening to break into a strangled squeal like a newborn puppy, snub-nosed and blind, helpless and avid, opening its eyes and finding itself in a world new as a wet painting.

Occasionally a corner of the old pattern appears. Seeing how attractive he is to other women, the fear feeling rises, but so far it's been dissipated in this Something Else that seems to be growing, something I can only call the new inside life. Or occasionally, when the relationship becomes too encompassing, I'm ashamed in face of his frank delight, half wishing he would stop and we would be separate again. But this never lasts, there's this powerful quivering pug-nosed puppy I'm holding, he's too eager to hold back for long.

Christmas Eve stands out as a day I won't quickly forget. I appeared at the office party, an elaborate friendly brawl, and hurried away to join Yule at the shop, we'd planned to spend the rest of the holiday together. The workmen had gone when I arrived, we cleaned up the remains of beer in cans, half-eaten hero sandwiches, and I carefully wrapped the remains of the Christmas cake. It was getting dark when we sat down on that huge red sofa in the far corner of the first floor to have a cup of coffee before closing up; we were in fact planning our evening. He was saying, "Let's go to the bistro on Third Avenue," when suddenly the front door opened and closed quickly. I couldn't see who had come in but a stab of fear hit me at the sounds.

Someone was walking in high heels. Yule bounced up and looked through the studio. "It's Liana." But he had lowered his voice and was standing still, watching. And the heels kept on clicking as he moved his hand, directing me to stay where I was, but I had already moved and was by this time near enough to see Daphne. She stopped suddenly, midway, and stared at us, her eyes darting first to Yule and then to me and then back to Yule again. She made a striking picture in her yellowish tweed coat, it was open at the front showing the fur lining, and some wonderful fur and tweed hat and remarkable high-heeled Russian boots. I knew immediately something was wrong, but it was too late to go back. By this time I was standing near him, and now the three of us were standing foolishly around looking at each other.

"I'll go talk to her," Yule was almost whispering as he walked off, pushing me back with his hand. I heard him say, "Hello, Liana," in that easy way he has of talking. "I guess you want to take the screen. Be all right, it's finished. Must be dry by now."

Daphne didn't answer at first. She continued staring at him for a while, then suddenly burst out in a loud trembling voice, "I thought you were coming to the country!" Her anger seemed so useless, almost pitiful—that great energy going into a dying flame. "We've been expecting you."

"I didn't say I was coming. You had no reason to expect me."

He started upstairs to get the screen, and seeing this, she started screaming. "You did, too. You promised Tom—he told me he called you yesterday and you said you'd come. And Tom at least is *not* a liar."

Yule turned on the stairs. "I told Tom I didn't think I could make it. I said I'd call him if I could."

"Well you can come now. I've got the car. I want you to come, Yule. Wait till you hear. Horace Lemon is coming—he'll cover the party in the column. Over a hundred people. . . . Planning to take pictures of the screen and of you." She was commanding him; there was a threat in the last. By this time he had reached the balcony and started down again with the big screen stretched around him like a great cloak.

"Why don't you have a drink, Daf? We left it in the desk, didn't we, darling?"

"You've got to get ready and come out with me!" she screamed.

Yule kept on slowly coming down the stairs. "It's no good, Daphne. I never said I'd be one of your boys."

He planted the screen against the wall nearby. I said, "I'll go get it," and went off for the bottle of whiskey. "Wait a minute—there's one here!" he called to me without turning, he was just opening the door in a cabinet under the stairs. I said, "Hello, Daphne," now that I was out in the open I had to say something, it sounded foolish but then I was afraid of her. As she looked up at me I saw the bright pink spots in her face and the way her mouth was sucked tightly in. "I want Yule to come on out with me," she said, rather quietly now, ignoring the greeting. "It's very important for him. Besides, he promised and we're counting on him. After all, it's his house almost, he's responsible for it. Such a chance for him—why the publicity alone is invaluable!"

I said, "It's all right with me—if he wants to go," and was immediately sorry I'd said it.

"I don't want to go. I'm not going. Just forget it now, Daphne." Yule had found the bottle and was trying to open it. "Just get it out of your head once and for all. Oh, this is Bourbon. Where's that Scotch—do you remember, honey? You like Scotch, I know—oh, here it is, here's the Scotch."

He carried the bottle and glasses to a breakfront where he stopped and began pouring the whiskey. He handed the first glass to Daphne but she didn't move her hand to take it, so he put it down near her.

"Well there's your screen, it's all finished and you can take it along with you. I'd better wrap it up—is it still raining?" Daphne didn't answer. She was staring at the screen, apparently studying it. I couldn't tell from her intent look what she thought of it but it seemed an odd reaction to the beautiful twelve-paneled screen for her bedroom with its impressionistic treatment of the flowers, waterscapes and animals around her place in Connecticut. "It's magnificent!" she finally said. "A work of art."

"Thanks. Now come on, let's all have a Christmas drink. You can take it along and take all the credit for it—after all, it's your design and your idea—I'll paint in your name on the bottom panel."

She ignored the drink. She seemed to be taking in the screen inch by inch. Suddenly she turned on her heel and walked quickly out of the place.

"My God, what's eating her?" I asked, but he only shook his head. "Did you promise her you'd go to the party?"

"Of course not. I told Tom I couldn't make it—and neither could you. He knew what I meant. Also that we were getting married."

"No? You didn't say that?"

"I did. I'd better just lock the door. Here, have a drink, honey. And don't look so scared. I can handle Liana."

I was ashamed of myself but scared I was, and took the drink gratefully. We had just finished our drinks, Yule was pouring water from a carafe I'd given him when Daphne opened the front door again and came on in. She was holding one hand in the pocket of her coat as she advanced, and she was smiling a peculiar hard little smile. She came the length of the studio and stood near the screen.

"I knew you'd change your mind," Yul said. He came toward her with a glass of whiskey, but she smacked it clean out of his hand.

"Is this screen absolutely finished?"

Yule nodded as he opened it up further, one panel was folded at the end. I was going to get cigarettes, I'd left my pack on the sofa; as I started off I heard a sharp rending sound and turning quickly I saw her ripping the beautiful silk with a sharp knife. Great zigzag holes were already gaping as Yule came bounding toward her in one of those quick moves. He grabbed her and held her, with her arms pinned behind her back.

"Let me go!" she screamed as she tried to kick him, but the way he had her she was teetering on her heels. "Let me go or you'll be sorry."

It was unbelievable, but there it was happening. She was kicking backwards against his legs when he shook the knife from her hand and it fell to the floor with a crash. I ran and picked it up, then threw it out the back window—it flashed in the dirty snow just as it sank under. But the picture of Daphne stayed with me: she was gnashing her teeth and kicking with some great wave of hopeless uncontrolled fury. The minute he let go of her arms she started toward him again, this time reaching to scratch his face, but he soon caught both her hands and held them carefully back this time, as he began calmly walking her through the studio toward the door. I ran ahead and opened the door and Yule pushed her through and set her on the street, locking the door behind her. His face was badly scratched and bleeding.

"Good God, what's the matter with her?" He didn't answer, he was shaking his head. "Do you think I'd better go out?"

"It might be charitable—but dangerous." He wiped his face with a clean handkerchief I handed him. "You can go if you want to, though—I'll be right here, she can't do much more now."

"I'll take her a drink, maybe that'll help." I went on out after her, bringing the bottle along with me, and quickly spotted the station wagon parked at the corner. It was one of those new wooden jobs with a deliberately rustic appearance. Daphne was sitting in front, her head bent over her arm. She glanced up as I came beside the car, her face wet with tears. The side window was open, so she couldn't have wanted to be left entirely alone. I asked her, "Is the other door open?" She nodded, and I crawled in and poured a drink into the small glass I'd brought along at the last minute. She took it immediately and drank it down, pushing the glass back in my lap without glancing in my direction.

"This is what you've got—after all your doctoring," she blubbered, still looking ahead of her. "A goddamned furniture maker. I guess you think you've picked a winner. Well you haven't. I could have done things for him—but you can't. You haven't got any money or any connections. You're nothing but a goddamned woman."

"What made you come to the shop?"

"Oh, I knew. Tom told me but I wanted to make sure. Stopped by your place and the super told me the whole story. They're probably up to his place, he said. Oh I saw the way he was looking at you—last summer. And Tom likes him, too."

"Want another drink?"

She shook her head. "Get away from me, Joyce. You'd better just get going." She started the motor. "I had a present for you, too."

"I don't exactly own him," I said. "You can see him any time you like, after all."

"Who wants to see him?" She was screaming again. "Dull sonofabitch. Plants—furniture—fish. Good God, what a dull bastard."

"Dull people are kind of interesting though."

"It's about time you stopped slumming."

"Daphne, wake up. What do you want with Yule—really now?" There for a second she looked alert. "Go on, say it. You might feel better."

"I don't know." She was sobbing for a minute, then stopped abruptly. "I just don't know. He's stubborn. You can't get near him— I found that out while I was out there in the country with him. Wait till you find out. Self-contained as a goddamned cat. Oh I don't know—I guess I just felt good when he was around, doing things around the house, stuff like that. There was something about him . . . that quieted me down."

"He wasn't yours—any more than he is now. You can still see him that way."

"He would have been. He's lonely. He hasn't got anybody but that awful family in Brooklyn. Bunch of uneducated wops. His sister works in a factory."

"And has leprosy, no doubt?"

"It won't be so funny when you're stuck with her around. The whole thing won't be so funny. Doesn't care about money or he'd be rich by now. You'll have one of those dirty marriages—with no money. You'll be sorry.'" She felt better now, I could see that. "Get out, Joyce. Just get out of this car."

I got out. The motor was running now, she was going into first, then the car moved forward and stopped long enough for her to lean out the window and holler, "Merry Christmas" as she tossed something back at me. I saw the beautifully wrapped small package come through the window, it skidded past my feet and landed in the wet street. I picked it up and carried it back inside, together with the small angel that had become dislodged in the flight.

Yule was waiting at the door. "Well, that's that," he said. "Thank God she's finally gone." I said, "I'm sorry about the screen," as we walked back to look it over. "Don't be sorry, honey. I hated that damned thing. Tried to talk her out of it but she insisted." I said, "I think it can be mended." It was slashed down the middle in five places, one panel of pines and rocks was less seriously injured but the stretches of silk showing foxglove, columbine and phlox were torn in half, and pieces showing sea pink and bleeding hearts were hanging out from the sides, while the curious panel of the "bad dream-eating animal" was hopeless. "Old Mo looks like he's coming through a barroom door," Yule commented. "Let's not bother with it now. It's hers—whenever she wants it I'll just ship it off to her. Come on, let's get out of here before she changes her mind and comes back."

CHAPTER FORTY-THREE

· · · · · ·

WE WERE GOING TO OUR FAVORITE PLACE ON THIRD AVENUE FOR Christmas Eve dinner, but what with the telephone calls that started coming in from Toni and Sol—first they thought they might come by, then they decided no, they couldn't make it, they were going to a party uptown, then yes, they were coming by, after all—it was too late to go anywhere by the time I was dressed. Then Yule arrived and we got so interested in trimming the tree with those red and gold apples and tiny electric lights that resemble candles, we forgot all about dinner. I was standing by the window, holding the cords that tied the apples on, when I thought there was something familiar in the black car I saw nosing its way into the empty space at the curb. "That's Sol and Toni now," Yule said. He stopped trimming. "Just look at them. Married couple who've just had words."

The first glance I caught of the magnificently dressed Meyers, they were sitting at opposite ends of the wide seat, Toni was staring before her, Sol was leaning forward muttering—probably those awful helpful cracks he always threw at the long-suffering Marvin, and it hit me Yule was right. The jolly pair *en route* to a merry tryst were actually two people hell-bent to unload their troubles, an impression which gained credence as we watched the unfortunate Marvin helping them out of the car, exactly as if they were patients coming from a spell at hospital. And then they were coming in—with their grand clothes and grim faces, smiling heavily and wishing us all the merries, and with Marvin carrying a package that was too heavy for Sol to manage. And Sol was saying, "Hullo, Joyce, Merry Christmas. Hullo, Mr. Yulie," and making for the sofa as soon as he'd removed his hat and coat as if that were an end in itself.

Toni went immediately into the bedroom where she threw her shining sable coat blithely across the bed, then straightened out to look at herself in the mirror and began piping in her high elfin voice. "Do you like this antique satin deal, Joyce? You can tell me the truth. But wait—first tell me, isn't the sable kind of overwhelming?" I looked at the spirited blush-pink dress with the great bell sleeves of sable and made appropriate murmurs, "Very becoming—pink was always your best color," when Sol trudged heavily toward the doorway. "You like that costume, huh, Joyce? That's my taste. Something like that you won't see every Tom Dickan Harry. I tell her whole families five kids could live years on what that cost. Here look, Yulie—what you think something like that?" Yule stood beside Toni. "Very good. Excellent," he said, but he was plucking in the fur at the wrists, indicating cuffs, and automatically the over-large sleeves on the tiny girl took on character and drama. Toni piped, "Say, that's what it needed. Oh, Yule, that's real great. I'll take it back Monday and have it fixed."

I was glad to see them, it was reassuring hearing Toni squealing again around the place, especially after the recent experience with Daphne. "You better open your present, honey. Maybe you want to put it on the ice—some of it, that is. It's rehoboams of champagne. It's awful awkward," she whispered, "those big show-off bottles—I mean they're hard to handle—but he insisted." Out loud, she finished, "The Meyers do things in a big way. Maybe you don't want to drink it tonight, you better save it for a party with people you want to impress." I said no, we'd open them tonight, one of them, anyway. Yule carried the heavy package downstairs where we soon found the rehoboams wouldn't go in the refrigerator and required special treatment. "He wanted to bring you a Methuselah," Toni hollered over the banister, "but I knew you'd have trouble with that." And Sol chimed in, "That's vintage stuff. A rehoboam only serves couple dozen people couple drinks apiece. Lissen, Joyce, if you use six-ounce glasses like we have at home you can only give a drink apiece, then you keep the other two bottles on ice, you got to have big buckets or else put them in the tub. Well you got the beginnings." Yule finally placed one of the bottles in a scrub-bucket which he started filling up with ice and wrapping in an old tablecloth. "Looks like we'll miss dinner at that— but don't worry, I brought some stuff along and I'll make something. You go on back upstairs, don't worry about your troubled guests, you're in for an earful. This is going to be a great season—I feel it in my bones."

Upstairs, Toni was in the bedroom again, Sol was sitting morosely by the fireplace playing with some twenty-dollar gold pieces. "I can't stand the noise he makes rubbing his money together like that," she whined. She was back at the dressing table. "I know what you're thinking, Joyce. I'm making up again, and you're right. I do it for consolation. I feed my face the make-up like other people feed their faces food. At least you can't get fat on make-up." I picked up the cigarette box I'd come after and started back. "Come on out now, Toni—it's not fair leaving Sol out there alone." She put on another round of lipstick and got up. "We've had a terrible fight. You don't understand what happened. He's going to divorce me, he says. We're through. Look, could I come back here?"

I reminded her, "It's only ten o'clock. By midnight everything will be different." But she didn't believe it. "Nothing will be different. I did myself in. I knew I was doing things all wrong—but I couldn't stop it. I tried to stop myself but I just couldn't—you know how that happens when you try to stop doing something and you just can't make it." I said yes, I did indeed know, and got quickly to the subject of my dress. Yule had designed it, telling the dressmaker exactly what to do, helping her first make a pattern, and then cutting the collar for her. "He cut that collar?" Toni didn't seem to believe it. "Yes, it's supposed to be like the collar worn by Mary Queen of Scots. Like it?" She looked it over silently, with only Sol's money-clinking and the firewood crackling coming in upon us. "You mean he really can design something like that? Well, it's terrific. I can tell he's awfully talented with his hands. Just the way he pinned up the sleeves on my dress, he's got talent like crazy. But a man hanging around dressmakers, I don't know, darling. He might be bisexual, of course I don't think he's completely homo. Sykes was bi, I know he was, he never actually admitted it but I've heard it all over."

I tried to explain. "Yule doesn't hang around dressmakers. He just can't resist making things—" but suddenly lost interest.

"Well don't worry about it, honey. Lots of girls I know have made very satisfactory adjustments with bi's. Remember Maggie Wyler? Well, she's married to Smith Wyler and if you remember he's a very successful bi. She says she wouldn't trade him for a heterosexual because with a bisexual you've got the unattainable already *attained*."

Every time she stopped for breath the sound of Sol's gold pieces clinked in the silence; Toni gritted her teeth and began talking all over again. By the time I'd managed to bring her back to the living room Sol had gone downstairs. "Maybe he's gone out by himself," she whispered, fearful of being left alone, but no, old Sol had only gone downstairs to get himself a drink of brandy, and next thing we knew he was coming slowly up the steps carrying a tray with a bottle and some glasses.

Toni glanced at Sol. "Oh you got yourself some brandy, huh, darling? You see, I told you Joyce would have brandy. Sol likes to drink brandy and champagne, he doesn't like whiskey very much, and I remembered the bottle I left here. I said it's so awful I'll bet she still has it."

"You gulls want some brandy? You got a tasty little place here, Joyce." Sol was back by the fire now, the money in hand. "Well, here's to you both. I saw some people outside looking up at your tree. Yule's down there cooking up some good-looking stuff."

"Gee, it's nice to see an unpretentious little tree like that—if you go in for that kind of thing," Toni cooed. "Wait till you see the pine trees on our terrace—with hundreds of electric lights that keep flashing in and out. Looks like something should say success to your chain of delicatessen stores. I said . . ."

"For our New Year's Eve party," Sol cut in. "Cost a pretty penny get those trees planted up there." He gave Toni a cold quick look. "You should see the rooftops they have in Hollywood holiday season. My friend Manny Wohlheimer paid ten thousand dollars get some Christmas setups on his roof—but it's something. A work of art. I got photographs I'll show you."

"She can't wait," Toni put in.

Sol glanced at her once again. "Well, Merry Christmas, gulls," he said, as he finished off his glass.

The conversation kept rising into tense little waves and receding into tense quiet. "Tell me about your penthouse. It must be magnificent by now." But neither answered.

"You tell her, Toni," said Sol.

"Well, I guess you have to see it. The chairs are Italian Directoire, the desk is Biedermeier, my bed is French Directoire. It cost a fortune, it scares me to think about it. But you know, decorating an apartment is a sado-masochistic experience, it has areas of sadistic snobbery . . ."

"Listen, that stuff she goes on, I tell you it's beautiful, Joyce. A picture. Chairs why we got one original Louis Seize, something could be in a museum. Something could bring a lot of money anybody needed to sell. You know Louis Seize—he says I should sit down but I says no, I'll stand up!"

"I can't tell whether it's terrific or terrible," Toni piped up. "This Miss Hooper, she's the one we had first, she kept talking about old English inns that have Elizabethan elegance. One day I just told her, I said Look Miss Hooper, I don't live on the River Thames, I don't want to go eel-fishing in the marshes on the Mediterranean coast— in fact where I come from an eel gets into the house the people move out."

Sol got up slowly and poured himself another drink, just as Yule appeared with the first morsels of food—hot deviled eggs garnished with anchovies and prosciutto cut paper thin and large slices of melon. Sol put his arms around Yule. "Yulie, listen, Sunny-boy, I want to tell you a little joke." Whatever he had meant to say he seemed to forget and instead started a spiel about a string of motels he'd bought, giving us all the facts of the purchase and the remodeling, as if we were vitally concerned and breathless for the information. "It's results that count," he would stop to say every so often, or "Nothing succeeds like success." Then, "Now you guess what the occupancy was after remodeling. Go ahead, don't be afraid. Just take a guess, Yulie, Sunny-boy."

"Wait a minute. I want Yule to tell me something. Yule, tell me, what are people supposed to do in their morning rooms?"

"Spend the afternoon," Yule advised, as he ducked downstairs, apparently to see to the rest of the cooking. Sol was just bringing him up to date on the financial itinerary of the new home, "It's costing me ten thousand every week—I've been at it ten weeks now—I always say a man can't spend money in his own home, what's going t'be?" but Yule continued on his way downstairs, and toward the end of the speech could be heard singing that damned *Baby How Long* again.

Suddenly the conversation gave out. In spite of the great gaiety the Meyers were affecting, the premonition that all was far from well kept nubbing me with its chill nose. Sol picked up his pieces and began jiggling them like dice. "Stop it!" Toni screamed. I knew we were in for a bad time.

Sol got up and walked heavily toward the window where he stood staring moodily down at the street. "Have you got any aspirin?" Toni asked. I had aspirin, but it was the wrong kind, next thing I knew she was putting on her sables and sallying forth to the nearest drug-store. I had planned to escape now by running down to the kitchen, but Sol crossed the room almost in a leap and took hold of my arm as if he'd got hold of a raft in a stormy sea.

"Sit down a minute, Joyce," he pleaded. His eyes, red and watery, now looked out at me like a pair of bleeding billiard balls as some odylic force forewarned me I was in for a session that wouldn't be quickly terminated. I had opened my doors to an erupting volcano, I knew that as I heard the first words, "Joyce, I've made a fatal mistake," and wondered once more what there was about me that produced in people an abrupt urge to unbosom themselves, usually of many an unholy matter I'd as lief they'd kept in their purdahs.

"Lissen I can tell you as a friend, you're not going let loose in the streets, there's things going on down there that Fifth Avenue penthouse strike me like a bang over my head. I can tell you, you got something about you . . ." His voice was muffled now, a gentle liquid tone crept in as he fished interminably for the big evasive word. "You're not a wiseacre, same time you've got a heart and still and all you're no-body's fool. I'm telling you, Joyce, this I wouldn't tell another living soul so help me, I wouldn't even tell my own brother, a pig with his mouth. You know something, lissen, a man making love to his wife, he's happy, yes? He's all relaxed, yes, he's talking to her and he's saying things. I mean a man like myself, I'm not Bernard Shaw, sud-denly she hollers, *QUIET!*" The word rent the atmosphere like a sheet being torn. "I gotta be *quiet* like I got sick maybe—like maybe somebody's dying. I gotta get up, acting like I went deaf and dumb. What do I do? I ask you, what can a man do? I'm pretty sore, I can tell you that much. I'm putting on my shoes, I'm going out, you think she apologizes? Nothing like it. She's lying there still, her eyes closed, I tell you, this I wouldn't tell another living soul. Maybe I drop a shoe, something like that, what does she say? *DO YOU HAVE TO BREAK DOWN THE HOUSE?*"

4 0 4

He lit a cigar and stared angrily at me, as if expecting an answer. I said, "She didn't mean it that way." Then, "You just didn't understand." But he said, "I understand. I understand more'n you think. Sometimes I think there's something about that gull, it's not natural. A man making love to his wife he should act like maybe he's not there, maybe he's a shadow, maybe he's somebody else. You explain me that one."

I held myself tight, laughing with my diaphragm—after all it was sad for him—as he continued. "Lissen, Joyce, I had love affairs. I had gulls all over—Paris, England, Switzerland—even in Sweden I had a sweetheart." He sounded as if having a sweetheart in Sweden was highly irregular, brave and subject to commendation like climbing the Alps. "In Sweden once I had two gulls, they were friends living together. One sweetheart I had in London, a fine society type—high up, she's been around fine places, you can see her name in newspapers. The way she speaks, you know right away you lissen, first words coming out of her mouth, she's a little queen. Gulls in Paris, them I don't crave, but a man goes to France he's not going sit still somewheres like a dummy. He goes out meets people next thing he's got friends all over him like plague locusts. So what'll he do nights he's by himself, no business transact—telephone rings and there you have it! I know women—New York, Chicago, San Francisco, London—I had all kinds, good and not so good, you know the type, cash and carry, what can you do? I tell to you, Joyce, I heard women saying all kinds of things, too—why a man treats them right, sometimes they're crying out like maybe they're seeing a ghost. And it's nice, too, hearing all those things. But I'm telling you, Joyce, what this Toni says to me, this I never heard nothing like it no bed nowheres in my life. A man going out charting an empire wouldn't hear nothing like this.

"You know women. They like to think they've got something good. Man like me opening plants all over, I'm an ambassador wherever I go. Pictures in the paper, newspaper stories, big public affairs. His own wife he can't get up, eat maybe a cheese and onion sandwich. He can't curl up, go to sleep—Oh no, he's got to *disappear*. It's humiliating. Lissen, you gulls lived together, you been thicker than thieves, tell me, what's she thinking about—lying there her eyes closed?"

"But, Sol, how would I know? What does anybody think about?"

"Lissen, Joyce, what anybody's thinking about, that she's not think-ing about. I'm not so dumb I don't know something funny's going on."

"But Sol, you know it's a strain—after all, a new house being decorated. And then that obstetrician, it's probably his fault—they cause a terrible strain—a woman trying to have a baby. Things will calm down once you have the baby."

"Baby!" The great black and white balls in his face showed spots of flame. "Oh my God, don't mention baby, please." The lights from the fire coming in and going out gave his face a ludicrous quality as they changed it from a dark shadow, with just the eyes showing, into a great round mask of white porky sorrow and then back to the dark shadow again. "She's claiming I haven't got babies in my genes! I got t'go to doctors and leave samples my manhood for X-rays yet. I got t'come home and wait, wait, wait while this doctor figures me out, have I got babies or haven't I got babies? He's in no hurry, he's not caring what's in my genes. Well then I finally get this doctor on the telephone and I get the answer. I've got babies my genes, all right, nothing to worry about, he says. Hundreds of babies, maybe. And so I come home tell her and we go out. We're going to have a night on the town. And I'm feeling happy again making love, I think this time maybe she'll be different, so there it is. I say Baby how are you now? *SHUT UP!*"

The front door banged and then Toni was coming up the stairs. Judging from the fresh staccato of her sharp little heels, I decided the trip for the right kind of aspirin had revived her old *élan*. Yule picked up the cue and came in with another round of champagne for a mid-night toast.

Daphne's present turned out to be a small gold finger ring with an exquisite enamel setting. I tried it on, and recognized it as one I had seen in a rare antique shop in the neighborhood. It was a poison ring, with a compartment for suicide pills. I found the spring and it snapped open. Toni came over and examined it in wide-eyed fascination. "That's for the exit pills," I explained.

"I wonder why she wants you out of the way," was Toni's final comment. Just then I caught Yule's glance and knew we were an audience of two, waiting together till the end of the show.

It was past midnight before I was back in Toni's deserted bed-room, listening to her talk while she fished around in the empty drawers for some compact she said she'd left behind. "Look, honey, is everything all right with you? Because you know you can tell me the absolute truth—no matter how terrible." I said everything was fine but she sighed unbelievingly, and continued walking around in her sables that seemed out of place in the plain little room. "I can see you're going to have Yule around for a long time. It'll be kind of dull for you—I mean housework and cooking and all." I inter-rupted to say I hadn't thought too much about the *modus operandi,* nor done much of it either. "A man should be able to give his wife a maid . . . Oh well, it's better than being alone. Even a bad marriage is better than no marriage. And there's something awfully nice about him. He's attractive, too—those eyes, they kill me. Look, you say he's a college graduate?" I nodded. "And a worker by choice? It sounds kind of crazy, dear. Take like Sol, you know he can't even read or write—and he's gone all the way to the top." I started to explain that Yule was different from Sol, but quickly lost interest in what was I saying. Besides, Toni wasn't listening.

"Well now, don't worry about the sex angle right away. It's all in how you train a man." I was hoping to avoid this, but there it was. "I've found out something new. You have to hold on to your fantasy while you're making love—the whole time, remember now—" There were sounds in the dining room, human voices, Sol's and Yule's, coming nearer. Toni gave me the rest in a throaty whisper. "It's all in how you train a man. The whole thing is to make him keep quiet. Remember now, nothing may go right for the first six months to a year even, but then maybe one day when you're least expecting it, even after you've given up the whole idea, bang, it'll happen, and there you are."

Yule and I stood at the window, watching the Meyers depart from our street. Sol was berating poor Marvin, his voice ringing out over the traffic sounds. "Whatsa difference Christmas Eve and any other time? You're supposed to be waiting from ten-thirty on—not sitting around coffee shops I should be going out looking for you." Yule watched them off with great amusement. "Whatever he does to Marvin, that little talking pixie will do to him. Must be tough on the old boy, a wife with a built-in wailing wall. Remind me to dream up another invention for him—an unhearing aid." And we made coffee and talked and laughed, and this was the best part of the wayward day.

CHAPTER FORTY-FOUR

. . . . . .

I REMEMBER AN APPOINTMENT I HAD WITH DR. HALSTED EARLY IN the summer. For some reason I'd been talking about old Mr. V and the spanking and the great cleansing power of laughter. "Ah yes, that," he said. "Well, laughter came before words. Now tell me, how long since you've had the fantasies?" I tried to tell him, but I couldn't remember: it was that long ago. I had to force myself to remember the market place with the prince riding up in his carriage, and when I did finally remember it looked like some faded old mezzotint. "The theater in there has burned down to the ground," I said. Dr. Halsted nodded. "I think these particular fantasies have gone for good. A woman coming out of frigidity into the kind of fulfillment you're having usually stops thinking about sex. Feeling good stops the preoccupations flat."

He had a new patient, he told me, an intensely promiscuous woman who kept blaming her lovers for her failures. "She thinks they're all at fault. Keeps looking for the one man, the knight on the charger, who'll change everything for her." He said one thing more on this subject. "You were lucky in meeting Yule and coming out of it with him, just at the right time. Because it might have been almost anybody. It's never the man who does it, no matter what you read in the romantic books. It's because you were well. No man in the world can make a woman well that way, but great God, the numbers of them that believe in that stuff. And the men, too—going around thinking the women are at fault." He expatiated more on my life situation, and then he said, "Well, you're finished here. I've helped you to some physical well-being. You know the techniques. You're pretty happy. That's all."

We talked casually. I asked him, "How did you hit on this kind of therapy?" And he told me. "I found out the verbalizing didn't help much, even made some people worse. It gave them an obsessive way of life, substituting the insights for their own *being*. Oh it helps some, but in a case like yours—where the experiences that caused the trouble occurred so very early in the pre-verbal era of your childhood—it wasn't much good." He, with many of the other doctors, found himself in a critical situation, with more and more people coming for help. Obsessed with his obligation to heal, he started experimenting with the very techniques he had learned as a student doctor in Germany. "The science comes from the East, from India, but the Germans adapted it for the West. It doesn't take the place of analysis. Instead it supplements it," he said. "It's the same work taking place on the deeper levels." I said I'd like to go on with the breathing techniques, to go further. "That's up to you . . . what you want to do with your life. All I can do is bring you down out of your head and into your physiological being. I've done that. I'm finished." I wasn't. "But these centers I've opened up, you wouldn't want to help me develop them further? After all it's a science that's well known in other parts of the world."

Dr. Halsted sighed. "So it is, but not here. And I'm not the one. For one thing, I'd lose my scientific standing. And there are other reasons, many other reasons." There hadn't been any dynamic research into the unconscious here in America, he said, and until there was there would be no dynamic therapy, and Anxiety Row would grow longer each year, and any cure would have to be accidental. "We can't get the big grants. We never will. Americans don't like to face mental ill-health. If we did we'd have to admit we're not the healthy perfect people you see in the dental advertisements."

So I said good-by. "Just go on out and enjoy yourself. Do the best you can." And there I was out in the street again, and not even missing Halsted.

I'm cured of my great trouble, the next note reads. The first part of the race has been run. I won by the skin of my teeth, by the perimeter of a hair. I was shooting with loaded dice, maybe we all are. I was playing with marked cards, I was running in a fixed race, but somehow I won.

Those cold old years in the pond have left a scar. And sometimes a shadow falls, I feel again the chill uncertain quivering in the air. Once more the darkening twilight descends, an unutterable loneliness stirs, and back there in the slimy blackness the croaks start up . . . Creatures float by, brownish green-flecked formless blobs with golden eyes and wide wide mouths, offering love and death, and death and love. Come back to the dark old drench of Monster Mill where poisonous toads lie down in the coils of deadly cobras and blink peacefully out at the passing shades. It can happen in a glance, a word shrilled in the public places of the great world, where the half-men have status and wield influence and offer protection, and quarter-men compete for the soft spot in the cobras' coils. And the memory stirs, dank air seeps up to the nostrils, I quicken and am drawn to the edge of the pond. But the figment fades. The grown man is too tall for the cramped tree house. And there is no return.

I don't know anything about "God's intentions," and anything I say would be just more talk. But there is so much of this talk, and the talkers are so sure of what they're saying, perhaps a small amount of unsure talk wouldn't harm anyone. I do have an idea, call it a hunch, that we were not intended to be wandering around in this darkness so long. I even have the idea that we are supposed to walk a ways over there across the borderland, to see that which we feel intuitively, even to experience some of the scope of the infinite through awakening our inner selves. No, it is not for everybody, only for those who feel the pinch of the mystery, the dryness here, and long for that of which Omar Khayam wrote, "One glimpse of it within the tavern caught, Better than in the temple lost outright."

Alcoholics say they sometimes catch this glimpse in the early stages of sucking off the bottle; heroin and morphine addicts that they see it after they have taken the needle, and peyote chewers that they achieve this bliss through the juice of the cactus plant. Apparently what they see is soon forgotten, or if remembered remains apart from the ordinary torments of living, giving them small help—besides which they pay a terrible price. Nevertheless the longing for the glimpse certainly seems to be there. The mystical cries of the beatniks who mix up God and bliss with drugs and the connection is not entirely phony.

I don't know how many of them have any idea that this same connection might be obtained through certain breathing exercises and other techniques called Hatha Yoga, and that far from leading to withdrawal symptoms and despair, they might find this the doorway to greater mental and physical health, perhaps even new experience and great refreshment. I don't know how many would want this kind of training and experience, even if it were available, or how many would greatly prefer the American Quick Quick Quick: doctors, needles, pills, anything but one's own well-equipped body. I wouldn't know where to advise people to get this training even if they wanted it, where there would be teachers dedicated to their work, gifted in the subtle art. Some do exist. It's a possibility these are the doctors of the future who will be available when people are more aware of their needs, and we are all less ashamed, less desperate to appear healthy and perfect, and when there is a greater body of knowledge currently available and socially acceptable. That will be a time when anybody who has stumbled into a science as old as time needn't be embarrassed to mention it for fear of being considered weird. Or perhaps this time is here now and being elaborately ignored like the sudden appearance of a poor relation at the Park Avenue apartment.

Night before last I ran into Cal, the last entry reads. I was having coffee in a little place downtown when I saw him, signaling frantically to me, and next thing there he was sitting with us at table, talking his head off. "Because you see, Joyce, I've had you on my mind. It's about that doctor—the one I sent you to." I said yes, thanks very much, and he continued. "I didn't know at the time he'd left for Mexico, but now I hear he's coming back." I said, "You mean Dr. Halsted?" And he said, "Oh no, not Halsted. He was in the group— but don't go to him. He's way out, experimental—he's spent years in India, that kind of thing. Oh he's had some cures, but I don't think the original group approves of him . . ." I started to laugh and just couldn't stop as he continued talking and staring at me.

I had gone to the wrong man.